ACTING AS FRIENDS

Michael De-la-Noy

ACTING AS FRIENDS

The Story of the Samaritans

Constable · London

First published in Great Britain 1987
by Constable and Company Limited
10 Orange Street London WC2H 7EG
Copyright © 1987 Michael De-la-Noy
Set in Linotron Plantin 11 pt by
Rowland Phototypesetting Limited
Bury St Edmunds, Suffolk
Printed in Great Britain by
St Edmundsbury Press Limited
Bury St Edmunds, Suffolk

British Library CIP data
De-La-Noy, Michael
Acting as friends: the story of the
Samaritans.
1. Samaritans, *Organization* – History
I. Title
362.2   HV6548.G7

ISBN 0 09 467500 7

For FREDO DONNELLY and SHEILA COGGRAVE
Repraesentativus
and in loving memory of
CAROLYN and ERNEST MOSSNER

'We are not professionals. We are acting as friends.'

A deputy director in the Midlands

CONTENTS

INTRODUCTION 11

1 A BENEVOLENT DESPOTISM 13

2 CARING FOR THE CARERS 41

3 AMATEURS AT WORK 62

4 ROOTING 90

5 LONG-TERM BEFRIENDING 116

6 BEFRIENDING IN THE OPEN 149

7 EMOTIONAL TIME AND SPACE 169

8 PUBLIC PERCEPTIONS 188

9 NOT LIKE AN ORDINARY DEATH 201

SAMARITAN PRINCIPLES AND PRACTICES 229

INDEX 231

INTRODUCTION

Without the unreserved co-operation of the Samaritans, no comprehensive book by a non-Samaritan could ever be written. Nevertheless it is necessary to emphasize that although the executive committee of the Samaritans satisfied themselves initially of my essential empathy as a writer, and the general secretary was kind enough to read a draft manuscript in order to have the opportunity of correcting factual errors and commenting upon value judgements, total editorial control has always resided with the author and the publishers. This is not another official handbook about Samaritan principles or codes of practice; it is an independent account and assessment of the history, purpose and practical functions of the Samaritans and of the scope of their work and potential usefulness in the context of society at large, written by an interested outsider. The ultimate responsibility for opinions, judgements and errors of fact is mine alone.

It is also essential to emphasize that on a wide range of matters there is a lack of uniformity between branches. To remind readers continually of this fact would be tedious, but it needs to be borne in mind that there is no definitive method of running a branch (the existence of a ratified set of principles and practices is another matter) any more than there is an archetypal Samaritan or one entirely typical caller. Those who work as Samaritans will find plenty here with which to disagree, facts that do not coincide with their own branch procedures and opinions that differ, perhaps radically, from their own, gained from years of personal experience. This book can only be read as one person's objective view of a national organization which bases its aims and modes of operation on a standard code of conduct and then leaves thousands of voluntary helpers a measure of freedom and responsibility in which to implement that code to the best of their human endeavour.

Initially, it was envisaged that in order to facilitate research I would be allocated a sort of liaison officer at the general office in Slough, through whom arrangements would be made for me to visit centres, attend training courses and so on. But so immediate and spontaneous were the flood of invitations and offers of unrestricted co-operation which I received from individual Samaritans on behalf of their branches that in the event the necessity for any sort of clearance through 'official channels' became almost entirely superfluous. Alas, because of the essentially confidential nature of the work of the Samaritans and the need to retain a large measure of anonymity it is, however, impossible for me publicly to thank an incredible number of people to whom I am indebted, not least to former callers who have talked to me of their need for help and the extent to which they felt they had received it. But I hope they will all know how much they have assisted me, and how grateful I am. With the exception of a handful of instantly identifiable people, mainly present or past full-time employees, who have given permission to forego anonymity, it can be assumed throughout that the names of every Samaritan and caller, and, when appropriate, the location of branches referred to, have been disguised. So far as the staff at the general office are concerned, I can only say they have consistently made my task an easier one, and turned the pleasure of their company into a privilege.

In 1986 I was granted an Authors' Foundation Grant by a panel chaired by Lady Antonia Fraser and nominated by the Society of Authors, which considerably eased the financial burden of research.

Michael De-la-Noy
London, 1987

· 1 ·

A BENEVOLENT DESPOTISM

'I first went to the Samaritans when my marriage was crack-
ing up. My husband's drinking had been very serious. He'd
left me, and I was very lonely, and I had the complete
responsibility for my son, who by this time was a drug
addict. Then my mother died. I was left without any relatives except my brother, and he always kept himself pretty
well detached. He is frightened of involvement, and yet he's
a Samaritan! As a Samaritan he might be quite good, because
he mustn't get involved with the callers. Perhaps he's a very
good Samaritan. Perhaps he's good with people who are not
related to him, people he feels he can escape from.

'I rang the Samaritans a lot, nearly always because of my
son. I didn't know how to cope. I was completely and utterly
and solely responsible. Sometimes, hysterically, I felt like
killing myself, because I didn't know where to turn, but by
the time I actually picked up the phone to ring the Samaritans
I usually said, "Is it all right to ring, because I'm not going to
commit suicide, but I don't know what to do and I feel very
miserable and I don't know who to turn to?" And they'd say,
"No, no, that's perfectly all right, fire away." Or I might
burst into tears, or something, and then talk. Or put the
phone down and ring them back. Sometimes I'd try to ring
them and couldn't get through because the phone was
engaged, and try three or four times, and in the end give up
and then recover anyway.

'If the Samaritans knew I'd rung several times recently, they'd ask me to come in. If I went in immediately, or if I went in, which occasionally I did, without ringing them, I'd get to see anybody, and sometimes it wasn't very helpful. Nearly always it was helpful over the phone, for some reason, but when I went in, once or twice I felt worse when I came out, because I felt that the Samaritan I'd met wasn't very understanding. But if they already knew something about me, because I'd met them before, they would be very concerned, and listen well, and make me feel sort of welcome. But once or twice I felt I was being a nuisance. I know they don't give advice, but after talking at some length on the phone I usually felt better, it clarified my mind. You see, the worst thing when you're living alone is having no one to talk to, to clarify what's going on in your head. Sometimes writing it down helps, but it's a slower process, and if you're feeling very emotional it's not so easy to write down. It's easier to talk it out, having some response of nods and smiles and "Yes" and "Go on" and "What does that mean?"

'But I remember on one occasion a woman being slightly aggressive and interrupting me and saying, "Well, that's not so, you've contradicted yourself." She sounded as though she was tensed up herself, irritated. I mentioned this to my brother, and he asked who she was, and I gave her Christian name, and he said, "Oh, I know her, she does get rather sharp at times." Which I thought might have tipped the balance for somebody who was feeling worse. I could take it in the sense that I didn't kill myself. But after seeing this woman I went away crying, when usually they had put my problems in perspective, or sorted out that I should come and see someone regularly. I was in fact befriended twice. I went back because I had experienced better results previously.'

It seems that every decade or so, one obscure, previously unknown person is liable to come up with a brainwave, a simple idea that captures the public imagination or fulfils a commonplace need that no one else has catered for. It may be double-glazing, or the invention of cats' eyes. In 1953, the year of the Queen's coronation and the conquest of Everest, it dawned upon an Anglican clergyman, the Revd Chad Varah,[1] that if people who needed to summon the police, ambulance service or fire brigade in an emergency were accustomed to dialling a telephone number, those in emotional distress might be encouraged to call for help in the same way. He had been led to this basic proposition partly through his experience as a parish priest, more particularly by an almost obsessive interest in the social and religious history of sexual harassment. 'I am not particularly modest,' Chad Varah admits, and he records that since 1935 he had been regarded 'as one of the chief exponents of the theology of sex'. In 1935 he was ordained deacon. He was twenty-four, and still a bachelor. Nevertheless, 'as a young priest', Dr Varah has told countless audiences throughout the world, 'I had attempted to teach youngsters about sex in my youth club, and I had started giving marriage guidance to young couples. As a result, I became very knowledgeable and practised.' It is this self-taught knowledge, and practice acquired at vestry level, that has formed the basis of his public platform ever since, and in large measure has been used to justify and underpin the philosophy and mode of operation of the Samaritan movement that developed from it.

Many children destined to head a large family need to achieve at an early age an enviable degree of self-assurance. Born in 1911, at Barton-upon-Humber, Edward Chad Varah was the eldest of nine children. Varahs – almost certainly Ukrainian in origin – had lived in Yorkshire since at least 1537, and Chad himself was named after the seventh-century saint who converted the Midlands and founded the church in Lincolnshire where his father was parish priest. He was educated at Worksop College in Nottingham, gaining an Exhibition in Natural Sciences to Keble College, Oxford.[2] From there he went on to

---

[1] He was appointed a prebendary of St Paul's Cathedral in 1975.

[2] In 1981 Keble College conferred upon Chad Varah an honorary Fellowship.

study for the ministry at Lincoln Theological College, where one of his teachers was the sub-warden, Michael Ramsey, later Archbishop of Canterbury. After serving three assistant curacies, Varah was inducted, in 1942, to his first living, Holy Trinity, Blackburn. He remained there until 1949, and for the next four years he was vicar of the Church of St Paul, Clapham Junction.

Not content with exploring the theology of sex in the course of his parish work, Chad Varah had begun to supplement his stipend by writing articles on the subject. 'So when, in 1952, the editor of *Picture Post* got no reaction from a dreary series of articles about sex, I was the natural person for him to ask to write something exciting,' he has recalled.[3] 'I contributed what was probably the first article ushering in the "permissive society".' He received letters from 235 readers, fourteen of whom he thought were suicidal. The 'dreary' articles to which Chad Varah refers in fact appeared in 1951, supervised by a 'panel of experts', which included the poet Charles Madge, one of the inventors of Mass Observation and at that time professor of sociology at Birmingham University. They were introduced by one of *Picture Post's* star journalists, Fyfe Robertson, and included pieces with riveting titles like 'What Should You Tell Your Children?', 'The Roles of Men and Women' and 'Some Common Worries, Real and Imaginary'. After courtship, marriage and divorce had all been dealt with, Chad Varah's 'exciting' contribution appeared, on 10 November 1951, under the banner headline, 'A Parson Puts His Case', but far from ushering in the Permissive Society, the advent of which is generally reckoned to date from the Profumo Scandal in 1963, it read like a perfectly responsible, indeed highly orthodox, Christian commentary, and contained the pithy remark, 'The solution to marital unhappiness is not easier divorce but harder marriage.'

After four years in Battersea, and inevitably already aware of

[3] 'Why and How I Started the Samaritans', the *Samaritan*, special issue 1976.

the tragedy of suicide through his work as a parish priest, Varah read that in Greater London alone three people killed themselves every day, and it occurred to him that 'the kind of counselling I had been giving to people anxious or depressed about their sexual problems might well be applicable to people with other problems.' It further occurred to him that if you were feeling suicidal you needed to talk to somebody about it there and then, and the best way you could speak to somebody was by picking up a telephone. Varah's awareness in 1953 of suicide statistics in Greater London coincided with an offer of St Stephen Walbrook, a magnificent Wren church in the City, closed for thirteen years after being bombed early in the war, a benefice he has held ever since. In addition to a verger aged ninety-seven, who lived to be 102, it was blessed, in those days, with the fortuitous telephone number MANsion House 9000.

Varah told the patrons, the Worshipful Company of Grocers, that if he did move in as rector he would want to set up an emergency telephone service for people tempted to commit suicide, and they agreed to the experiment. It was started in such an *ad hoc* way that no serious consideration was given to a name by which it was to be known. Within days, Chad Varah was being quoted in the press as referring to 'Good Samaritans', and 'The Telephone Good Samaritans' became an instant if temporary sobriquet. Within a matter of four or five weeks the word 'Good' had thankfully been dropped from the official title, and for the next ten years 'The Telephone Samaritans' became the forerunners of the Samaritans. Yet so potent is the imagery of the New Testament that when speaking to the *Daily Mirror* in December 1953, Chad Varah was still apt to explain that 'If a case is sufficiently urgent, a Good Samaritan will dash to the caller and try to comfort and help him or her.'[4] And so carried away with enthusiasm did he become that within a month he had told the *Daily Mirror*, 'I want to spread the organization so

[4] Samaritan, *n. & a.* Native or language of Samaria (*good* – genuinely charitable person, w. ref. to Luke x: 33 etc.). *The Concise Oxford Dictionary.*

that there are at least two Samaritans for every four square miles of Greater London and the suburbs.' At this time, the 'organization' consisted of precisely four volunteers, two of whom were Chad Varah and his secretary. Neverthless, journalese already had the upper hand, the *Sunday Chronicle* breathlessly reporting on 13 December that 'in desperate, anxious undertones' a man on the run from the police had 'pleaded with the kindly-voiced priest who answered his call to grant him sanctuary in his church.'

'Telephone Samaritan No. 2, pretty twenty-four-year-old Vivien Prosser of Wimbledon' (the *Sunday Chronicle* again), Chad Varah's secretary, had taken the first call herself, because the rector was out. During the first twelve months, about 100 callers were spoken to on the telephone or interviewed in the vestry. Although an average of two such pastoral consultations a week would constitute a very small proportion of the total numbers of parishioners to whom a parish priest in a busy inner-city area might be expected to minister, they had at least three factors in common which made them unusual and newsworthy, time-consuming and often emotionally draining; the majority had arrived from outside the parish, all were feeling suicidal or in despair, and those who had already attempted suicide were guilty of a criminal offence. Furthermore, by having contemplated suicide they had attracted to themselves a social stigma, for in 1953 the subject of death still remained – as it does today – one of the last taboos in our society, and suicide in particular was regarded as antisocial and irresponsible to a degree.

Those two callers a week clearly represented merely the tip of the iceberg, for although suicide rates may fluctuate, sometimes quite irrationally, today 13,000 new callers a year contact the central London branch of the Samaritans alone, and there is no reason to imagine that a similar number of distressed or desperate people were not walking the streets of the capital in 1953. Had they all converged on St Stephen Walbrook at once, the fledgling operation would have been squashed at birth. As it was, within a matter of months the two callers a week were swelling by geometrical progression, assistance from voluntary helpers was needed to interview them, and a good deal of initial help was actually being offered by fellow sufferers. 'Chad saw that a lot of clients waiting to see him were befriending each other,' John Eldrid, an Anglican priest who joined the Samaritans in 1958 and is now the full-time director of the central London branch, has recalled. And Chad Varah himself has said that his small band of initial helpers were doing more good than he. 'They had no qualifications at all but great human qualities. They were simply listening to callers and making coffee, providing just what the clients mostly wanted, a listening ear, with no advice or preaching, just a great deal of warmth, tolerance and acceptance. They did not necessarily approve of everything the callers had done, but they offered acceptance of them as suffering human beings.'

There were, in the earliest days, perhaps some dozen helpers. By 1956 there were still only twenty, but in three years they had dealt with 350 callers. Recruitment tended to be by word of mouth, and of course, for a variety of reasons, the earliest volunteers, like so many of their successors, tended to leave. Originally they were known not as volunteers or Samaritans but as 'rector assistants'. The first Samaritan volunteer to be enrolled immediately after the founder and his secretary was Mary Meikle, who rejoiced in the number 3/1. A volunteer who can remember being referred to as a rector assistant as late as 1955, the year he drifted into St Stephen to offer his services, was Roger Martyn (44/1), who eventually became the Samaritan's first honorary legal adviser. With no training or experience of any kind, he was sent within minutes of volunteering to see if he could be of assistance to a man in distress at Wimbledon Station. Because the numbers of callers were initially quite small it was possible, even with a small staff, to devote a considerable amount of time to individual cases, although when the vestry was in use interviews might have to be conducted in the church in competition with the organist. Roger Martyn's recollection of his first night duty, on New Year's Eve 1956, places in perspective the level of activity at St Stephen

Walbrook thirty years ago compared to that of almost any Samaritan branch today: absolutely nothing happened.[5]

Roger Martyn's mercy dash to Wimbledon Station may have furnished Chad Varah with the case history he wrote up for *Picture Post* on 30 June 1956, in 'the first of the *Picture Post* reports on the desperate men and women the Suicide Samaritans have SNATCHED FROM DEATH.' London, even then, was described by Varah as the 'biggest, loneliest city in the world'. The article is remarkably orientated towards religion, and it is written (ghosted, perhaps, in the office) in a journalistic style impossible to parody. A workman reading a newspaper, and a man waiting to jump under a train, meet, providentially, on the platform. As the 'impatient man' leapt forward, the workman caught him roughly by the collar.

' "You silly fool!" he hissed.

'After what seemed an interminable delay, the doors closed again and the train moved grindingly on. The workman pushed a newspaper under the nose of his companion, who was drawing deep, sobbing breaths. "Read that," he ordered, stabbing at a paragraph with a calloused forefinger, "and if you'll ring these Samaritans I won't hand you over to the police, which is what I oughter do. Funny, I was reading about 'em just before you tried to do yourself in, and thinking it was a lot of rot. But I'd say they're just the people you need." '

'Gradually I found my senses again. They even encouraged me to find a job,' the reformed suicide reported from the caption beneath a photograph of himself driving a van. This picture, like all the others liberally illustrating the thrilling adventures of the Suicide Samaritans, taken during heart-to-hearts on station benches and frantic phone calls from telephone boxes, were shamelessly faked. They do not write articles like that any more, but no wonder some potential volunteers still harbour the notion that being a Samaritan

[5] The fact that in 1956 a new volunteer had been allocated the number 41 does not mean there were at that time 41 volunteers; when a volunteer left, their number was not reallocated. In 1956 there may in fact have been only twenty volunteers *in situ*.

involves the glamour of rushing around seeking souls to save.

'Befriending' was the therapeutic term Chad Varah soon gave to 'the listening acceptance and personal caring' that he estimates was all that was required by seven out of eight of the people who called at the vestry or telephoned, and there are still Samaritans today who regret that the term Befrienders was not officially adopted, as it has been in some places overseas, instead of Samaritans, with its obviously Christian connotations, derived from the parable of the Good Samaritan. For the word 'Samaritan' is one reason why, although the Samaritans are now forbidden to proselytize, a good deal of identification with religion has undoubtedly rubbed off on to the movement. The early core of 'rector assistants' actually banded together into a Company of Samaritans, holding special services of dedication and admission. Not only was the founder a priest but the first two full-time assistants at St Stephen were clergymen, and for ten years only clergy were appointed, by Chad Varah, as branch directors. 'It added tone,' the present general secretary, the Revd David Evans, suggests. For an organization staffed by amateurs to be dabbling in sex and suicide was considered by many in the medical profession, the police, the Church and the social services to be foolhardy, to say the least, and certainly the wearing of a collar back to front was felt by society at large to confer an aura of respectability. A more positive advantage in recruiting clergy as local directors lay in their vocational understanding of confidentiality.

'It was very difficult for someone like a doctor to be a Samaritan,' says Mr Evans. 'There are ethical problems over the possibility of appearing to treat somebody else's patient. On the whole, the role of doctors has been as consultants.' A faint atmosphere of religiosity may linger, but nowadays women outnumber men as directors by just over two to one, there are four medical directors and precisely three clergymen. As for the term 'befriending', this does now have a firm place in Samaritan terminology. From the moment a caller contacts the Samaritans he or she is regarded as in some sense being befriended, and support offered to a caller after initial contact, and for a limited length of time, is officially known as 'on-going befriending'.

Even while vicar of St Paul, Clapham Junction, Chad Varah had regarded himself as 'possibly the busiest parson in the C of E.' The setting up of his experimental emergency telephone line had of course been work undertaken in addition to routine duties as a parish priest which at St Stephen Walbrook involved a certain amount of ceremonial, for St Stephen is the parish church of the Lord Mayor of London, and within three months he decided to disengage from befriending (but not from counselling, 'which I was quite capable of giving') in order to concentrate on administration and on enquiries from well-intentioned innovators overseas. 'I shall never again pick up the emergency telephone,' he told his rector assistants. 'But I will answer letters, and I will select you, instruct you, deploy you, discipline you and, when necessary, sack you.' Not for nothing did some of his recruits refer to him as the Boss. 'It was,' recalls Jean Burt, who became a Samaritan volunteer in 1958, 'a sort of benevolent despotism. He gave very firm direction. And we needed this, because we were so inexperienced, and there were no national standards of training to fall back on. So we used to have our own training classes, and every Monday, at lunchtime, Chad used to hold a meeting of all the volunteers, and there was practically a one hundred per cent turn-out, because we were all so frightened of making mistakes. People brought their sandwiches and the meeting used to last about an hour. We learned a lot about the callers, and about ourselves.' A volunteer who offered his services within the first six weeks has said that 'in those days, the only way you were trained was by doing the work, meeting the clients and learning from your mistakes.' Undeterred by the despotic atmosphere, however, in 1971 Miss Burt quit a civil service post in the Cabinet Office to become assistant general secretary to the Samaritans, being made an MBE in 1979 for her work. She later served as joint general secretary, resigning in 1984. After thirty years she is still a volunteer at the central London branch.

Eight years after the war the condition of St Stephen Wal-brook remained deplorable. One outside wall of the outer vestry consisted of nothing but plywood, and the room itself was heaped with builders' rubble and old organ pipes. All this mess had to be cleared up, but even after the church had been restored, Jean Burt remembers conditions at St Stephen as being 'remarkably cramped and sometimes bitterly cold,' an impression echoed by another volunteer who joined a year later than she, who has written, 'Almost my first impression of the Samaritans when I joined in the autumn of 1959 was an engaging atmosphere of rather dotty scruffiness. We were herded together in the outer vestry which continued to retain a distinct air of the war damage it had sustained. This not over-large room had to contain the volunteers, the staff, the clients, an assortment of tables, desks and chairs of varying age, the all-important telephones, and, almost as important, the tea and coffee-making impedimenta. Although we were totally untrained in any psychological or sociological disciplines we were soon made aware that there were certain cardinal prin-ciples to be observed, the breach of which would involve instant dismissal; absolute obedience to one's superiors in the branch, complete discretion, no false sentimentality and above all the knowledge that the client's needs were paramount.' But although they were dealing in matters often literally of life and death, the prevailing atmosphere, he says, seemed primarily to be one of laughter, friendship and a certain openness.

The two volunteers on duty at night slept on bunks in a tiny room in the tower, with telephones on a shelf opposite the bunks, and cold linoleum in between. A hoaxer took to tele-phoning on a regular basis to inquire if the volunteers were awake, and one night a lady rang to say she had chucked her cat out of a fifth-floor window, and what was she to do with the body? John Eldrid was one of those who slept in the tower when on duty at night; it was not until 1964 that the crypt was converted, at the expense of the patrons, to ensure that perma-nent Samaritan premises would always be available when the living changed hands. Eldrid's arrival heralded a nucleus of full-time support beginning to gather around Chad Varah, including a second priest, the Revd Eric Reid, and Mary Bruce, a psychiatric social worker who came over from St Bartholomew's Hospital in 1958 to help consolidate the experience of the past five years and to set up properly structured training classes. She remained with the Samaritans until 1965. 'One of the significant things about the Samaritans,' says Mr Eldrid, 'is the way it has changed so little in essence from the early days. Of course, thirty years ago people were not as permissive as they are now. Not only was attempted suicide still a crime, but so was all homosexual activity, and in withholding information from the police Samaritans were not protected by law. Some of the volunteers used to get worried about not giving information, and two things Chad Varah had to fight hard for were the necessity for volunteers to be open and non-judgemental about sexual matters, and the absolutely overriding necessity for confidentiality. These days a lot of the things he fought for are considered quite normal, but even to offer befriending rather than counselling was an entirely new concept. One of the people who helped us gain acceptance among statutory and other voluntary bodies, and also enabled us to understand certain psychological and psychiatric problems better, was Richard Fox, the doctor in charge of the emergency clinic at the Maudsley Hospital on Denmark Hill. He became consultant psychiatrist to the Samaritans. Most branches will now have a psychiatric consultant – not to interview the callers, unless they wish it, but as a consultant to the director.' Dr Fox was in fact appointed consultant psychiatrist in 1963, and he was soon being telephoned by the Samaritans for permission to send callers who were obviously in need of psychiatric care to the Maudsley for admission. 'I was impressed by the quality of the referrals for admission,' he says, 'and eventually I even referred a client back from the hospital to the Samaritans for befriending. At that time the Samaritans were held in great suspicion by the medical profession, and Chad Varah had been searching hard for respectability.'

Eric Reid was thirty-seven when he arrived from Ireland,

with a training in psychology and philosophy (he had been ordained into the Church of Ireland), and along with John Eldrid he was appointed a deputy director. His Samaritan number was 332, which would indicate that over the first six years one new Samaritan had been recruited, on average, every week, although of course by no means all of them had remained as volunteers. He was attracted to the work on a full-time basis because, he says, 'I liked the whole idea of befriending by ordinary, down-to-earth people, and I had always been interested in social work within the Church. Although I did my stint of parish work for twelve years, I'm not a parish man.' One of the most remarkable rescue missions Reid got involved in during the ten years he worked at St Stephen occurred on receipt of a letter from a man which read, 'By the time you receive this I shall be dead.' The only hint of an address was a hotel room number in the five-hundreds, and a London postmark. Reckoning there were few hotels in London with more than 500 bedrooms in those days, he and Chad Varah exercised some rapid detective work, and tracked down the writer of the letter, who was rushed to hospital suffering from an overdose.

'I would say about thirty per cent of the clients – a word we always used then and one I prefer to callers – were, in our opinion, suicidal,' he recalls. He also remembers 'many a good set-to' with the founder. 'We argued about all kinds of things, but he admired you if you stuck to your guns. One of my faults was that I wasn't always prepared to let go of clients that easily, and finish off befriending. So much of our work was still experimental that I don't remember any rules or regulations being laid down in writing, other than the sacrosanct rule of confidentiality. Much of our time was spent devising preparation classes – not training classes; you can't train someone to be a Samaritan, you can only prepare them. Chad generally took the classes in sexual problems, and it was very noticeable how high the drop-out rate of new recruits was after those. I suppose it was the shock! I remember one volunteer was horrified at the thought of anyone having oral sex.' Eric Reid resigned from the Samaritans in 1967 to become chaplain to a psychiatric hospital.

In 1979 he was appointed an honorary canon of Newcastle Cathedral, and in 1987 he retired after twelve years as secretary to the Hospital Chaplaincy Council.

Despite Chad Varah's initial dream of spreading to the suburbs, for six years the church of St Stephen Walbrook seemed likely to remain the single centre for the Telephone Samaritans in the United Kingdom, the one address and telephone number available 'to help the suicidal and despairing'. 'I don't think the idea of expansion outside London ever occurred to Chad Varah in the early years,' says Jean Burt. 'He was too busy seeing callers and corresponding with people from all parts of the world who wrote to him about their problems.' Looking back on an era of almost unbelievable expansion that eventually did take place, she remembers that when new branches got started in the austerity of post-war Britain it was never easy. 'There was an acute shortage of everything, premises, volunteers and money, and as always, as soon as you advertised for new volunteers to man a centre you induced a disproportionate influx of new callers.' But in 1959, the year that was marked by a six-year grant from the Gulbenkian Foundation, Edinburgh, under the ecumenical leadership of Presbyterians, Roman Catholics and a Presbyterian minister, Professor James Blackie (henceforth known as James 1/2), achieved the distinction of becoming the first of a galaxy of branches eventually destined to cover every essential catchment area in the United Kingdom. Looking back on the decision to open a branch in Edinburgh, one of the original Scottish volunteers has written, 'I tremble at what had to be done. There were no models on which to build, except St Stephen, and London was so different. It is interesting, first, to note that Chad let us be different, indicative perhaps of the Samaritan spirit to improvise and to be flexible, and secondly the warmth and commitment of ordinary people who worked for hours – cleaning, scrubbing, painting, training, fixing rotas, doing duties. To a schoolteacher, sadly accepting so many of the restrictive practices of that profession, finding kindred spirits – bus drivers, university lecturers, chars, housewives – willing to get stuck in and try to do something for other people was an eye-opener.' Despite the apparent lack of models, within twelve months three more branches had been established, one of them in Liverpool, the first English branch outside London and the third formally to be recognized, set up by a future suffragan-bishop of Buckingham, who became Christopher 1/3, and who managed to acquire from the Postmaster-General the eight-millionth telephone installed in Great Britain. The other two branches were in Scotland, in Glasgow and Aberdeen. Another half-dozen centres took root in 1961, in Bradford, Bournemouth, Hull, Jersey, Portsmouth and Belfast, where, of all places, a Presbyterian director joined forces with Anglican, Roman Catholic and Methodist colleagues. A former Lord Mayor of Belfast chaired its finance committee, and the branch was opened just ten weeks after an exploratory meeting had been held in the Chapter House of Belfast Cathedral.

'There was a good deal of evangelical religious fervour in the early branches,' a former member of the executive committee recalls, 'and the setting up of the earliest branches was often a bit chaotic. You'd get a group of ten Methodists sitting round a table saying "We ought to have a branch", and the next week they'd started one. Hence there was no systematic recruitment, and very often people weren't selected or trained. Anybody who turned up was put straight on the telephone. But as branches spread, new branches were able to draw on previous experience and disasters.'

Press publicity had by now taken hold of public imagination overseas, particularly in Europe, South Africa and India, and centres supposedly based on Samaritan principles of befriending had come into existence in Salisbury in Rhodesia, in Karachi, Bombay and Hong Kong. They tended, however, to depend upon professionals to the exclusion of volunteers and to be strongly orientated towards denominational religion, and sometimes also they were based on psychiatric hospitals. In 1960, in order to try and steer a good deal of misplaced enthusiasm in the direction of his own concepts of 'listening acceptance and personal caring', Chad Varah organized a conference of overseas branches in Switzerland. 'Imitations of varying inadequacy' was how he later described the earliest attempts at forming Samaritan-style branches overseas, and he admitted that efforts to let the 'Samaritan ideal' influence the work of other organizations had not, at this stage, been success- ful. In the United States, needless to say, 'students of suicide' emerged, and even an American Association of Suicidology, from whom, in 1974, Chad Varah was to receive an award. But a good deal of flexibility in approach by countries with traditions different to the British occurred. Istanbul produced the Com- rades in the Spirit; Israel, the Helping Hand. The simple word Friendship was chosen by the Parisians, the Belgians opted for Tele-Welcome, and *Telefonseelsorge* (Pastoral Care by Tele- phone) was the rather appealing name adopted by the Germans.

But before the 'Samaritan ideal' had taken a firmly rooted hold throughout the world, a major breakthrough in social attitudes, destined to alleviate the task of the Samaritans at home, was about to be accomplished. For some years, attempts had been made behind the legal and political scenes to have the felony relating to attempted suicide removed from the statute book, and one influential campaigner had been a remarkable woman, Dr Doris Odlum, who became an inspiration to three generations of Samaritans. A child psychiatrist, who had served from 1954–58 as president of the European League for Medical Hygiene, she was born in 1890 and educated at St Hilda's College, Oxford. In 1916 she had stroked the London School of Medicine for Women's eight in the first women's race ever rowed, against Cambridge University. She was also a national fencing champion. Having already been consulted over the 1958 Mental Health Act, which altered radically the status of patients in psychiatric hospitals, Dr Odlum was now recruited to help draft the 1961 Suicide Act, and in the same year Chad Varah invited her to become consultant psychiatrist to a newly formed branch in her home town of Bournemouth. From then on she devoted a vast amount of her time to Samaritan work, contributing to the movement's magazine and in 1974 being appointed president for life, a role in which she played an active and stimulating part until her death eleven years later, at the age of ninety-five.

By the start of 1963, with attempted suicide no longer a crime, the total of Samaritan branches in the United Kingdom, including branches still on probation, had risen to twenty-three, a dozen new centres having been set on their feet the previous year, in Birmingham, Cambridge, Croydon, Derby, Dundee, Guernsey, Halifax, Nottingham, Manchester, Reading, Salisbury and Stoke-on-Trent. This was the year the suicide rate for England and Wales (the rate for Scotland is always calculated separately), having slumped in 1941 to 9.0 per 100,000 of the population, was to reach a peak, 12.2 per 100,000 of the population. (It is currently 8.2 per 100,000.) Also in 1963 the existing twenty-one fully recognized branches became incorporated into a company limited by guarantee, with the name 'The Samaritans'. Those twenty-one founding branches were Aberdeen, Belfast, Bombay, Bournemouth, Brighton, Cambridge, Dundee, Edinburgh, Glasgow, Hong Kong, Hull, Jersey, Karachi, Liverpool, London, Manchester, Portsmouth, Reading, Salisbury in Rhodesia, Stoke-on-Trent and Woolwich. For the next four years they were to be served only by a full-time secretary and an honorary bursar.

A Memorandum of Association spelt out the object for which the Samaritans had been established: 'to assist persons who are suicidal, despairing or in distress and thus reduce the incidence of suicide by providing a service in each area where a branch is formed to enable such persons to receive immediate help, compassion and friendship from members of the Association selected and prepared for the purpose, working under direction; and also, in accordance with normal procedure, counselling or referral for treatment or advice from members or non-members of the Association having specialist or professional skills.' A precept clearly enshrined in the Articles was that 'the business of the Association shall be managed by the Council', and no longer could the Samaritans be charged with being run from a church in the City by a benevolent despot. In particular, the Articles granted to a council of management the right to recognize and to close down a branch, and forbade members of a branch that had been closed down to form a separate association of any kind having a name incorporating the word 'Samaritan'. Thus by becoming a company (licensed by the Board of Trade to omit the word 'Limited' from its title) the Samaritans were enabled to lay claim to copyright in their name and, by implication, in their activities. A very distinctive and beneficial feature of the Samaritan movement was clearly laid down, too. 'A director of a branch', one of the Articles read, 'shall be given wide powers in the management of the branch to the intent that the primary objects of the Association may be pursued without undue restriction; and in particular when, in the opinion of a director there is a possibility that a client may commit suicide, he shall be empowered to take such steps as he reasonably thinks fit to avert that possibility.' It is interesting to note that in 1963, those who called upon the Samaritans for help were officially referred to as clients, and continued so to be called for some considerable time; today such terminology is generally thought too clinical, and anybody currently telephoning or visiting the Samaritans is usually (although not invariably) referred to as a caller.

In addition to assuming responsibility for endorsing or closing branches, the council of management was empowered to appoint branch directors. Initially the council was to consist of no fewer than twenty members, and the first council was elected by the subscribers to the company. There were thirty of these, all but three of them men (one of whom described himself as a gentleman); two were bishops and another twelve were clergymen, one of whom later became a bishop. Membership of the council was restricted to Samaritans, any one of whom might be removed from the council 'if he becomes of unsound mind'. There is no recorded instance of such a disaster, but the condition of someone's mind is often difficult to determine. Just as difficult to ascertain is whether the Samaritans have achieved their stated objective of 'reducing the incidence of suicide'. If suicides fell to zero there would be no conclusive proof that the Samaritans had achieved such a miraculous event, and even if a caller were to report back – and many have – that through support received from the Samaritans he had refrained from killing himself, such testament would only amount at best to circumstantial evidence. The argument about prevention is presented early in order to dispose of it early, for in a way it is irrelevant. Because, from empirical evidence, it is impossible to prove that the Samaritans have ever prevented a single suicide, no argument follows that they should not try, and most Samaritans would regard one life saved in thirty years as a worthwhile achievement. In any event, the aims of the Samaritans extend far beyond the explicit attempt to prevent suicide – to the alleviation through compassion of distress at every level, and even to the comforting of a caller who they believe may be dying of their own free will. In the face of such a harrowing experience as that, semantics about statistics and evidence tend to pale in importance.

Nevertheless it has been claimed that the decline in the suicide rate after 1963 was attributed to an increase in the number of Samaritan branches, and hence the number of callers. This may be so, although unfortunately saturation coverage of the country by Samaritan centres did not prevent the suicide rate from creeping up by 0.7 per 100,000 of the population between 1975 and 1985. However, there was certainly an undeniable correlation between the expansion of Samaritan activity and a decline in the rate of suicide between 1964 and 1975, a rate which may look small and seem to reflect little fluctuation as between, say, 11.5 per 100,000 of the population in 1959 and 12.2 in 1963, but a suicide rate of 11.5 per 100,000 in 1959 represented about 5,250 deaths, and a suicide rate of 12.2 per 100,000 in 1963 meant that almost 5,750 people had killed themselves, an additional 500 per annum, or a rise of around ten per cent. While the Samaritans were slowly getting underway between 1959 and 1963, by which time they had established (by the end of 1963) thirty-five branches, the suicide rate, as indicated, had risen to 12.2 per 100,000. But between 1963 and 1970, during the greatest period of Samaritan expansion, it fell steadily and consistently – to 11.7 in 1964, by which time there were forty-eight branches, to 10.8 in 1965, when there were sixty-five branches, to 10.4 in 1966, when there were seventy-three, to 9.7 in 1967, with eighty-eight, to 9.4 in 1968, with ninety-six, to 8.9 in 1969, with 107 branches, and to 8.0 in 1970 when, by that time, there were 117 branches. By 1975, with 165 branches in existence, the suicide rate had fallen to 7.5, the lowest level ever recorded.

The decade of the sixties saw an avalanche of new centres, among them, in 1964, Leicester, where for the first time a non-clerical director (a solicitor) was appointed as one of a team of co-directors. With the arrival of every new branch there arrived, also, an inevitable proportion of volunteers who turned out to be less than suitable, for nothing resembling a uniform procedure for selection and training had yet been established. 'There was trouble sometimes in the early branches,' Jean Burt remembers. 'Directors could become a bit too dictatorial, or just unable to cope. You also had unruly volunteers. Not everybody can work under direction, and a lot of people came into the Samaritans in the early days thinking it was going to be terribly glamorous, with a lot of rushing about and drama, and some of them wanted to do their own thing, which would have been far too dangerous. Mistakes were made also in opening branches which were not really viable, in small catchment areas, where there was perhaps more enthusiasm than real need.'

For better or worse, between 1961 and 1969 no less than 102 Samaritan branches came into existence, just over half the total achieved in the period 1959 to 1986. On average one branch was established every four weeks in 1963, in Bedford, Cheltenham, Doncaster, Guildford, Hastings, Havering, Ipswich, Oxford, Southampton, Stafford, Weybridge and Worcester. A similar rate of progress was maintained the following year, with thirteen branches appearing, at Leicester, Bristol, Colchester, Coventry, Exeter, Folkestone, Grimsby, Macclesfield, Norwich, Reigate, Scunthorpe, Shrewsbury and Torbay. The busiest year of all was 1965, when seventeen branches were opened, at Bath, Bolton, Cardiff, Chelmsford, Crewe,

Dumfernline, Eastbourne, Harrow, Kilmarnock, Leatherhead, Leek, Maidstone, Newcastle, Northallerton, Orpington, Sheffield and Wolverhampton. The next twelve months saw a further eight branches established, in Falkirk, Leeds, Lincoln, Lowestoft, Luton, the Medway, Northwich and Southend. Fifteen more centres got going in 1967, in Basildon, Basingstoke, Brent, Chester, Darlington, Newport, North Devon, Redbridge, Rochdale, Slough, Swansea, Swindon, Tunbridge Wells, Whitehaven and York. Another eight branches opened in 1968, in Brighton, the Chilterns, Kingston-on-Thames, Huddersfield, King's Lynn, Northampton, on Teesside and at Ware. This remarkable decade closed with a fine flourish, eleven more branches opening in 1969, at Bexley, Blackburn, Canterbury, Carlisle, Great Yarmouth, Lewisham, Putney, Walsall, Warrington, Watford and Worthing.

But this almost reckless enthusiasm led to some bizarre events. One branch was actually run single-handed by a clergyman who, it was alleged, would cheerfully leap from the pulpit on a Sunday to answer the telephone. A Non-Conformist minister managed to split his branch in two by having sexual relations with some of his volunteers, and engaging in psychotherapy with the callers and then making a charge for his services. An Anglican clerical director was so incompetent he handed over the day-to-day running of *his* branch to a semi-recovered alcoholic, who photocopied four case records and sent these off to the *News of the World*, who declined to publish them. One of the first members of the new executive committee recalls, 'The whole of the administration in the early days was done by a lady with rheumatoid arthritis and an old gentleman who had a background in accountancy. They kept all the records in the loo at their little home in Oxted. But they did it magnificently, organizing conferences and writing to people, and they kept the whole thing ticking over until it just got completely beyond them.'

The branch in Manchester, the seventh to be established, had been launched, in 1962, largely under the leadership of an Anglican priest, the Revd Basil Higginson (Basil 1/7), and in

1967, the numbers of branches having already trebled since Incorporation four years previously, he was appointed the first general secretary. Much of his seven years in office (he was compelled to resign through ill health in 1974, and died two years later) was spent travelling the country, offering advice and practical help to local citizens intent on starting a branch in their own town. He inspected premises, ensuring that the need for adequate financing was understood, and that potential volunteers realized the kind of commitment they were taking on, especially in terms of hours of voluntary service required to man a branch. It was said after his death that his memory about branches had been phenomenal, that he was able to recall precisely 'their history, troubles, triumphs, premises, personnel and clients'. Trouble of a major order arose in 1972, when the opening hours of one branch located in a seaside holiday resort became so haphazard that the matter had to be discussed by the council of management. 'It took the council four hours to arrive at a decision,' Jean Burt, by then assistant general secretary, recalls. 'And a decision to close the branch was only made after there had been numerous attempts to get the volunteers to maintain the high standards necessary. The thing was played right out until it became obvious that with the present people in control it was not viable at all. So the council decided to close it, which was very traumatic. The honorary solicitor and I had the awful job of actually going personally to do it. We called one evening to collect the keys, and to place the assets in a separate account. Eventually the lease had to be wound up, too. We took away all caller records, and lodged them with another branch seventeen miles away, who had agreed to do a holding operation. I'm happy to say that a very good branch rose from the ashes eight years later.' This was the only occasion when a branch has ever been closed through misdemeanour, although another was at one time reduced to probationary status, an act, says the present general secretary, 'which concentrated their minds no end'.

Branches tend to run so smoothly today, with a degree of dedication that often involves volunteers undertaking many more duties than they originally committed themselves to, that it is a salutary reminder of times past to recall how novel and unexpectedly difficult some of the early enthusiasts found it to establish a routine and a set of essential guidelines for operating. In 1973, two years after the Ealing branch had been founded, one of their members was writing to the *Samaritan*, a quarterly magazine founded the year before, to bewail the difficulty of welding into a team 130 volunteers, 'few of whom regularly meet more than one in ten of their colleagues'. Support for branch meetings aimed at further training had been disappointing, he said, and when a meeting was convened to discuss the lack of support, only half the branch membership turned up. One vital matter thrashed out was a policy over temporary closures during summer holidays, when the numbers on duty might be down to two, the telephones were ringing and half a dozen clients were waiting to be seen. It was agreed that in those circumstances a 'Closed' notice had to be exhibited, giving the telephone number and the time of re-opening. Just two years into the life of the branch, two perennial problems all too familiar to Samaritans young and old received an airing: 'How long must we suffer the minority who telephone us several times a day?' and 'Why has the branch not given directions on sex calls?' Another ominous question on the agenda was, 'How should we deal with a client carrying a weapon?' By the end of December 1973, out of 143 branches being manned by 17,285 volunteers, ninety-two were in fact already offering a twenty-four-hour service at the branch premises, and the forty-six still unable to achieve this ultimate goal were having calls transferred to volunteers at home or in other branches. The practice of volunteers taking calls at home would be severely frowned upon today.

An atmosphere of inspired chaos and improvisation can stimulate and strongly appeal to the pioneer spirit, and a former vice-chairman, who joined in 1969, got some of his frustration at the way the Samaritans had developed off his chest when he resigned in 1985. He had joined the movement, he explained in the *Samaritan*, because 'it was something I could do where I could give of myself, that the giving was of value to someone else. The Swinging Sixties swung to a halt, and all the open, challenging, optimistic things which were there for us retreated into the drab Seventies and the fearful Eighties, and with the changes the Samaritan movement became middle-aged before its time. It became necessary to justify one's existence, to be more accountable, so there was more control, organization, measuring. The Samaritans became semi-professional, confused by the worst of both worlds.' He went on to regret the modern need for organization, training, hot-lines, standing orders, manuals and directives, 'all the paraphernalia of a recognizable organization'. What he described as 'Chad's Little Army' used, he said, to be a guerrilla movement in an uncaring society; now it was more like a pillar of NATO. A colleague from Teesside responded in a letter by saying he could understand the disillusionment displayed, but somewhere, he felt, there was wrong thinking. It was only natural to look back with nostalgia at the movement as it had been in the beginning, but any organization which did not adapt would die. 'We *have* to evolve,' he wrote, 'as we and our task grow bigger. Only our refusal to succumb to disillusionment may stand between our callers and the abyss. Our nostalgia is a luxury they can't afford.'

By contributing articles to *Forum*, a magazine devoted to sex under the banner of education but whose correspondence columns were sometimes so erotic as to verge on the pornographic, Chad Varah had risked being cold-shouldered by the Establishment, but in 1969 the mantle of respectability fell upon the Samaritans when its founder was made an OBE. Presumably the civil servant known as the Ceremonial Officer, whose job it is to compile the prime minister's honours lists, had, like a volunteer named Susan, writing in 1972, 'missed the highlight of Chad's sex lecture'. These spicy performances lingered long in the memory of those volunteers he trained personally. 'Tonight I'm going to talk about sex, about heterosexual sex, homosexual sex and abnormal sex,' an Australian Methodist remembers the rector of St Stephen Walbrook beginning a training session. Again, 'All keyed up for the King-dom of Heaven, we got Chad on sex,' a founder member of the branch in Edinburgh has recalled. 'In our cold climate we didn't have problems of sex – at least, not until Chad arrived.' Sex, for Chad Varah, has remained something of a speciality. In a book called *The Samaritans in the '70s*[6] he contributed sections on *Befriending the Sexually Frustrated* as well as *Befriending the Homosexual*, and one of his more esoteric publications was titled *Telephone Masturbators and How to Befriend Them*.

'In my view, the Samaritans actually started as a sex counsell-ing agency, with suicide prevention growing out of that, and Chad's attitude towards sex has always been a threat hanging over the organization,' says one of his admirers. 'He once wrote a book on sex in which he insisted on writing all the words in their original Anglo-Saxon, so it was "fucks" and "cunts" all over the place, and Doris Odlum was the only person who was able to persuade Chad not to publish this bloody book. If it had been published it would have caused a furore, in and out of the Samaritan movement. When he went to branches to give talks on befriending people with sexual problems he deliberately went out of his way to shock as many people as he could, with, I think in part, the laudable purpose of removing from the organization people who were going to be shocked. But the consequence of this was that we had branches all over the country threatening to leave. The first job I did when I was elected to the executive was to visit a branch in Surrey to close it down, because Chad had given them a talk on sex and they were so outraged they were threatening to leave the movement. We decided they were really rather a nice lot and didn't deserve to be closed down. Wherever he went we had to send people to damp things down afterwards. I'm sure Jesus Christ would have made a terrible pope, and in Chad Varah we had a brilliant, charismatic, creative person who started something quite new but, as his creation expanded, he proved not at all to be the person to carry out the bureaucracy.'

[6]Constable, 1973.

Three years after Chad Varah had featured in the honours list his adolescent offspring received its most influential flood of publicity: eleven episodes of a television series called *The Befrienders*. Based on archetypal case histories, it went out, in 1972, at peak viewing time on Saturday evenings, and was seen by an estimated eight million viewers. The result was a heavy response from young callers and youthful volunteers. Some branches recorded a two-hundred per cent increase in calls during transmission, but commenting at the time on the quality of the programmes, a volunteer from Reading who was also a television producer wrote to the *Samaritan* to say that many fellow Samaritans had found the series unreal, and many television professionals had found it trite. Left only with a relationship between client and volunteer to explore, he thought the programmes lacked dramatic content, for a Samaritan was essentially a passive listener. The clients, too, he thought unconvincing and uninvolved, but he concluded that the series had probably been good for the Samaritans. Quite apart from the bonus of free publicity on television, it has always been the case that in the United Kingdom, volunteers have been easier to recruit than overseas, for in this country there already exists a tradition of charitable and voluntary service, which perhaps is one advantage of the existence of a distinct and clearly identifiable middle-class. It was soon recognized by the Samaritans that the poorer the country overseas the more difficult they would find it to recruit volunteers prepared, or with the time available, to offer their services free of charge. In many developing countries it is common practice for people to take two jobs, when the work is available, just to make ends meet, and – again, when the work is available – whole families tend to seek employment from a very young age. Often, too, when a Samaritan branch did get established, there were no social services to back it up. Nevertheless, by the mid-seventies there were branches, in addition to Hong Kong, Bombay and Karachi (and excluding branches in Europe and affluent countries like Australia, Canada and the United States), in Zambia, Brazil, Malaysia, Singapore, South Korea, Calcutta (where one of the volunteers was Jacob de Mel, Bishop of Calcutta and Metropolitan of India), Delhi and Sri Lanka, with many more in the course of preparation. In 1974 twenty-two delegates from branches all over the world met at St Stephen.[7] The result was the setting up of an entirely independent organization called Befrienders International, The Samaritans Worldwide, and on 2 November 1974, twenty-one years to the day since establishing the Telephone Samaritans, Chad Varah resigned as director of the London branch to become the president of Befrienders International. He resigned from this post, together with the honorary presidency of the central London branch, on 2 November 1986.

So far as setting up new branches in the United Kingdom was concerned, the years 1970 to 1973 remained as busy as the Sixties had been. The first year of the new decade saw ten new branches, in Barnsley, Bognor Regis, Coleraine, Dublin, Hartlepool, Perth, Peterborough, Sunderland, Truro and Weymouth. In 1971, the year the Duchess of Kent became patron, a further eleven branches followed, at Barrow, Chesterfield, Durham, Ealing, Kirkcaldy, Mansfield, Preston, Wakefield, Weston-super-Mare, Yeovil and in North Hertfordshire. In 1972, still at the rate of one a month, branches or groups were appearing in Bracknell, Bury St Edmunds, Cork, Hamilton, Hereford, Lancaster, Pendle, Plymouth, Scarborough and Wigan. The other two branches set up that year marked a dramatic widening of Samaritan horizons: a Scottish Correspondence branch and a branch specifically designed to befriend in the open air, at Festivals. This was also the year Chad Varah received the Albert Schweitzer Gold Medal. Yet a further thirteen branches were founded in 1973, in Ashford, Bangor in Northern Ireland, Bridgend, Brierley Hill, Elgin, Gloucester, Hillingdon, Horsham, Inverness, Milton Keynes, Newry, Retford and Taunton. Although by this time the scope for further expansion was inevitably shrinking, thirty-seven

---

[7] A decade later the numbers of branches overseas had reached ninety-nine, no less than forty-three of them situated in Brazil.

more branches remained to be born. Five appeared in 1974, at Derry, Enfield, Grantham, Rhyl and Solihull, seven in 1975, in Aberystwyth, Ashington, Ballymena, Craigavon, Limerick, Omagh and Telford, and another half-dozen in 1976, at Galway, Harrowgate, Haverfordwest, Tamworth, Waterford and Winchester. Buxton, Rotherham and Southport were equipped with branches in 1977. The Scottish Borders and Farnborough were covered the following year. In 1979, Blackpool, the Isle of Man and Stockport each acquired a branch, and so, in 1980, did Dumfries. Bury followed in 1981, Matlock (since closed) the following year, and in 1983 Banbury became independent. Bangor in North Wales and Gwynedd became operative in 1984, Sligo and Shetland followed in 1985, and in 1986 Ennis, Caithness, Newbury and Newport, Isle of Wight brought to an astonishing total the establishment of 198 centres in twenty-seven years, a rate of progress which averages out at nearly one new branch every eight weeks over an unbroken period of a quarter of a century.

·2·

CARING FOR THE CARERS

One of the salient features of the Incorporation of the Samaritans in 1963 was the degree of autonomy granted to branches, so as to enable the movement to serve national needs at local level without the handicap of a top-heavy bureaucracy, one of whose functions might well have been to distribute funds from central sources. The reverse became the case. Each branch was made responsible for financing its own centre, and for handing over to the general office a proportion of its annual income, raised by itself, as a contribution to central running costs. That proportion is currently seven and a half per cent. According to the present general secretary, between 1963 and 1969 the general office consisted of a few boxes filed under somebody's bed, and later on of 'a couple of rooms in a vicarage out in Iver, for some reason'. It was not until 1969, by which time 100 branches scattered all over the British Isles were clamoring for advice and administrative support, that the Pilgrim Trust contributed £5,000 towards the purchase of a six-room semi-detached house in a residential area of Slough. It was going cheap because a road development scheme, which in the event fell through, was scheduled, and the house had been earmarked for demolition. Into these rather unpromising premises Basil Higginson moved eighteen months after taking up his appointment as general secretary.

Eventually two extra rooms were added, and today, the general office is staffed, in addition to the general secretary,

David Evans, by an assistant general secretary, Simon Armson, an administrative officer, Mrs Vera Feeney, who started work as secretary to Mr Higginson, three secretaries, a bookkeeper, an accountant and a publicity assistant. Funds have recently been supplied by British Petroleum for the employment for two years of an assistant to build up a data base. It was while he was chaplain to University College, Swansea, from 1969 to 1971, that Mr Evans first became a Samaritan volunteer, and eventually director of the Swansea branch. In 1971 he was appointed chaplain for social work in Birmingham, and again became director of the local Samaritans. Between 1972 and 1975 he was area representative for the West Midlands Region. Following Basil Higginson's resignation, Evans became joint general secretary, and since 1984 he has been designated general secretary. In the same year, Simon Armson was appointed assistant general secretary. He came to full-time work with the Samaritans with administrative experience in health service management, allied to personal knowledge of no less than four Samaritan branches, Birmingham, Shrewsbury, Telford and Oxford, in each of which he worked as a volunteer.

In 1975, David Evans inherited a movement receiving one million calls a year, of which 210,000 were coming from first-time callers, a situation that meant that one family in forty now had a Samaritan caller in their home. A survey that year carried out by National Opinion Polls, based on a random sample of 2,125 people picked from the electoral register in England, Scotland and Wales, was designed to gauge public awareness of the Samaritans and the likelihood of someone calling them. Ninety-two per cent of all those questioned had heard of the Samaritans, and the majority were reported to have a correct idea of their purpose, the level and accuracy of knowledge being highest among the younger age-levels sampled. Only seven per cent overall thought the Samaritans concerned themselves exclusively with suicide, a remarkable discovery for a movement which by that time might well have become almost wholly synonymous with suicide prevention. Equally satisfactory was the finding that only one per cent thought of the Samaritans as a religious organization, but it was a disturbing revelation that three out of five people questioned entertained the notion that the Samaritans were some kind of welfare agency. The report contained 10,000 statistics, hopefully more accurately compiled than a return sent in that year from a branch which reported fourteen unwanted female pregnancies and one male.

In so far as the Samaritans have evolved a hierarchical structure, it consists, at the top, of the council of management, who meet three times a year, and are ultimately responsible for the work and conduct of the Samaritans in the United Kingdom and the Republic of Ireland. As each branch is represented on the council usually, but not always, by its director, the size of the council is too unwieldly to deal with detailed business, and this is normally undertaken by an executive committee, meeting eight times a year and consisting of the chairman and three vice-chairmen, thirteen regional representatives, medical consultants and holders of a number of honorary posts – the bursar, solicitor, publicity officer and youth officer. The local branches are grouped into regions, each with a representative, elected annually by the regional branch directors. On a day-to-day basis, the branches are supervised either by a team of deputy directors or by 'leaders'. Once a volunteer has been accepted by their branch they automatically become a member of the Association, and they cease to belong to the Association – in other words, they stop being a Samaritan – when they resign from membership of their branch, or endure the disappointment of being asked to leave. There is no such thing as a Samaritan floating around in suspended animation. On moving house a volunteer must apply to join his new local branch, and there is no guarantee that he or she will be accepted without a period of retraining.

At the core of the Samaritan operation there resides a set of seven principles and seven practices, established by the council of management in 1981. For some volunteers, they read like a second revised version of the Bible; for everyone they serve at the very least as a basic yardstick for conduct, and by a careful if not perhaps too rigid adherence to them it is felt that every Samaritan everywhere, despite that element of autonomy the branches like to retain, can be assumed to be acting at any time of the day or night in accordance with one another and in the spirit of a quite definite philosophy. The council regard their set of fourteen cardinal principles and practices as a contract with the public. Among other things, they enshrine the necessity for preserving confidentiality, and they absolutely forbid a Samaritan to impose upon a caller their own convictions with regard to politics or religion. They make it plain, too, that in contacting the Samaritans a caller never loses his freedom to make his own decisions, including the decision to end his life.

It is interesting to note that there is a major difference of emphasis regarding confidentiality as between the Samaritans and the Church. No priest, Anglican or Roman Catholic, is permitted to reveal any information imparted in the confessional, even with the permission of the penitent, but the fourth Samaritan principle lays down that everything a caller says in asking the help of the Samaritans is completely confidential *within the organization*, and goes on to stress that a Samaritan volunteer is not permitted to accept confidences if a condition is made that not even the branch director should be informed of them. In order to be able to discuss a situation within the centre, the Samaritans in fact exercise a kind of collective confidentiality. But the Samaritans will refuse to reveal the fact of a telephone call or visit having been made to them, even by a child, without the caller's permission, and they will not disclose, again, unless they have permission, facts relating to a crime. This point was dramatically stressed in 1975 when the West Midlands police were hunting Donald Neilson, a notorious kidnapper who became known as the Black Panther. The director of the Stafford branch said at a meeting that if the Black Panther contacted the Samaritans their code of confidentiality would prevent anyone informing the police, and he was taken to task by the chief constable, who accused the Samaritans of neglecting their public duty. But in fact many gruesome crimes attract imposters, and the Birmingham branch had no less than two Black Panthers, neither of them Neilson, checking in. There is one exception in law which obliges disclosure of information to the police; receipt of information relating to an act of treason or terrorism, so that if someone telephoned a Samaritan centre threatening the life of the Sovereign, or to say that they had planted a bomb (as indeed they did in 1983, when the central London branch was alerted to the bombing of Harrods), the call would be reported immediately, whether the volunteer taking the call believed the threat to be a hoax or not. If a Samaritan was subpoenaed to appear in court as a witness in a criminal case he or she would be obliged to attend, but they could decline to testify by trying to seek the same protection accorded by custom to a priest, who would never be expected to break the seal of the confessional.

When it comes to setting up a new branch, the first criterion has always been not whether the area it is proposed to cover still remains uncatered for but whether, in terms of population, it is large enough to justify a twenty-four-hour emergency service staffed by unpaid volunteers in premises they must raise their own funds to run. There is nothing more demoralizing for a volunteer who has undergone eight weeks of intensive training and geared himself up to cope with some fairly grim situations than to sit around for four hours at a stretch with nothing to do. 'Now that the coverage of the country is so complete we are getting enquiries from groups of people in places too small to carry the commitment,' the general secretary says. 'A branch can open with about seventy volunteers, on the basis that publicity will bring in the other forty you need, but what many people don't realize is that to do even this you have to receive something like 350 applications, so as to allow for people who drop out of their own accord and the loss of people you regard as unsuitable. And they don't realize the boredom factor. It's not right to mount that sort of operation where the usage is going to be so slight that there will be a lot of blank shifts. Our experience is that you more or less know how many callers you will get from a given population.' When it is proposed to open a new branch, or grant full status to an 'associate group', the regional representative is responsible for taking the proposal to the executive committee. If the committee thinks the proposition worth investigating further, a steering committee is formed, headed by a local convenor. A public meeting is then held, to attract a nucleus of potential helpers, to encourage initial financial support and to make sure that the social services are kept informed of possible Samaritan involvement in their area. Contact is encouraged with a neighbouring branch so that they can offer assistance with the selection and training of the first volunteers. When a new branch becomes established, one of its first priorities is to elect a branch committee, to take charge of administration and fund-raising. Once open, the branch is placed on probation for at least a year. By trial and error it has often been found that the first available premises are not necessarily the most suitable. A front door adjacent to Barclays Bank, British Home Stores and the police station may seem conveniently central but it does lack privacy. On the other hand, the ideal Samaritan centre is not too far removed from the bus or railway station, and it needs to be reasonably quiet yet easily located.

In the dozen years since 1975 the numbers of contacts made annually with the Samaritans, by telephone, letter or personal visit, has doubled to around two million, some 380,000 now being first-time callers.[1] The number of volunteers is currently registered at about 21,000, 6,000 short of the numbers required to maintain a really efficient service round the clock in every branch, where ideally at least three Samaritans will always be on duty, two to man two telephones and a third to answer the doorbell. But it is not unknown in the smaller branches for only one Samaritan to be on duty at a time, a practice very much deplored but occasionally inevitable. Even in those branches with a theoretically healthy membership, three volunteers sharing a shift can be run off their feet. 'Although 27,000 volunteers is a realistic figure to aim at,' says Mr Evans, 'in a way, the sky's the limit, because there are always occasions when branch lines

[1] In 1985 the Samaritans received 2,154,233 calls, an average of 5,901 a day.

are engaged. But certainly we need another 5,000 or 6,000. Although in recent years we have opened a few new branches, the numbers of volunteers has stayed steady, which amounts to a possible real decline. We lose upwards of thirty per cent a year. Considering the time we invest in selection, training and support, it's disappointing, although there are other organizations that have an even higher turnover.'

A branch with only two emergency lines really needs a minimum of 130 members, and 160 would be ideal. It has been estimated that if a branch inserts a third line, it immediately requires an additional forty volunteers to complete the rota. 'In some branches, with very large populations, we simply haven't got enough volunteers to cover the third line that we need,' says Mr Evans. 'We are worried about this rejection of people who get the engaged signal. We try not to block both lines with long calls, and sometimes we transfer to an ex-directory line and bear the expense of phoning the caller back. But not all callers want to give their number. At this point we may have two volunteers on two lines and someone at the door as well. It is good to have one, sometimes two, lines in each branch not advertised to the public. We use them, for instance, to ring in with messages, so as not to block the emergency lines ourselves, and if an ex-directory phone is picked up and put down we know the branch is busy and we ring back later. They can be used for fixing up the duty rota, or consulting a leader or a director on call at home, again allowing us to keep the emergency lines open as much as possible.'

It rather seems as if a Samaritan is liable to remain a volunteer for fifteen years – and sometimes much longer – or to drop out after three, often for perfectly practical reasons; pregnancy, enrolling for a degree course in further education, moving home or changing jobs. And Mr Evans placed his finger on one particularly sensitive spot. 'It's hard to cope with a string of sex calls when you have otherwise blank shifts, and you wonder what it's all about. Sometimes you can almost hug a genuinely distressed person.' Women Samaritans take a very large number of calls from men wanting to masturbate while engaged in conversation on the telephone, and not surprisingly, some women feel able to deal with this aspect of their work in a more detached way than others. 'Two of my friends became volunteers,' a member of one of the busy London branches explained, 'and the reason they both left was the number of sex calls they had to deal with. I think a lot of people feel they are going to sort out dramas all the time, and be able to help in a practical way, and even after they've completed their training they still have false expectations. But if you go on duty and for the fifth time in an evening somebody asks you what colour your knickers are, you tend to get a bit cheesed off with it, frankly.' This volunteer, married to a Samaritan and a member of her branch for the past eleven years, cited as another cause of people dropping out the possibility of personality clashes. 'Then, again, some people just find they can't cope, or a crisis comes up in their own life they have to deal with, and they find they can't deal with that on top of their Samaritan work.

'I think you could become stale, or cynical, if you did nothing else except your duties, and you stayed very much within your branch. But because my husband and I both have Samaritan duties outside our branch we've made a lot of friends. If you have a spouse who isn't a volunteer there can be some conflict. Although the Samaritans always insist that a spouse should be happy about their partner's involvement, there can be some uneasiness occasionally.' Mr Evans stressed the opportunities for maintaining interest. 'The average length of time for a volunteer is about three years, but a change of role in the branch will keep up morale. There are lots of roles for keeping up enthusiasm – rota secretary, membership of the committee, acting as a leader or a deputy director. Although it's not a rule, a lot of branches are now leaving people in a post not longer than three years.'

In 1980, a volunteer from Bognor, writing in the *Samaritan*, said she thought that 'in a small branch such as ours, boredom can be a problem. The large city branches probably have calls practically non-stop, whereas we can spend the whole shift chatting to our colleagues, pausing only to seize gratefully upon a long-term caller and reluctantly obey standing orders to limit him to ten minutes. It can be hard to accept the maxim that we joined the Samaritans to be there, not to be busy, but it is something we have to accept.'

Between 1978 and 1980, fifty-seven volunteers resigned from the branch in Reading, twenty per cent per annum of the branch membership. During that period, one of the volunteers telephoned all those who had left to try to ascertain the reasons, and found that fourteen had done so for the perfectly good reason that they had left the district, eleven because of ill health or old age, thirteen because of a variety of changes in personal circumstances, including pregnancy and promotion at work, and three had felt the time had come to leave because of long service. Of the remaining fifteen, the volunteer carrying out the telephone survey concluded that nine had never enjoyed a real commitment, expressing comments like, 'It was not what I had expected', five had felt doubtful about Samaritan methods ('We ought to be able to do something for our clients, not just listen,' one former Samaritan told him), and two were apparently dissatisfied with the leadership in the branch, feeling they could have done a better job themselves.

The image of an organization run by middle-aged, middle-class women, dressed in sensible shoes, twin sets and pearls, to which many female Samaritan volunteers themselves subscribe, is not borne out by the facts. At least a third of Samaritan volunteers are men, most branches outside London and the Home Counties are staffed by local people with regional accents, and many more Samaritans pertain to lower-middle-class status than to middle-class. And, unlike many voluntary organizations, the Samaritans seem to make no appeal whatsoever to the upper-middle-class; among some 175 volunteers elected or co-opted to the council of management in 1984, not one had a title. However, there is still within the Samaritans, in common with most other voluntary agencies, an overwhelming dearth of volunteers from ethnic groups other than white and established British. At a conference of 300 Samaritans drawn from every part of the United Kingdom and Ireland it would be rare to spot more than one coloured face. Mr Evans places the chances of more than five coloured or ethnic volunteers turning up among 1,000 delegates to the annual conference (excluding visitors from overseas) as most unlikely. 'I have no idea why this is. As their situation has been politicized, maybe it is less likely they will volunteer for what they see as a white agency. But then we don't receive many calls from members of ethnic communities, either. Occasionally you do receive a call in a Birmingham or Yorkshire accent and something doesn't add up, and you suddenly realize in spite of the accent you are talking to a West Indian or an Asian. Their expectations tend to be different, towards marriage, the family, parents, grandparents and so on. But no specific training has yet been given to help with this. I think almost any branch would fall over backwards to encourage ethnic volunteers, but they are not coming forward, and in company with many other organizations, we don't know the answer – unless we ran a black branch, but it might be very inefficient in terms of resources.'

A deputy director who did have a coloured volunteer in her branch said she thought he might be one of so few because of 'an image we've got that we shouldn't have. In a lot of voluntary organizations we tend to be middle-aged, middle-class women, people like me, but it's largely a question of who's got the time.' Robert, her West Indian colleague, has got spare time because he is out of work. 'I don't think a West Indian accent, for example, would be off-putting to a white caller,' she said. 'A Sloane voice is much more likely to be. But I don't think people in a crisis really care whose voice they get, quite honestly.' Robert said he had never experienced any problems with people talking to him. 'I even had a caller the other day moaning on to me about coloured people. We have a gay volunteer who's sometimes on duty with me, and he had a caller recently complaining about gay people! When we first volunteered we were both asked what our attitude would be if that sort of thing happened. If you're going to get the hump about it you can't act as a Samaritan.'

The key person in every branch is the director, for he is the man or woman ultimately responsible for the morale of the volunteers, upon whose performance the lives of some of the callers could depend. And one of the most reassuring aspects of Samaritan organization, despite some disadvantages it brings in terms of a lack of continuity, is the way in which directorships turn over every three years or so. A stretch in office of five years is tolerated, but no more. This gives the branch a regular chance to renew enthusiasm under new leadership, and continually reminds all those who hold office that they remain first and foremost a Samaritan volunteer. The chances are that a director will have had several years' experience as a Samaritan. In 1980 a branch in the Midlands chose a local government officer of twenty-nine, but he had been a volunteer since the age of twenty. In 1986, a branch in Yorkshire acquired a director of twenty-seven, who joined the movement when he was only seventeen. A fair proportion of directors are in their early thirties. Anyone taking on the directorship of a branch at whatever age assumes considerable responsibility. A young male director in the Eastern Region, on the point of stepping down after three and a half years, explains how his successor, a woman, came to be appointed.

'I think it's important to remember that the director of every branch is appointed by the council of management, not by the branch, so that the director is the Samaritans's man or woman in a certain branch. The branch only nominates. When a director resigns it is the responsibility of the branch chairman to set up a working party to consider the needs of the branch. Our working party consisted of two committee members, one representative from the leader team, and one representative from the branch. We approached at least fifty per cent of the volunteers to sound them out. We talked to everyone in the leader teams, because they work most closely with the director, and everyone on the training team and the interviewing team.

'We came up with about eight names. But there were not even one or two who were willing to take on the job. Nobody we had considered suitable wanted it. It was too big . . . it wasn't the right time . . . But two names emerged as favourites. One still remained determined not to go forward, so the other woman said she would. The regional representative was consulted. She came down and met Betty quite informally, over dinner, but she did manage to conduct an interview in those circumstances. She then had a meeting with the working party, and said she was prepared to put Betty's name forward to the council of management, and the working party reported back to the branch committee.'

Every one of the 182 directors may see his or her task in a different light, and will certainly bring his or her own gifts and handicaps to the job. A schoolmaster in his late thirties, who professes to shyness but hides a tough interior behind a winsome veneer, gives an account of his own approach:

'As director I'm responsible for the volunteers as well as the callers, and I refuse to be responsible for people I don't know. So I interview each volunteer, and the interview usually lasts anything from an hour to an hour and a half. It's difficult to keep it shorter than that. I want them to get to know me as much as I want to get to know them. They think I'm quite an authoritarian figure, but I'm not! I investigate how, during training, they have experienced asking about suicide. Has it been difficult for them? Have they always asked about suicide? If not, why not? Have they had any calls that they found particularly difficult to cope with? Was there anything about our work that took them by surprise? Was it what they expected? They must have given some thought to being a Samaritan before they came along and volunteered their services, and I do sometimes distrust people who say, "It was exactly as I expected it to be," because I don't think it can be. I really don't think it can. I always ask, "Have we disappointed you in some way? Did you expect that we were going to do wonderful things, wave magic wands and make everything better?" And I'm pleased to say that in almost every case people say it's better than they expected it to be. The thing that makes it better for them is the fellowship and support they get from other volunteers.

'I spend a good twenty-five hours a week on Samaritan work.

I suppose it is a lot, but you don't do any more than you want to do. I do it because I find it rewarding. Make no mistake about it, I get a great deal out of it. And at the same time I'm looking forward to handing over to somebody else!'

With the continual growth of new branches over the years, not necessarily evenly spread across the country, the regional boundaries into which the United Kingdom branches are divided have been altered four times since 1966. Recently it was found that one region possessed seven branches, another twenty-four. For members of the Truro branch, located in the South West Region, to meet up with members from Haverford-west involved a round journey of 600 miles. While Carlisle remained in the North West Region (it has now been reallocated to the North), this branch was separated from its fellow regional branch of Bangor by 400 miles. So at the end of 1985 a major reshuffle took place, leaving only two of the previous dozen regions unaffected. Twenty-five branches changed regional affiliation, and a new, thirteenth, region was established to cover South Wales and the Marshes. The largest region at present is the North East, with sixteen branches. The remaining twelve regions consist, on average, of about four-teen branches each.

Regional representatives are elected annually by the branch directors in their region. Their appointment is ratified by the council of management, of which they automatically become a member, as well as a member of the executive committee. This involves nine meetings a year. In theory it would be possible to combine the job of regional representative with directorship of a branch, but probably ill-advised. Previous experience as a director, on the other hand, is considered almost a *sine qua non*. A regional representative who has only been doing the job for a short time explains how she envisages the job and what she is trying to make of it:

'I was told it was a doddle, that I wouldn't be half as busy as I had been as a director, and then I received a four-page job description. But in fact the task is mainly representing the views of the executive committee to the region – views you may not share – and representing the views of the region, which, again, you may not share, to the executive. It's a very effective way of passing information backwards and forwards. You are consulted when a new director appointment has to be made, and you have to interview the person who may be appointed, and discuss with them all the aspects of being a director, which is why you need to be an ex-director yourself.

'You oversee regional spending, things like the publicity budget, the budget for befriending in the open, and for training in the region, and you help to mount regional training conferences. In my region I have thirteen branches, and I am responsible for support of the thirteen directors. But I never visit a branch unless I'm invited. I'm quite sure that if I said I want to come to a branch they'd be delighted, but I prefer to be invited rather than inflict myself. I also chair the regional directors' meetings, three or four times a year, and put together the agenda. We may discuss callers who are of concern to a number of branches, or any particular aspect of work that's come up at the executive that needs to be discussed with the directors, or anything that the council of management has decided upon which they want to discuss. You have to be re-elected each year, and it's generally for three years, and of course you continue as a volunteer in your own branch.'

One of the most crucial group of Samaritans in any branch are the leaders, a kind of back-up team who form part of the decision-making hierarchy, between the volunteers on duty and the deputy directors, and whose task also is to supply an instant source of comfort and support within the branch. 'Caring for the carers is their most important task,' is how one director put it. 'You don't know what's going to be thrown at you during the course of a duty and sometimes it's quite traumatic.' One branch on the east coast has eighteen leaders, who work in pairs over a twenty-four-hour shift, one as leader and the other as deputy leader. The leader remains on call at home, 'and thus can remain more detached, and defuse any heavy situation in the centre.' If a caller wanted the Samaritans to ring for a doctor, the leader would undertake to do so. Leaders are also responsible for discipline. One explained: 'If I was seriously concerned about the capabilities of a volunteer I would talk to them first, at the time if possible, but failing that I would arrange to meet them and hear what they had to say about the situation. If it was a matter of not following one of the practices or principles, and they felt unable to accept these conditions, then I would take it further, to the deputy or the director. But usually I find that if you just talk to a volunteer about any matter of conscience they manage to work out the correct solution for themselves.'

A Samaritan from one of the London branches recounted her experience of the role of a leader. 'It varies from branch to branch. Some do a twenty-four-hour duty, some a twelve-hour duty. And some branches have leaders who change with each shift. If the leader needs help he will go either to the deputy director or the director. In point of fact, in my branch we don't have leaders as such, we have deputy directors, and we do a seven-day stint. We are on duty as a deputy director from midnight on Sunday until midnight Saturday. You go about your normal everyday work and you carry a bleeper, so that if you are not available at the end of a telephone and the centre needs you urgently, they bleep you. A leader, or deputy director, is in charge of decision-making on the shifts. If a volunteer has a difficult call, someone obviously dying, for instance, they would consult the leader. If a leader has had a disturbed night every night for seven nights, by the end of the week you're feeling a bit shredded, to say the least.'

Deputy directors usually take on a specific task in a centre. At a branch in the East Midlands, one deputy is responsible for initial training, one for on-going training, one for callers and one for volunteers. 'One thing that our volunteers here find very reassuring,' said the deputy director who looks after the welfare of the volunteers, 'is that they are never alone. There's always someone else on watch with them. There is always a leader to whom they can refer, and the leaders are very good at helping them to express their own feelings after they have spoken to a caller. It's my job to speak to a volunteer if they've done something silly, like promising to go out to see a caller when they've finished their watch and going off without reference to anybody else. This sort of thing can all be done in a hurry, with the best possible motives, but really it isn't on. Then there are volunteers who are having a hard time themselves. They won't always ring me, they may prefer to speak to some other friend in the branch, or even outside, but if they want particularly to talk to me, that's fine. If anybody is having a break because of some personal difficulty, or they are ill, I keep in touch.

'But my main task is to support volunteers when they have taken a really difficult call. Things like silent calls. A long, silent call can be very distressing. You feel an absolute failure at the end of it when you've been trying to get someone to talk for half an hour and then the phone goes down. They can really be quite hard to deal with. And then there are the people who ring – we do get them occasionally – who have quite made up their mind they are going to take their own life, and really just want to tell somebody. But they don't want any help, they don't want us to go to them, and that's hard. The caller ends the conversation, usually. We don't have absolutely firm rules about it. Although we respect everybody's right to make their own decision we do not accept that they have a right to involve us in their death. So we will not actually sit and talk to somebody while they die. That's too harrowing for a volunteer, we feel. It used to be that you stayed with them until they were unconscious, then rushed them to intensive care, by which time some vital organ might well have been damaged, resulting in kidney failure or a stroke. So now you do not enter into any contract to stay with someone while they die. If we have a caller on the phone who has overdosed then we would make it clear to the caller that if they passed out on the phone, if they lost consciousness, we would do everything we could to get help. And that's not asking them if we may, that's saying, "If this happens, this is what we shall do." And then the caller has the choice of hanging up or allowing us to help, because we feel otherwise that it's much too heavy for the volunteer.

'If something like this happens, you do need to talk it through afterwards, because you can't take it home. You can't talk to anybody else about what has happened. So we need a very strong support system within the organization. I may go home and say, "I've had a terrible time, it's really been awful," but you can't go into the details at home in the way you can in the centre. And it's hard, sometimes, when you worry about what you've done. You may feel OK when you leave the centre but later you need to ring someone. I think – I hope – that's what we're good at. I think we do support each other.'

To make quite sure that Samaritans *are* supporting one another, and of course that they are providing the most effective service possible to callers within the guide-lines laid down by the fourteen principles and practices, a system of branch visits has been inaugurated. These are conducted, about every two and a half years, by a panel of experienced Samaritans, many of whom will have served as directors, and who will therefore have personal knowledge of the stress involved in running a branch. Regional representatives are encouraged to put forward the names of suitable Visitors, but a final choice is made by the executive committe. All Visitors attend training weekends. The best they can hope to gain during a necessarily brief visit is an overall impression of a branch and its atmosphere, and every effort is made to dispel the impression that somehow a branch is under threat. What the Visitors are most anxious to experience is the relationship that has developed within the branch be-tween callers and volunteers, and they tend to ask themselves two basic questions: would I care to be a caller at this branch? And could I feel happy as a volunteer here? Visitors work in pairs, and always come from two different regions. They attend a branch meeting so that they can meet as many volunteers as possible, and they inspect every aspect of the branch work – funding as well as caller-care.

Samaritans come in every shape and size, and from every corner of the British Isles. Among the 20,000 people at present manning 380 emergency telephone lines, some live in the leafy lanes of Horsham, others overlook the industrial wastes of Gateshead, the slag heaps of Ebbw Vale, the rolling green of the

Lowlands. Yet although the movement embraces geographically nearly as wide a diversity of accents and attitudes as the nation itself, those 20,000 disparate individuals do seem to be welded into some sort of recognizable entity. They possess more in common than a shared philosophy or frame of mind. Some are more modest and self-effacing than others, some better drinking companions, others less unimaginatively dressed, but taken all in all a distinguishable aura of gentle tolerance and patience emanates from Samaritans, a noticeable inner quiet one does not encounter at a cocktail party, where strangers look over your shoulder or try to get into an argument. Like monks and nuns, who consciously but politely distance themselves from personal involvement so as to preserve their emotional chastity, Samaritans create conditions for instant, disinterested contact rarely possible elsewhere in our frenetic age. The contrast between delayed adolescent neurosis let loose at an Open University summer school and the relaxed, mature revelry at a Samaritan conference could not be greater. This temporary, professional celibacy, the peace treaty they seem to have signed in the battle between the sexes, for example, enables the men, especially, to relax. While many Samaritans smoke like chimneys and laugh an awful lot, they disarm criticism by their lack of aggression. They do not try to score points off one another, nor off those they meet outside the circle of Samaritan colleagues, so that when a Samaritan asks quite a personal question, designed to elicit information about your marital status or possible sexual orientation, the question comes after a relationship has been established and as an act of friendship. It never stems from prurient curiosity. They look you in the eye, and make you welcome without overwhelming you with *bonhomie*. These are of course overall and generalized impressions gleaned in the course of restricted research, but they represent very positive impressions, all the more distinctly etched and registered for being, in the normal round of life, such rare experiences.

Somehow or other, the Samaritans also survive, most of the time, their own and other people's grief on a scale almost

incomprehensible to an outsider. During a recent annual conference, for an hour and a quarter Mother Frances Dominica,
who runs a hospice in Oxford for children, calmly introduced
a succession of slides showing boys and girls, babies and
teenagers, and just as calmly spoke of everyday life in the house
as they and their families and the staff and the Duchess of Kent,
who pops in to help every now and again, contemplate the ever
present reality of premature death. 'I was all right until the dog
came on the screen,' one Samaritan said afterwards. 'That was
too much.' After half an hour the hall had become a gently
lapping sea of hankies, with men and women quietly wiping
away the tears that had become a kind of common denominator
of their own voluntary calling. And of course Samaritans are
vulnerable to body blows from all sorts of directions. At the
same conference, a talk on child abuse resulted in a female
volunteer who many years before had been sexually assaulted
by her father becoming so suicidal she had to be professionally
befriended.

And to say that Samaritans come in every shape and size is no
exaggeration. If you meet a Samaritan he may be a handsome
young left-wing idealist, with thick black hair and wearing
filthy dirty jeans, who rolls his own cigarettes and speaks with
flattened-out Midland vowels. Or she may be a cosy middle-
aged lady ideally suited to running the local post office. Or a
young freckle-faced housewife wearing a mushroom-coloured
skirt. He may be a West Country farmer, too young to have
begun such a worrying paunch and too busy ever to have
cleaned his fingernails. They are the sort of people who nearly
always eat well and live in comfortable surroundings but are
prepared, like boy scouts from good homes, to put up with any
deprivation at a weekend conference, including packeted soup
at every meal, served to an unbroken string of announcements
about cars parked improperly, claims for travel expenses,
orders for Sunday newspapers, requests not to slam firedoors
after one o'clock in the morning. And their reading habits, if
conference bookshops are anything to go by, are catholic, to say
the least; copies of *Adrian Mole* rub shoulders with *So You*

Think You're Attracted To the Same Sex?, *The Body Electric* with *Divorce and Your Money*, *Living With Multiple Sclerosis* with *Father and Son*.

Snatches of Samaritan conversation at conference time, caught on the hoof, can be instructive, too. A rather roly-poly volunteer from Scotland recalls how the Samaritan who had trained him had said that he had found he could only be himself as a Samaritan. 'And I've found the same,' he says. 'I can now talk to anyone about sex, about anything.' A rather earnest young man with a beard, gripping a pint of beer, gets into an argument in the bar with a colleague from the same branch about whether they are there to prevent suicide. 'I am!' she snaps. Someone else can be overheard to say, 'We are neurotic about confidentiality,' which is almost a heresy. Discussing the subject of training new volunteers, one old girl in tweed skirt and brogues, with a twinkle in her eye, says it is important to ask potential Samaritans if they have transport to get to the centre long before you start worrying whether they get upset by homosexuals. 'We don't encourage journalists to join,' comes over as rather an unnerving aside. A young wag called Martin suggests the Samaritans should automatically reject freemasons, too, and everyone looks suitably shocked until he explains it was a joke. Someone really lets the cat out of the bag when she is heard to offer advice on the treatment of new recruits. 'Don't tour the premises and let them see the files and so on,' she suggests, 'not until they've definitely been selected. They'll only find out things they shouldn't know.'

Whether Samaritans are jovial by nature or driven to drink through the stress of their work, they certainly let down their hair at conferences. A gay Quaker turns a corner of the bar into a cabaret; an actress lets off steam about the group to which she has been assigned, every member of which, she complains, refused to admit they had any hang-ups. 'I told them not to be so ridiculous,' she hisses into her soup at lunch. 'We all have hang-ups. Mine's the group I'm in!' A very glamorous volunteer who looks as though she ought to be an actress too, adorned with chunky blue earrings, a silver bangle round her ankle and wreaths of imitation coral round her neck, vigorously makes the point that there is no conceivable way you can dodge rejecting unsuitable candidates; rejection, she says, is rejection: 'You can't wrap it up.' Silently suppressing his mock resentment, a chubby young man with greying hair and piercing blue eyes whispers behind his hand, 'That's my leader over there. I can't *stand* him! He thinks we shouldn't ask new volunteers about personal problems at all!' Suddenly the door of the telephone kiosk bursts open, and a Samaritan mum from Surbiton bursts out. 'My daughter's got a First, my daughter's got a First,' she shrieks, 'I must hug someone,' and she flings her arms ecstatically round the first person she sees.

· 3 ·

AMATEURS AT WORK

Being a Samaritan is not a job for someone primarily seeking a lot of personal contact and direct involvement with other people. The majority of those who approach the Samaritans do so on the telephone, and after spending perhaps half an hour listening to a tale of woe, the volunteer, once that call has been discontinued, may never hear from the caller again, nor ever know for certain what effect their attempt to offer compassion, understanding, sympathy, care and reassurance has had. Yet at a period in our social evolution when, so far as such things can ever be accurately measured, kindness and consideration towards fellow human beings seems to be at a premium, when an atmosphere of alienation, at home, in school, at work and on the streets seems to have become the standard environment, and indifference to the lot of neighbours common practice, the Samaritans, with their deliberate policy of distanced involvement, their exchange of first names only, their use of numbers instead of surnames, their often faceless and always essentially anonymous offer of help, have become the organization towards which millions of people throughout the world instinctively turn at times of acute, sometimes suicidal, crisis.

The way in which housewives and solicitors, farmers and school teachers, accountants and clergy, bank clerks and supermarket supervisors are selected and trained as Samaritans varies from branch to branch, and while there is always a danger that a small yet busy branch, desperately trying to maintain double-manning round the clock with only sixty-five members, may be tempted to cut corners and accept volunteers they have doubts about (a potential drug-pusher once very nearly slipped through the net), the business of accepting suitable candidates and rejecting others is one the Samaritans take very seriously. With an almost constant need to recruit something like 7,000 volunteers every year merely to replace the thirty per cent of members who die, retire or resign, the movement wants a further 6,000 new members in order to improve existing services. 'A lot of people think we select just anyone,' a vice-chairman told a conference on selection held at Leeds University in 1986. 'In fact, our experience in my branch is that whenever we have accepted someone after training about whom we had our doubts, we have lived to regret it.' It has been estimated that about eighty per cent of those who make an initial inquiry about joining the Samaritans arrive for a first interview, twenty per cent having themselves decided not to go forward on realizing more fully what sort of work or commitment was involved, and only thirty per cent (some, again, having made their own decision not to proceed) are eventually accepted at the end of their period of training.

On receiving a telephone call from a potential recruit, some branches send out an initial application form, others invite a group of new volunteers to a social gathering prior to an initial interview. The first question usually asked is why the applicant applied, and behind the answer sometimes lies, in reality, a need not to become a Samaritan but to seek the help of the Samaritans. Two or three Samaritans in every branch have probably at some time in their life, quite often after joining the Samaritans, been a caller, and a number of potential callers seek contact with the Samaritans in the first place by seeming to apply as a volunteer. Providing an answer to the question 'Why do you want to be a Samaritan?' may prove the hardest test for applicants, seeming to make them sound smug ('I want to help other people.'), or unsure of their motives ('It just seemed like something I ought to do.'). There is a fear of acknowledging the very real possibility that altruism does not exist, that seeking to help other people makes one feel better when perhaps it should not. People often think it necessary to justify their motives, and they feel equally nervous about being judged by them, and then found in some way unworthy.

Having surmounted (or maybe stumbled over) this first hurdle, the applicant will probably be asked whether they hold religious or political attitudes which they feel could be *useful* (and on the form supplied to interviewers at one branch, the word 'useful' is underlined) as a Samaritan. Is this a trick question? Samaritans are strictly enjoined not to exhibit to callers any religious or political beliefs. They will also almost certainly be tested out on their feelings about abortion and homosexuality, and invited to discuss the things that shock them. They will be asked to throw their mind back to the biggest emotional crisis they have ever had to deal with, and to recall how they coped with it, and they will be asked if they have ever contacted the Samaritans before.

Questions about suicide loom large. *'Don't* be helpful if they're surprised by the question,' the interviewer is instructed on one questionnaire. The assumption that we all suffer from depression at some time is enshrined in a question on this subject, and the applicant is asked to talk about their friends, and to say how they think their friends would describe them. Information is prised out, too, about the applicant's home life, about whether they are married, single, divorced or living with someone to whom they are not married. Not every gay applicant would at this stage feel sufficiently at ease to disclose the fact, although others may make a point of doing so.

The procedure followed by a branch in London is to write, in the first place, to someone volunteering to be a Samaritan, inviting them to read a succinct but fairly detailed summary of Samaritan work and what is involved. It emphasizes, for example, that apart from helping a Samaritan to be available, the Samaritan's family will be positively excluded from that part of their life. 'You will not be able to discuss your work with them, for our clients' business is strictly confidential,' they are warned. They are told, too, that 'your own experience of distress will have enriched you and probably deepened your compassion and understanding. Equally, you may feel you have become too vulnerable to take on other people's troubles. If you are at present experiencing trouble or its immediate aftermath you may wish to be advised to postpone your application to a later date.' Only after the applicant has read and digested the fact sheet, and still expresses a desire to join, is an initial application form sent out. This starts with the daunting question, 'Why do you wish to become a Samaritan?' and invites information about physical disabilities, treatment for mental illness and previous contact with the Samaritans as a caller. Item 12 reads, 'Complete the following statements as spontaneously as possible: I feel encouraged when . . . It really bothers me when . . . I feel confident when . . .' And a referee is asked for.

Another branch, which sends out an application form straight away, asks new volunteers when they first heard about the Samaritans, and why they are volunteering now. 'I think this is actually quite a good question,' the director says. 'Why now rather than last week? Why now rather than six months ago? Has something happened to draw the Samaritans to their attention? And on the initial form we ask, "What makes you feel you are suitable for Samaritan work?" But I don't like that question. Some people feel they have to write an essay. I would much rather know the bare bones about somebody and develop the details at an interview. We are more articulate than we are literate, and it is easier for people to talk than to write.

'The application form is really just an indication of intent. It also includes an availability slip, and gives the person applying a chance to decide if they've really got the time to give to the kind of commitment we require. A lot of people are very vague about the Samaritans when they first offer their services. Some still think it's a religious organization. In our branch they are interviewed by just one person. Other branches have two people conducting the interview. Some branches even have a second person take over the interview half-way through. Everybody thinks theirs is the best method. Personally, I don't believe there is a best method. The matter of taking up references is also a contentious issue. In my branch we don't ask for them, because I think an applicant should be assessed on their own merits and not on what somebody else has to say about them. I don't know how many Samaritans would be recommended for Samaritan work by their employer or a friend, because these people don't know what it's like to be a Samaritan. It's not like recommending somebody for a job. At the interview and on the training course we have the means of assessing suitability better than anyone else.'

Debate about the best way to conduct selection interviews waxes strong. Those in favour of the technique of interviewing by panel maintain that a Samaritan needs to be able to relate to more than one person, and no opportunity to do this arises at a one-to-one interview. A clash of personalities is less likely, too, and while one member of the panel is questioning the interviewee, another is free to take notes. The overriding objection to three or four selectors meeting a new recruit, put forward by those who prefer the one-to-one approach, is that such a method is just too intimidating. 'People are being asked very personal questions,' an area representative points out, 'and if one selector is not competent to cover every area then I believe that two or three one-to-one interviews are preferable to the recruit having to face a panel. Many people who go for an interview do not realize before they get there how deeply their personality is going to be explored. Not many people are ever asked in the whole of their lives how they will be able to cope with behaviour and feelings. When a Samaritan is selecting candidates, he is not acting as a volunteer but as a selector, and he requires very special skills. He needs to be courteous but persistent, and sensitive but prepared to challenge views expressed by the candidate. Above all, he must be prepared to be tough, and for a Samaritan that isn't always easy. Whichever way you choose to conduct the selection process, we must always remember that selection is about creating an environment in which the candidate can do well.'

Skills required for rejecting candidates exercise the minds

of many Samaritans as much as those skills required for recommending they go forward for training. 'The application form should make it quite clear that you are only applying to be considered, and that for many reasons, not by any means detrimental to you, you may not get in,' a leader from the North East suggested at the conference in Leeds. 'We should be very careful not to raise people's hopes and expectations too high.' There seem to be as many ways of turning down a candidate as there are of conducting interviews and training classes. Some branches write a letter, some do the dreaded deed face to face, some on the telephone. Asked on a show of hands how they themselves would prefer to be rejected, a discussion group of some thirty Samaritans drawn from across the country seemed equally divided. One volunteer said he thought that whatever method was used it was important to put candidates out of their misery within twenty-four hours of an interview. Dismay was expressed at the disclosure that some branches funked the problem to the extent of sending out a cyclostyled letter, with even the director's signature stencilled. It was felt that not enough explanation was offered in the course of interviews to prepare the candidates for the possibility of rejection, so that because the Samaritans were in some positive way regarded as being run by 'good' people, those found unsuitable must feel morally tainted. Some branches apparently try to soften the blow by suggesting other areas of voluntary work where the candidate's particular aptitudes would fit in better, but as one selector emphatically put it, 'We never do this because it sounds as though you are offering a second prize.' Perhaps the most contentious issue regarding rejection is whether any reasons should be given. Many – perhaps most – branches offer no explanation at all. 'If any explanation is to be offered, be wary of putting it in writing,' is the advice of one director. 'People have a genius for misinterpreting letters. In any event, we are certainly under no obligation to justify ourselves, and if we are to offer reasons, one reason is sufficient. It should be some factor they will readily recognize in themselves, and not something they need feel badly about. It all comes down to making clear in the interview the whole range of reasons why certain perfectly admirable people are just not suitable for Samaritan work.'

If at the initial interview an applicant seems totally unsuitable, some branches take the bull by the horns and say so there and then. Others promise to communicate a decision within three weeks. Such factors as 'sensitivity', 'warmth', 'flexibility', 'ability to communicate', 'ability to listen' and 'ability to tolerate others' are assessed, and the interviewer is asked to consider whether they would be happy to work on a shift with the applicant, and whether they would feel happy confiding in them. If the impression is more favourable than otherwise, the applicant is accepted for training, on the understanding that at any stage they may be dropped, and likewise are free to leave. 'We should be very careful only to assess on observable facts,' one training officer strongly believes. 'It is almost impossible to assess such nebulous things as honesty and loyalty at an interview. One thing I'm certain of: we should do everything we can to eliminate unsuitable candidates before they go into a training class. This involves a commitment of sixteen hours over two months, and if you then reject them at the end of *that* they feel much more let down and unworthy to work for the Samaritans. They really feel they have failed. They are bound to. Obviously someone who has not measured up in training classes cannot be allowed to proceed, but it really is our responsibility to sort out our selection procedures so that these sort of disappointments are kept to a minimum.'

Like examinations, all interview situations are strictly unreliable, and many are looked back upon with laughter and incredulity. A Samaritan once interviewed by a fellow volunteer may, within half a dozen years, have become her interrogator's director. 'In an interview, everyone is on their best behaviour,' a leader who spends a fair amount of time selecting volunteers explains. 'And I think it is very revealing what people choose to tell you about themselves. I make it clear at the start that no one is going to be rejected because of anti-social behaviour, like attempting suicide. We have all sorts of people in the

Samaritans and we all have our own problems. I emphasize that the fact that you become a Samaritan doesn't guarantee immunity from stress. I always ask if they have ever contemplated suicide, because from knowledge of how a volunteer has coped with their own emotional problems you can make an assessment of their attitude to other people's. You get a gut feeling. I'm sorry, but I do get a gut feeling. I always ask applicants to give me an example of something they think they're not very good at, or an area in their own life where they think they haven't coped very well, and this is revealing in two ways. It tells you how they did actually cope, and what their attitude to it was.

'The things I look for as an interviewer are a responsiveness to others, an ability to establish a rapport with another person, and someone who has a fair amount of experience of life. But I make a distinction there, because we do have some quite young people coming forward. You can't expect a great experience of life from them, but everybody has potential, and if they haven't got experience then you look for the potential. Above all, we are looking for people who are honest – honest with you, honest about themselves and honest about their feelings.'

The question 'Why do you want to be a Samaritan?' is reserved until the end of the training programme in the case of a branch in the north-east region. 'The question about their motive is the question most people find most difficult to answer,' the director has found. 'I always ask it when I conduct the final interview, because by then they are much more relaxed, and we know them pretty well. At the initial interview, many people just don't know why they want to be a Samaritan. It isn't that they can't articulate it, they genuinely don't know.' Something into which he inquires very closely is the ability to make friends. 'Someone I can think of came along recently and didn't really know why he had come forward, and then told us his mother had thought it would be a good idea. Well, you think twice about that, don't you!'

'Interviews in my branch are quite intensive because we need to probe deeply to make sure that the applicant isn't going to be rocked by being a volunteer,' a member of the selection panel at a large branch in the Midlands explained. 'We take three weeks to inform applicants of the outcome because the report I make out is read by a group before a decision is made to accept someone for training. And although I use the word training, I don't actually believe you can train people to befriend. We develop skills, we're not trained. There are fewer misconceptions among applicants about the work we do than there used to be because we send them a packet of information, but they still don't realize how much they are supported when they come on duty. Samaritans are required to consult among themselves, and this comes as a revelation, too. If at the end of the three-week delay we turn someone down we never give a reason. There are some things you can't tell people.

'Basically, you've got to be stronger than the caller. If someone presenting themselves as a volunteer is going through an emotional crisis of their own, they are not ready to become a Samaritan. Which is not to say they won't be later on. Being a Samaritan is quite demanding, by any stretch of the imagination. In my branch, trainees take a phone call before the end of their training so they can discuss with the director how they felt they were supported. People get very anxious about their first call, and the sooner they take it the better. But what I always try to get over to new recruits is that taking a call as a Samaritan isn't all that different to having a friend ring you up in distress. We are not professionals. We are acting as friends. A professional is someone who has gone through a recognized training in a specific subject and come out with an accepted qualification at the end of it. I would most certainly accept the analogy that we are amateurs. Oh yes, absolutely. Absolutely. The word amateur comes from *amare*, love, and this is the basis of the caring we hope to give.'

The value of support for one another offered by volunteers in the branch was echoed by an experienced Samaritan, who said, 'Thank God we don't work at home, and thank God we always work in pairs. Very often, if you've had a really hairy call and you've been on the telephone for an hour and a half with someone who sounds pretty desperate, an hour and a half's concentrated listening, you need to blow off steam with some-body, and the great thing is, there's somebody else in the centre with whom you can nearly always discuss the call, and off-load it to some degree. This is especially necessary if you feel somehow you haven't been of any help. Sometimes you just feel so helpless, and that's when you most need support and reassur-ance from another volunteer.' And sometimes, of course, a caller can arouse in a volunteer strong feelings of resentment. One of the most able, and gentle, members of a training team told her class of recruits, 'Callers do sometimes make us very cross! And that is something you will need to recognize and come to terms with.'

Just as having experienced suicidal feelings in the past is no automatic bar to membership of the Samaritans, neither is physical disability, and a number of volunteers are confined to a wheelchair. The only handicap to their joining a branch may be ease of access to the centre, as some Samaritan premises, unfortunately, can only be reached by a flight of stairs. Many branches number among their members at least one blind Samaritan. This might at first seem like an insuperable dis-advantage, when it comes to making notes after a call, or interviewing a caller face to face, for the loss of eye-to-eye contact undoubtedly invalidates a major dimension inherent in any personal meeting. But Ada, a cheerful widow in her mid-sixties, claims she overcomes most problems by her gift of a retentive memory. 'I had to develop that,' she says, 'when I went totally blind in my mid-twenties. When it comes to making a report, I dictate everything at the end of my shift. I've been a Samaritan now for ten years, with one break when I had a personal bereavement to cope with. You're no use to other people then. I act as a guide and mentor to recruits during our training sessions, and find blindness no disadvantage in my work at all.' Unlike many blind people, Ada smiles much of the time, and only feigns bad temper when reprimanding her dog.

A blind Samaritan in Manchester contributed some forth-right comments on the selection of blind volunteers in an article he sent to the *Samaritan* in 1985. He urged the disabusement of certain myths about the blind; they are in no way especially wise, he wrote, with no special sixth sense or compensation. On the contrary, blindness brought its own 'crop of special hang-ups'. He said he would think very hard about accepting someone in the process of losing their sight. 'What such a person does not know is the extent to which he will have to reorganize his practical and psychological mode of life.' Some astringent advice included the following: 'Don't worry about your building. If a blind volunteer falls down your stairs it's his fault, just as it would be your fault if you fell down them. Once he knows where they are, it's up to him; they won't move.' He made the point that a blind volunteer must exercise the same responsibility as anyone else about getting to the centre on time, and should not look strange or 'off-putting in any way.' During thirteen years as a Samaritan, he wrote, 'visitors have talked to me very easily. A few have asked whether I have something wrong with my eyes, but once they know I can't see they forget about it. Most don't mention it at all, and I think some don't notice anything unusual, particularly when they are very distressed.'

The numbers of Samaritans married to a fellow Samaritan appear reasonably small, but the numbers who are married and whose spouse has in some measure to support the active Samaritan, and indirectly the work of the branch, is considerable. 'I think the Samaritans make very heavy demands on spouses,' a London-based volunteer considers, 'although when a Samaritan first joins we make sure that their husband, wife or partner understands they must turn up for duty. Sometimes at night, if you are a leader or a deputy director, as I am, you get phone calls at home, interrupting your home life. You may have to go off and do some fund-raising, and the pressures can be quite strong to help out with a variety of additional chores. Fortunately most spouses are very supportive, but you do get some who say enough is enough. And I think the strain on them can be quite considerable. This is the reason some volunteers drop out. Merely by supporting their partner in his or her work, a spouse is making a very real contribution, but they don't get the job satisfaction, and the more you can involve them in branch activities the better. They are never going to be told by a caller, "If it wasn't for you I wouldn't be alive."

'When I am on call to the centre at home, I deal with calls at night on an extension downstairs, but initially the phone rings by the bed, and inevitably it wakes up my husband. I think some people actually arrange to sleep in separate rooms so that the partner isn't disturbed. But a director can't do that or you'd be sleeping apart for three years. So before a director, or even a leader, takes on the job, I think they've got to sit down and have a good, hard, frank talk with their partner, and ask, "Are you prepared to put up with this, because if you're not, then we won't enter into it at all." But I honestly don't think directors know what is involved until they become a director. I think leaders do, because they know how often they've rung their own leader, but every leader in the branch can be ringing the director. So it's often much better to have a system of duty directors, where a duty director stands in for a week at a time and the director is only called as a last resort. It's very difficult to assess the disruption to family life until you're in the middle of it.'

Questioned about her religious attitudes when she first applied to join the Samaritans fifteen years ago, a mother of two sons has certainly found over the years that her personal attitudes have not just been useful but essential. She has a full-time job as a personnel officer in an industrial town on the Welsh coast, and as a Roman Catholic she attends Mass every Sunday. Her Church remains opposed to a whole range of activities to which Samaritans callers 'confess' every day of the week – abortion, homosexuality, masturbation, adultery and pre-marital sex – which many sections of society now regard as either natural or, in certain circumstances, excusable. How does she square her joint allegiance to the official teachings of the Catholic Church and to the non-judgemental approach of the Samaritans?

'I do square it,' she says, 'and I don't find a conflict. When I first joined the Samaritans I found I had to think this through very carefully, to see whether there was going to be any great conflict, but in fact there isn't, because for one thing we're not offering advice, we're not saying to people, "If I were you I would do that, or I would stop doing that," and in one sense we're not really concerned with their actions. We are concerned with callers as people, so that what they do and what they are are two different things. We all do things that we know are not really right, but we don't stop loving each other because of them, and I think you have got to say to yourself, "I am concerned with this person and how they feel, I'm offering them friendship and care, and I'm not passing any opinion on what they're doing, because it doesn't concern me." I'm not in the Samaritan centre to run their lives or to moralize.

'At the end of my probationary period I was interviewed by the director, and I mentioned to him that I was concerned about an abortion issue, which at that time was right at the centre of discussion. And he said, "Well, you know, you're not there to give advice." And that really opened it up for me. I realized I had in fact been thinking about it from quite the wrong angle. And once I began to look at it from that point of view I found it applied to all sorts of things that might have been problems had I not had that wise word at the time.

'I think I was motivated to become a Samaritan through my religious belief, in so far as I feel we all have a certain responsibility for each other, that we can't exist in a vacuum. No human being can really cut themself off from other people. And if your own life is pretty stable, at least for the moment, then you ought to be being of some use to somebody else. You don't know when the tables are going to be turned, and you're going to find you need support. But I think all Samaritans are aware of this, that for a time you are on one end of the phone, but within a matter of days or weeks you might need to be on the other end, as a caller. Because we're all very vulnerable. So yes, my religion did motivate me. It has also supported me in being a Samaritan, because from my point of view, speaking as a Catholic, it isn't possible to do this kind of work without prayer. And I think that any offering of yourself to other people has to be based on prayer if it's going to be valid. That doesn't mean to say I would ever go and tell anybody that I prayed regularly before I went on duty, but I do. Samaritans with no religious belief are often better Samaritans, but that is the way I find my support, and perhaps they have other ways of finding theirs. There are really super Samaritans who have no beliefs at all. But I don't know how they cope with it. The most difficult thing for me was coping with one caller who had a terminal illness, about twelve years ago, and I've never forgotten that girl. It was something that really got to me at the time, and I thought that once she had stopped contacting us, because she was too ill, the only use I could be to her was through prayer. So I used to remember her at Communion each Sunday. And in a way that comforted *me*. I felt I wasn't totally cut off from somebody whom I cared about very much. Becoming a Samaritan has totally changed my understanding of people and their problems. Totally.'

The former joint general secretary, Jean Burt, remembers a Catholic priest who was also a Samaritan. 'Girls used to come to him pregnant, and he used to say to them, "Look, as a priest I cannot advise you, but here's the number of the pregnancy advisory service." Which seemed to me very sound!'

Why *do* people become Samaritans? One answer out of thousands was supplied by a television producer in Hampstead, married with two children, whose husband is also a Samaritan. 'I've been a Samaritan for ten years. My husband joined first. At the time he joined, one of our neighbours, also a Samaritan, asked me, "What about you?" and I said, "No, no, I don't want to join the Samaritans, I've got far too many friends who burden me with their problems anyway, I'm not taking on other people's problems as well." So I didn't join, and it wasn't until about two years later, when Bill had been thoroughly involved in the branch in various ways, that I actually happened to go out one night on a flying squad with him. A flying squad is when a caller rings into a branch, and is obviously in such a suicidal state that you are fairly certain they have made, or are about to make, a suicide attempt, and you stay with the caller, or ring for an ambulance, or bring the caller back to the centre.

'Now, in our branch you don't have to be two Samaritans on a flying squad. A husband can take his wife, or vice versa, and on this occasion Bill was called out and I went with him.[1] We arrived at this lady's house. She was very distressed and had taken an overdose, and her husband had called the Samaritans. He had telephoned the police as well, and they arrived. He was frightened, basically. Bill asked to be allowed to talk to the wife, and eventually the police went away. I drove the lady to the centre, and Bill sat with her in the back. I'd never been there before, and Bill said to me, "Will you take her into the interview room and I'll make some coffee, then I'll come in." So while he was making the coffee she was talking to me, and by the time he came back with the coffee I had got most of the problem. And I'm afraid after that I thought, well, maybe I could do it. Maybe this *was* something I could do. I don't think I thought I *should*, but that I could if they would have me. I can actually live without it. I discovered that when I had three months off, about eighteen months ago.'

Every story behind every Samaritan is different, as it is with every caller. Three years ago Maureen, a charming and elegant woman who lives in a small, comfortable house by the Thames in Berkshire, decided the time had come to reshape her life. She was already doing voluntary driving for a local hospital, attending art classes twice a week and acting 'as an agony aunt to nieces and people who rang me up and bent my ear for an hour', but then she also decided to volunteer to be a Samaritan. 'I was looking for directions, really. I was looking for something to do in the useful line. I was too old to get employment, and I'd had a very rocky three or four years. I haven't any paper qualifications of any sort. However, I have been through quite a lot in my life, one way and another, and I thought, surely the experience that I've had can be of some use to somebody. I was nattering on

---

[1] Many branches would strongly disapprove of a non-Samaritan attending a flying squad call.

about this one day and a friend of mine said, "Why don't you try being a Samaritan?" She had been one. It was something I had thought of, actually, some years ago, before my home broke up, only I didn't realize, as so many people don't, that you don't do it at home, and I didn't really see my husband being prepared to be woken by calls in the middle of the night. So I didn't think about it any more, but later I thought, now I am free I could do it. So I went along, and took a training course, and decided, yes, I would like to do it.

'How I relate my own unhappy experiences to my work as a Samaritan I don't really know, except that there are certain things I know about – bereavement, for instance. Cruse[2] know much more because they've made a study of it, but I do know that when you've lost somebody, you want to talk about that person, and that you're mostly stopped from talking because it embarrasses everybody. People cross to the other side of the street because they don't know what to say to you. They don't like to talk about the person who's died, and if it's someone you've lived with for many, many years and has been part of your life, you desperately want to talk about them. I mean, they're part of your life, you can't write them out, and to have to put up a wall of silence between you and them is very painful.

'I've lost two children. I've been divorced. In the year I was divorced my brother died of cancer, and I was visiting him every day when his wife couldn't. And within a year, my mother died. And I moved three times. Life was kind of hectic. But I somehow came through. I sometimes think that when all these things happen at once it is a sort of blessing, because you are kept so busy and so occupied with everybody else you haven't got time to sit around and feel sorry for yourself. But I did come to realize people's need to talk about certain things, and when people go through a very difficult time they need to talk about it sometimes over and over and over again. I was very lucky. When we sold the house and my husband went off, an old friend

[2] The National Organisation for the Widowed and their Children, 126 Sheen Road, Richmond, Surrey.

of mine decided to share a house with me. So I wasn't immediately on my own, as a lot of people are. I did have someone to talk to.

'I lost the children a long time ago, one at ten months, in what they call a cot death, which I'd never heard of before it happened, and my second son was drowned when he was four. I have one married son left. I was married for twenty-four years, and then my husband fell in love with someone. I knew that he wasn't a philanderer in any sort of way, he was a one-woman man really, so I knew it must be serious. I hoped it might blow over, but it didn't. So eventually we sold the house and I got a divorce. It was three or four years before I decided to offer myself as a Samaritan. When I was interviewed, I was asked, would it worry me if I talked to people who had been divorced? Would it revive old hurts, and so forth? And I said no, I thought I'd got over that, the bitterness, which is inevitable. It's so sordid, working out finances. Other than that they didn't ask very much, so I didn't tell very much. I don't like telling people unless they ask. I thought I'd forgiven my husband a long time ago and I've really worked hard not to be bitter. In many ways it's been good for my soul, if you know what I mean. I just feel it was awful when it happened, but that it's been what you might call a growing experience. I've had to cope with life again independently.

'If you are a woman and you're divorced and you're not working, not only do you lose your emotional security and your financial security but you lose the structure of your life, you lose your job, the job of running a house, the whole thing you do. And you lose half your friends. You are literally thrown out as naked as the day you were born, to pick up the pieces and to start life all over again. I was lucky, because I had a house, and a roof over my head, but a friend who is staying with me, she was left with practically nothing to live on at all, and she had a total nervous breakdown. In fact, she tried to commit suicide. She was between life and death for three days. So I lived through that. She was with me when she did it. She was in hospital for six weeks.

'Funnily enough I've hardly had any experience as a Samaritan of callers suffering as a result of lost children. It's like losing a limb. It's like losing a whole part of yourself, like having an arm cut off. It's extremely painful.[3] Before I became a Samaritan I was never tempted to ring them. I was never suicidal. It sounds very stupid, but when I had small children I remember quite distinctly suddenly understanding there was a purpose to life. It was like being born again, and ever since then I've had a kind of faith. Very individual. I've never been a church-goer. When I had to go to church a lot of it was all mumbo-jumbo to me, and boring, just plain boring, but I now understand what they're trying to say. I also had the feeling that suicide is no escape, because there is a theory, believe it or not, that you can't escape; if you don't meet it this time you'll meet it next. It's reincarnation, basically. I tend to believe in reincarnation. There's no evidence, but it makes sense. How else do you explain the people who are much more evolved than others? How do you explain the Mozarts and the Leonardos? I think that I was either a ballet dancer in my last incarnation or I'm going to be one in my next. I'm a frustrated ballet dancer. I love dancing. The thing that gives me greatest pleasure is to move my body to music. For one year, I went to a very good ballet school, and I really got very keen, and then my mother took me away. But I've always liked to use my body.

'You can't sort out your own problems by being a Samaritan. It's nothing to do with that. What happened to you has no bearing, necessarily, on what happens to the other person. Everybody has to handle problems in their own way. That's the trouble. It's very difficult to give anybody any keys. The real thing is to try and throw back to the person what they're saying so that they can talk it out and sort it out themselves. It's a great skill. I don't think I'm very skilled at it, but I know that is what is really necessary.

'Since I've been a Samaritan I did call them myself, once. Not

[3] The Compassionate Friends, 6 Denmark Street, Bristol, specialize in befriending bereaved parents.

my own branch, though. I had been a volunteer about two years and I was frightfully upset about something to do with my family, and it was midnight and I thought, I've got to talk to somebody, but I can't phone anyone at midnight, and I suddenly thought, I'll phone the Samaritans. I'll phone another branch, which I did. And of course, when I started to try and explain what was bothering me I burst into tears. I wasn't making much sense to them because I was crying so. The business of trying to explain what was upsetting me helped me sort out my thoughts, what it was that caused me such distress. So from the point of view of being a Samaritan it was a very revealing process.'

Another volunteer who had occasion to become a caller reported his experience in the *Samaritan*. 'Whilst I was a caller,' he wrote, 'it made me aware of Samaritan techniques being applied by the volunteer. I realize now, with hindsight, that I took a tremendous risk in making the call. Had the volunteer offered only techniques I should have been rendered even more dispirited.' But it seems he was fortunate in encountering the ideal Samaritan approach towards which all training and theory aspires. 'She gave me her undivided attention,' the caller wrote. 'She was warm, but not patronizing; she was gentle, but not wet; she was strong, but not critical; she was in control, but was considerate. Her tone of voice said it all (literally and metaphorically) and I could sense her support during silent spells.'

It is sometimes assumed that if the Samaritans recruit a wide variety of volunteers, married, single, divorced, old, young, middle-aged, heterosexual, homosexual, they will inevitably arm themselves with a catholic cross-section of society and thus be equipped to cope with every variation in the human condition. First of all, they never will recruit one of every kind; by the very nature of the role Samaritans are expected to play (a non-directional, essentially acquiescent one) they are unlikely to attract intellectuals, only people of average intelligence, and those who are not particularly creative or ambitious – although like all small ponds, the Samaritans will inevitably attract minnows with aspirations to swim to the top against less fierce competition than they would ever encounter in ICI or politics. Samaritan volunteers will tend to be passive rather than active, decent rather than holy, sensible rather than brilliant. And of course people do not volunteer because they fit into a particular slot, nor are they chosen to fulfil a special role, to top-up the required quota of black one-legged bisexual single-parent volunteers. And therefore a homosexual caller wishing speci- fically to speak to another gay, for example, has no guarantee that a gay volunteer will be on duty, nor indeed any guarantee that his problem would be handled more effectively if one was. In the normal course of his or her duties, a Samaritan with specialized knowledge or experience, or unusual personal orientation, will in fact have relatively few opportunities to make specific use of them. A general awareness and sympathy are what are called for and expected. But an extra-curricula role certainly exists for someone like Leslie, a transvestite,[4] in the way of helping to educate fellow Samaritans through branch meetings, seminars and conferences. An alarmingly heavy smoker, he drives an almost silent Daimler and lives alone in a compact semi-detached house on a new suburban estate in Surrey, furnished with numerous typewriters and an ansafone.

'As far as my branch is concerned, I'm just an ordinary Samaritan. They know all about me, but whatever I may do for the Beaumont Trust[5] has no bearing on my work as a Samaritan. They are quite distinct. I have done two seminars on transvestism for the national conference at York, and I travel the country visiting various branches. But when I'm on duty as a Samaritan, if I get a call from my sort of people then I handle it just as any Samaritan would.

'The biggest problem for transvestites is that the vast bulk are terrified, guilty, secret people. They are frightened to death of

[4] Almost always a heterosexual man (and very often married) who experiences an overwhelming compulsion to dress as a woman.
[5] A counselling agency of the Beaumont Society, which exists to help transvestites to meet, and enjoy a social life. The address is BM Box 3084, London WC1N 3XX.

discovery, largely because of what they perceive the public's attitude to be, which is in fact often better than they think it will be. I spent forty-five years of my life dressing behind closed doors. I knew I was transvestite when I was nine. All real transvestites know by the age of puberty. I "came out" quite simply because I'd reached the end of the line. I finished up with ulcers, and I was verging on the suicidal. Now I live largely as Jean. I travel as Jean, I give lectures as Jean, I've appeared on television as Jean. It's no offence. And to the best of my knowledge, no one's ever realized who I was. You wouldn't know me as Jean. Well, you might from the photographs on the wall.

'When I applied to join the Samaritans I told them I was a transvestite because that is now my policy. I make no secret. They weren't really interested. I said, "Of course, you wouldn't meet me as my other self." They said, "Well, it's useful to have somebody who knows something about this subject, for helping callers." What I try to do is help Samaritans to recognize what a caller is, which he may not know himself, as between a transvestite and a transexual,[6] or a fetishist, who are more likely to be sex callers. Understanding about transvestism in Samaritan branches varies enormously, which is one of the reasons I'm trying to do so much. Some branches have virtually no knowledge of the subject. They are quite unable to distinguish between a transvestite and a transexual, a fetishist or anyone else. I think it's a weakness in the training programmes, because transvestism doesn't form part of the training as a subject in its own right. But there is a growing awareness of it. But then, it would be impossible to train Samaritans in depth in every single area. It's just not possible. And Samaritan training, of course, is on-going. I know of only one other Samaritan besides myself who is a transvestite. But statistically, there must be many more.'

If it is true that the many thousands of Samaritans who have

[6] A man who feels himself to be a woman trapped inside a man's body, and may ultimately wish to undergo surgery in order to regularize his gender.

pioneered and consolidated their movement over the past quarter of a century are in a fair degree typical of the era through which they have lived, it should come as no great shock to discover that despite the interviewing process and the training, designed at the very least to curb any exhibitions of irrational prejudice, those who would prefer not to fraternize with, never mind befriend, transvestites or homosexuals have sometimes slipped through the net. A decade after the Wolfenden proposals to legalize all homosexual conduct in private between consenting males over twenty-one had passed into law, a gay Samaritan who felt it necessary to remain anonymous wrote an account for the *Samaritan* of his experience at the annual conference.

He had, he said, left the conference with a feeling of profound and painful alienation, for one of the women delegates had, apparently, remarked that she thought homosexuals were disgusting and she would prefer not to talk to them. He pinpointed the problem as one of a lack of understanding, and suggested that in training classes, homosexuality should be presented as a condition, not a problem. 'Most heterosexuals,' he wrote, 'are unaware of the emotional anaesthesia to which homosexuals are subjected, and of the profound and intense sense of aloneness, alienation and needless guilt that is inflicted upon them by our culture. Verbal queer-bashing is alive and well and not unknown at annual conferences, or in our branches.' Unfortunately, Dr Doris Odlum herself had seen fit to refer to homosexuality as a 'problem' when writing a series of articles for the *Samaritan* called 'The Male Predicament', adding the astonishing assertion that the situation in which men are attracted only to other men was 'of course . . . extreme and comparatively rare.'

Samaritans were swift to reach for their pens with which to beat their breasts, and letters appeared in the following issue expressing dismay, and suggesting that the lady in question should examine her motives for being a Samaritan, and resign. A gay volunteer from Reading, however, thought his own homosexual orientation had seemed to his interviewers to offer advantages over the heterosexual applicants, but he failed to explain how.

Although at times we pride ourselves on living in an enlightened age, physical as well as verbal queer-bashing remains alive and well, and it must remain extremely probable that, whereas in many Samaritan branches gay volunteers are known to their friends as such and serve from time to time as branch directors, there will still lurk within the movement a number of volunteers, both male and female, infected, like society at large, with 2,000 years of Judaeo-Christian hate. Perhaps far more remarkable is the number of clergy and others who from the start have stood out against the prevailing culture and climate, so that today, distressing though the experience recounted not so very long ago must have been, it almost certainly represents a minority attitude within the Samaritans, whose members, while seeming to be so ordinary in their homes, undertake tasks when on duty which most of their friends and neighbours would never dare contemplate. The press officer of Gay Switchboard reports, 'We have a good working relationship with the Samaritans, and in general they handle calls from gay people in a sympathetic and supportive way. We have a number of callers referred to us from the Samaritans but we don't keep statistics; many Samaritan callers feel a stigma attached and wouldn't tell us they had come via the Samaritans, so that actual figures would be rather meaningless. The Samaritans send our annual report to every branch. In some provincial branches problems about accepting gays still exist, but in London especially the situation has been excellent for a number of years.'

The double-edged experience of Geoffrey illustrates in a most striking way the two sides of a single coin. 'A few years ago,' he says, 'I volunteered to be a Samaritan, and when I volunteered I told them that one of the reasons I was volunteering was that I had once called them, and that I had found it very useful in the circumstances, and one of the things that I thought was important was not to assume that everybody was part of a solution or part of a problem. I also told them that I was gay, and that really seemed to throw them. I had gone for an interview, and I was interviewed by two people, and when I told them I was gay you could see them sort of doing, "Of course, officially we know it's perfectly all right to be gay, but . . .". There seemed to be all kinds of alarm bells ringing. They rang me up and said they wanted me to have a second interview with a sort of higher-up person. So I went and had a second interview with a higher-up person, and what it basically came down to was whether I was going to start preaching gay lib down the telephone. There were lots of sort of odd questions about that. And they then said, "We'll accept you for training." But by that time I just felt wrong about the whole thing. I just felt that I was going to be patronized by them in some way, that I would have to conform to some idea they'd got of what a respectable gay person was, that there wasn't a genuine accepting of gay people, there was a particular category of gay person that was all right, which they presumably decided I didn't fit into. I just felt odd about it. So in fact I wrote to them and said I'd thought about it and I'd decided I didn't want to pursue this. And they wrote back and said, "If we can ever be of any help to you please let us know."

'There had been a gap of about nine months or a year between my being a caller and offering to join the Samaritans. I was teaching at the time. But it was during a year when I was back at university that I had this mad, passionate affair, with this boy. He was a boy of seventeen. I was twenty-six. It was lovely! *Absolutely* wonderful! I met him at Victoria Coach Station, and he asked me the time. And within a week he was living with me. He came from Macclesfield. After six months I went away for three weeks, and it was all tears and tragedy at his end, because I was going away and how would he be able to live without me. This was a holiday I had organized ages before, in India and Sri Lanka. So I went. And while I was away I was convinced I was attached to him, and when I got back he'd gone, with somebody else, just like that. And I was totally thrown. I've never been so thrown. It was a combination of jet lag and being just really upset, and a bit drunk, and I came home to the flat and I was just in a state. I was in *such* a bad state! And this is where I think the Samaritans are wonderful, the way they provide a kind of vehicle that nobody else does. Although I've got lots of friends I can talk to about being gay, I didn't want any of them to see me in such a state, because I really felt very ashamed of myself, being in such a state.

'And so I rang the Samaritans. I got this chap who was just so good. I talked to him for about half an hour, and then I put the phone down and had a few more drinks. Then I felt a bit better and I rang them again, but I got a woman. And I didn't want to talk to her. She wanted to talk to me, although I'd asked for John or whatever his name was, and she wanted to start all over again. I didn't want to go through it all over again, so I said, "No, I want to speak to John." Then I had a very kind of calm conversation with him. He was just extremely good. I'll tell you why. He managed to make me feel as though he had experienced similar things without ever suggesting for a minute that he had. I think that was really it. I also felt, talking to him, that in his mind there was no censoriousness about me saying I'd had a sexual relationship with a seventeen-year-old boy, quite apart from the fact that it's illegal. So far as he was concerned, it was just a relationship that had gone on the rocks. And he never said, which I knew was perfectly true, "That's what you get if you have relationships with seventeen-year-old boys."

'It took me months to get over it, partly because the boy went on living with me for two and a half months. I couldn't get him out of the flat, and he was having affairs with other people. So at this stage it was all just a great disaster. But the Samaritans provided at that crucial moment exactly the right kind of safety valve. I wasn't actually asked if I was feeling suicidal; I think I had said fairly early on I was not going to commit suicide, I just wanted to thrash it all out with a complete stranger. And I was weeping down the phone! Later, in fact, I did feel quite suicidal, on several occasions, but I never rang the Samaritans again. I don't know why. The time when I thought I felt most like it was about six months after the whole thing was officially over, and I really thought I had got over it, and I met this boy and his new boyfriend in a pub, and I just couldn't cope. And I was so cross with myself for not coping, and I walked to a bridge, and I was quite determined I was going to throw myself off this bridge. Anger is quite a good defence mechanism, and I know what it was – I stopped when I was crossing the road to avoid being knocked down by a car, and I suddenly started to laugh, and I thought, how can I be telling myself I'm about to commit suicide if on the way to do it I'm trying to avoid being knocked down by a car! Anyhow, I suddenly found it all very funny.

'So that was my experience of the Samaritans, which was that at the receiving end they were extremely good, but when I was a real person, not at the end of a telephone, I didn't like them so much. And what was so odd was that I encountered two such dissimilar experiences at the same branch.'

Rejecting a potential recruit is one thing; a job most directors find far more distasteful, and some will actually shrink from performing personally, is asking an established volunteer to leave. This is allowed to be done without any explanation being offered, and for the Samaritan concerned it is often a crippling experience because, for better or worse, the Samaritans often become a crucial part of someone's life. Judging from an account of a volunteer's experience of being sacked from the Medway branch in 1979, published in the *Samaritan*, her director handed responsibility for the deed to a leader, 'who was very good, very kind, [and] obviously found it a difficult task. He coped with my hurt, then my anger, then left. From then on, as far as the branch was concerned, I ceased to exist. My name was removed from the volunteers list. My card went from the availability book. It was as though I'd never been.' Unable to speak to former Samaritan friends for fear of seeming in search of sympathy, and unable to explain her sense of loss to non-Samaritans, she found she had no one to turn to. 'It would have been nice to have had occasional contact during that first week,' she wrote. 'There must be a better way.'

Her article provoked a flood of reminiscences. 'No reason was given for my dismissal, although I was given the dubious comfort of being told it had nothing to do with my work,' one former Samaritan wrote. 'A request for an interview with the director was refused. The sense of disillusionment is deep. I really believed in the goodness of the Samaritans, but an organization which can practise such double standards – one for callers and the complete opposite for its own members – can no longer be credible to me.'

'Where else in these days can a person be accused, found guilty and punished without knowing the crime and without being able to defend himself?' another wanted to know. 'I have never heard a convincing reason for this ruling, and suspect it is mainly designed to make things easier for directors. Unfortunately, an insecure or small-minded director can so easily convert the directorship into a petty dictatorship. If anyone disagrees with him he can just ask him to leave and no one can do anything about it.' It must also be a fact that as long as a director can fire volunteers at will, his power to do so may well staunch criticism of his conduct or of branch procedures for fear of the consequences. There are, however, according to a former director of the Norwich branch, Dr George Day, who has written a pamphlet called *What a Young Director Should Know*, 'certain offences [that] demand instant dismissal – e.g. breaches of confidentiality, being drunk on duty, unwelcome behaviour or sexual irregularities at the centre, and *wilful* disobedience of the Directives.' What might amount to 'unwelcome behaviour' he does not say, but he is quite specific about sexual irregularities. 'Bluntly put: volunteers must not sleep with their callers. Penalty: dismissal.'

Just as dramatically he goes on to explain that 'callers often become embarrassingly infatuated with their befrienders, and fantasize about them like mad. Volunteers must be sternly warned that when they suspect this is happening they must inform their leader, and discuss how to deal with the situation without harming the caller's self-respect or precipitating his parasuicide. All the more so should the volunteer inform the leader if he himself finds he is beginning to reciprocate the caller's feelings. His befriending that caller must cease. If he is hell-bent on consummating his passion, he must resign and cease to be a Samaritan.'

In an article two years later reviewing the whole procedure for dismissal, a volunteer from the Putney branch expressed the view that if 'dismissal is necessary it should be done with love and care and accompanied by follow-up from the individual's friends within the branch. This offer of continuing contact is essential. Whatever the circumstances,' he wrote, 'there can be no justification for dismissal, suspension or warning without a face-to-face interview.'

The problem of easing a Samaritan out of a branch highlights more than anything the importance of appointing suitable directors, and in order to supplement informal training of directors at regional meetings plans are being drawn up to extend training opportunities for new directors. One of the dangerous weaknesses at present within the movement is the reluctance, quite often, of the most able Samaritans to shoulder, even for three years, the very considerable responsibilities and time-consuming tasks that fall to a director, and the consequent danger that a second or even third choice, of a less than adequate member, deficient perhaps in the most basic management skills, who nevertheless regards themselves as the most experienced and competent Samaritan in the branch, will be called upon to fill the post by default. When this occurs, the chain reaction of lost morale, ending with callers being cared for by jittery volunteers who have lost confidence in the leadership within their branch, could prove catastrophic.

·4·

ROOTING

There can scarcely be a more important task for any branch than the selection of a team to undertake the training (or preparation, as some prefer to call it) of new volunteers. Yet overall there is a haphazard approach to the job of training that makes an assessment of its merits at a national level practically impossible. The reason for this stems, like so much in the movement, from the historical decision to allow as much autonomy as possible to the branches, and a direct result is the deliberate refusal to impose from on high any consistent and officially approved training programme. The Samaritans were thirty-one years old, with virtually all their branches already set up, before the council of management, in 1984, got around to appointing a National Training Co-ordinator, and then, for the first eighteen months, only on a part-time basis.

Norman Whiting, with twelve years' experience as a Samaritan and a career behind him in teacher training, was the man chosen for the diplomatic task of trying to filter a co-ordinated national training programme through the network of regional and branch training officers. At sixty-one he rather resembles a well-intentioned monk let loose at a public school mission, but he has swiftly acquired a reputation among area representatives for the quality of his teaching materials, and a quiet and unassuming modesty belies his abilities on the public platform. 'Training had grown up without very much co-ordination,' he explains. 'And it was eventually recognized that there was a need for greater communication between the council of management, the regions and the branches. But the movement might not willingly have accepted a full-time appointment to begin with. The council are very careful about what some people think of as professionalism, and there are areas of resistance to the appointment of salaried staff. I think when they chose my title they were being very cautious about the idea that 'training officer' might imply dashing around telling people what to do.

'I'm expected to be the professional adviser to the movement on training matters, and to develop training materials. But I have no formal authority to go to a branch and say you are doing this or that wrong.'

Mr Whiting depends primarily upon nothing more than goodwill and establishing a personal authority for getting across to thirteen regional and 180 branch training officers any ideas he may formulate for improving methods and materials – training officers whose own tasks in the past have been defined 180 different ways. Until recently it was even left to the regional representatives to decide whether their region should have a training officer.

'We are far less unified on training policy at national level than many other voluntary organizations,' says Mr Whiting. 'I suspect this is all to do with the way the Samaritans developed. It is partly a result of branches feeling very strongly about their autonomy. The acceptance of broad policy is one thing, but if we tried to lay down a national policy on training I'm sure there would be tremendous resistance. I don't think the council would accept, on behalf of the movement, any attempt to impose a standard preparation course. I'm sure it wouldn't be accepted. But while autonomy in the branches has the advantage of producing original ideas and freshness, it has the disadvantage, all too easily, of allowing very poor practices to be continued.'

One result of the lack of a standard preparation course is that because many branches frankly do not trust the training given elsewhere, it is common, although not universal, practice for branches to insist on retraining a volunteer who may move into their area, after giving many years of uncriticised service in another branch. Some directors allow an experienced Samaritan undergoing retraining to carry out a certain number of duties during the training course, but there is a strong argument that while the Samaritans claim to be desperately short of volunteers it is absurd to tie up volunteers in retraining just because they have moved house.

'If you lay down the law too much, people are going to resent it because they feel insecure,' says Jean Burt. 'My views on retraining are that every branch can do its own thing, but retraining, when we are so short of volunteers, does seem dotty.' Mr Whiting accepts that the case against almost automatic insistence on retraining seems to argue for greater standardization of training courses. 'But', he says, 'I think it is worth looking to see if we can answer this problem not so much by implementing a standard national preparation course – which I'm damn sure wouldn't be accepted anyway – but by doing everything we can to up-grade the quality of initial preparation where it is found to be manifestly inadequate. Changes are often brought about when a new director takes over. I had a long talk with a director recently, who said that the preparation course in his branch had been considered quite inadequate by a lot of people for a long time, but it was one of those inertia things, and there were some prestigious people involved, and no one quite liked to grasp the nettle. The last course had contained one or two pretty disastrous sessions, and he was now about to grasp the nettle himself.'

Allied to the argument about retraining volunteers when they move from one branch to another is the question of whether, after some length of time, all volunteers should undergo a refresher course, or even take a sabbatical. 'I think for everyone it's different,' says the assistant general secretary. 'It may be a good thing for someone to take a break when circumstances in their life alter, rather than because five years are up. It's all too easy to take for granted an involvement with the Samaritans and not take account of changed circumstances. There is an increasing trend in many branches towards retraining people after a certain length of time, the assumption being that it's not a bad thing anyway, and that people who have been in the movement for some time would benefit from having the opportunity to stand back and reflect on it. There's no reason to have a break for the sake of it, but perhaps we ought to look at the whole question of sabbaticals and retraining more than we do.'

To an outside observer, one of the most striking factors about involvement with Samaritan work is the sheer range and intricacy of personal problems with which callers are beset, and it must surely be a stark fact of life that soon to be added to these will be the distress, and almost certainly suicides, attributable to Aids. An inquest in Southwark was told in 1987 that a thirty-four-year-old London man had killed himself in the mistaken belief that he was a victim. After sixteen hours of training, how well-equipped with hard, incontrovertible knowledge regarding lesbianism, transvestism, drug abuse and so on were new Samaritan volunteers? 'Our training courses are a bit like training doctors,' Mr Whiting explained. 'Can the medical student, in training, meet every contingency? I don't think you can say that at the end of any initial preparation course you are going to be ready for every contingency, and if we were to try to cover everything before a volunteer went into Samaritan service we would need a vastly longer preparation course. There is an overseas branch which insists on four-hour training sessions once a week for six months. Are they x-number of times more effective than we as Samaritans? I doubt it. There is a sort of cut-off point, at which you say. "This person doesn't know it all but he knows enough to make a start." And after all, all Samaritan training is on-going, or it should be.'

Norman Whiting's responsibilities extend to the training of experienced Samaritans for particular – sometimes unglamorous – tasks within the branches. Writing in the *Samaritan* in 1986, a volunteer from Norwich complained that 'Some volunteers who do their duties at the centre with commendable regularity steadfastly refuse to play any part in the supporting activities of the branch, like publicity, fund-raising, talks, selection, training, the rota, the treasurer's work, the house-keeping, committee membership. They joined, they will tell you, to be Samaritans, not to do the chores.' And he went on: 'Largely to blame for this unfortunate attitude is our recruit-ment publicity and our selection and preparation of new volun-teers, which all concentrate exclusively on listening and befriending, as if the other branch activities are the poor relations which you want to keep well in the background.'

Confronted with this criticism of training policy, Mr Whiting said, 'One can extend this to training people in local publicity. In this sort of field I am sometimes brought in to help plan, let's say, a residential school on publicity and fund-raising. I have a responsibility for anything that can be called training. I think we've got to help people to learn more about running a com-mittee in a voluntary organization. There's an awful lot of time wasted. But diffusion of ideas is the principal problem. The training of leaders is vital, but even if we run two leader training schools a year, you can only attract to them a minute proportion of the leaders at work in branches all over the country. I'd like to get more money into the regions to start training leaders at regional level.'

Meanwhile, at a quarter to nine on a Saturday morning, a training team and a bunch of new volunteers are meeting for the first time. Everyone has arrived early, for what the branch calls an Acquaint Day; together with the training team there are other long-term Samaritans, chosen as 'mentors' to help steer the volunteers through an eight-week training programme. The centre, which is rented, is in a dreary street off a busy thorough-fare, on the first floor of a hideously ugly pebble-dash building, partly boarded up, with a crate of empty milk bottles on the steps. Closing the door to shut out the babble of voices (any inhibitions seem to have broken down within minutes) the training officer, recently appointed by the director and running his first course, explained there had been no need to advertise for recruits. 'This is a middle-class area,' he said, 'and let's face it, we're all middle-class.' This seemed like a *non sequitur*, but not to the training officer, who was a balding man of about forty

wearing a thin blue vest. 'Some centres might get eight applications a year, but we run three training programmes every
twelve months and usually have about sixty new volunteers. We
have seventeen on this course. Some are former Samaritans who
have been away for a time and are taking a refresher course.' He
seemed unclear why five of the seventeen had not turned up,
but very clear that the branch was proud of their traditions and
training methods.

Before the session got under way, in a room furnished with a
xerox machine, strip lighting and double glazing, there was a lot
of kissing by Samaritans of one another, and a young man had
his beard tweaked by the training officer. Everyone had taken
note of the sign on the wall, 'Thank you for *not* smoking', or
else, most unusually for Samaritans, they were all non-smokers,
and in an atmosphere of quiet expectancy the branch director, a
lay preacher and grandfather who had been a Samaritan for
fifteen years, opened the proceedings. He was hot on statistics
but not so up-to-date on terminology. The branch had been
founded in 1970, he explained, because a policeman had been
murdered in the area and a queer had been beaten up. No one
blanched, and the connection between those two events and the
founding of a Samaritan centre remained a mystery. The
branch, he said, was staffed by 196 volunteers [if true, an
exceptionally high number for the type of area], there were
always two on duty, and last year they had taken 18,365 calls on
the telephone from a catchment area of 400,000 people, not
including 5,800 click calls (people who had rung in and then
rung off). Of those who had contacted the branch 3,508 had
been new callers, 1,479 or forty-two per cent of whom had had
suicidal thoughts or impulses. Last year, 19,296 hours had been
put in by volunteers on manning the centre – possibly nearer
20,000 hours when administrative tasks were taken into
account. Only that night, the shift of two, who had come on
at 11.20pm and stayed at their post without a break until
7.20 in the morning, had dealt with twenty-seven telephone
calls.

He ran through some national facts and figures too. Although suicides per head in Britain were low compared to the rest of Europe [only two countries are lower, in fact], in 1984, 4,834 people had killed themselves. It had been guessed that 200,000 attempted suicides were made annually in Britain. [If the guess was correct, that would be an attempted suicide every two and a half minutes.] He ended by telling the volunteers he would require from them dedication and reliability, a minimum of one duty every ten days and four overnight duties every year. It was stressed that unsocial hours had to be covered, even Christmas Day. On-going training, administration, delivery of talks and attendance at conferences 'so that we don't become parochial' were additional activities that would take up their time. 'You will get the feeling how we understand, love and care for one another,' he told them.

The training officer referred to Samaritans as Sams. He wanted new volunteers and their mentors first of all to spend two minutes talking to one another to find out who they were, then they were to stand up and introduce their partner to everyone else. 'This,' he said, 'is all about listening, and understanding what we hear.' As everyone was talking at once, in a small room, it was a wonder anyone heard or understood anything. It later transpired that quite a few had not. After four minutes the training officer said, 'Right, we'll start with you beautiful people,' indicating an exceptionally ordinary looking couple. Harry introduced Joan. Joan, it transpired, had been a Samaritan for fifteen years; she was the wife of a doctor, and after suffering an accident she had come back to undertake a refresher course. 'She feels her only talent is to be able to provide a listening ear,' Harry said. Joan spoke about Harry in such an upper-crust voice that not one word was intelligible. Bill, dressed in brown corduroy trousers, a blue pullover and open-neck shirt, sported a monkish haircut, and steel-rimmed glasses that gave him an uncanny resemblance to Himmler. He turned out to be a Catholic priest, and he had previously served as a Samaritan in Rome. Mark, neatly dressed in a blue jacket, was a bachelor of thirty who was just about to lose his job, and had volunteered to be a Samaritan because he had been struck by the number of lonely people in London 'and would like to do something about it'.

Jenny's mentor introduced her as a divorcee with two sons, who lived 'very local' and would therefore have no excuse to be unpunctual. She loved concerts and books 'and all the things that make life worthwhile'. Mavis, Jenny's mentor, was blind, and had her guide dog with her. An 'insurance technician' called Pete, a stocky little man who was going bald but had a ginger moustache, mentioned to his mentor that he was 'ex-territorial army'. Jennifer, young and rather pretty with long straggly hair, apparently told *her* mentor that she was a 'seemingly intelligent person', which drew a laugh when it transpired that Jennifer was a spiritualist and healer. So was the next volunteer to be introduced, a secretary in the probation service and a 'practising Christian'. Christine (the new women volunteers outnumbered the men by two to one) was a solicitor, who thought she might be able to help over problems of bereavement because much of her practice was concerned with probate. A young looking man called Andrew had been married twice; he, too, had been a Samaritan before. The youngest volunteer was Linda, only nineteen, who worked in a local school as an audio-visual technician; she was comfortably plump, wore a blue skirt and green anorak, played badminton and helped with the Brownies. A middle-aged woman worked in the Foreign Office and liked walking and photography.

The 'Hello, I'm . . .' session closed with the training officer and two members of his team reading an extract from *The Wind in the Willows* in such flat, monotonous voices that they reduced one of the great works of twentieth-century literature to the level of a bus conductor singing out the stops in Oxford Street. Then coffee was served, in disposable containers. Still no one smoked. Next came a film called *Can I Help You?* intended to encourage discussion about Samaritan attitudes and the problems volunteers are called upon to face. A slight touch of unreality was provided by a young coloured actress in the role of a volunteer; they are so few on the ground as to be verging on the unique. A male caller asked to speak to a man. 'Well, you're over twenty-one, it is legal, you know . . . Have you discussed it with your wife?' The same chain-smoking Samaritan, who called everyone 'Love', interviewed a couple with a baby, with 'no money, no job, nowhere to live and not married – at least, not to one another.' The volunteers seemed to be running in circles a bit, with a backlog of callers waiting to be interviewed and looking suitably depressed. One woman who attempted to offer advice to a caller was ticked off at length by the leader while they both squatted on the landing. She seemed about to burst into tears, when the doorbell rang. 'Well, aren't you going to answer it?' said the leader. After the film show, the volunteers and mentors split into groups to discuss what they had seen, but no very definite views were formed, or at any rate expressed. Mark was somewhat surprised by 'the ton-up Granny,' as he described one of the volunteers in the film, who turned out to be a member of the branch he was hoping to join. 'One person's attitudes will suit some callers, someone else's another's' the lady from the Foreign Office felt.

'The purpose of all your training,' a member of the training team with a soft north-country accent explained, 'will be to help you come to a decision as to whether you want to do the work. My own view is that you've all been training all your lives. But we are rooting for you. We do need you. However, the decision-making process will largely be your own.' He explained that the mentor they had been given was someone who would hold their hand 'because we know it is stressful. We cannot do this work without support and we don't expect you to.' In private conversation, he later referred to those volunteers likely to be weeded out straight away as 'the real basket cases'. The training officer emphasized the commitment to time and told the volunteers to turn up punctually for their first training evening, three weeks hence. 'This,' he said, 'is a commitment I demand.' There was no hurry to disperse. The recruits seemed quite reluctant to drift away.

During the course of the next three weeks the volunteers were interviewed, and one 'basket case', Pete, the insurance technician, was politely shown the door; pressed again and again for a motive for wanting to be a Samaritan, he had declined to offer any reason at all. A well-fed young business man in his mid-thirties, dressed in a neat city suit and blue-and-white pin-striped shirt, who had failed to materialize on the Acquaint Day, rolled up five minutes late, and despite the training officer's admonitions about punctuality, he greeted Linda, who arrived twenty minutes late, with a kiss. The evening had got off to an even odder start. For the benefit of those who had not been present on the Acquaint Day, the director again unburdened himself of his list of statistics, and repeated word for word the ostensible reason the branch had come into existence; 'a queer' had been bashed up by a group of youngsters, he said. One would have thought that in the intervening three weeks at least one member of the team would have taken him on one side and brought his vocabulary up to date. He said he hoped the new volunteers would soon catch 'our sincerity and togetherness as a branch', an irony seemingly lost on everyone in the room. There was a good deal more in the traditional vein of a lay preacher, about everyone being human, about empathy, caring and the expenditure of time, and how his own life had been 'enriched and expanded' by meeting callers. 'I'd love,' he said, 'to go on talking all the time,' another remark that no one felt inclined to contradict. Then it was the turn of the volunteers and their mentors to talk to one another, for ten minutes, and this they did with gusto.

The director and the training officer took it in turns to run through the Samaritan principles, lacing each one with an appropriate home-spun anecdote. A member of the branch, for instance, had recently seen a girl on an underground platform (there were, the training officer said, three attempted suicides on the London Underground every week) who looked about to throw herself under a train, so the Samaritan had gone up to her and said, 'I'm Anne, can I help you?' and she and the girl had had a chat and then the Samaritan had gone on her way. That, said the training officer, was an example of being available at any hour of the day or night to befriend. 'Don't forget or break the principles and practices,' the director told the volunteers. 'If you do, I shall have no hesitation in asking you to resign.' He was himself due to retire as director in four weeks' time. No one seemed cowed, or queried a single item on the list of Dos and Don'ts.

Then the training officer said, smiling broadly, 'Now I'd like to introduce you to a very interesting person. I happen to share a house with him, so that I find it very interesting.' This very interesting, if very oddly worded, remark was likewise received in stony silence. The Very Interesting Person, a stocky Welshman with a lot of grey beard, wrote on a board, 'What Am I Doing?', and quickly demonstrated that depending on which word had the stress placed on it, the question could be posed four different ways. Moral: when eventually they lifted the telephone and said, 'The Samaritans, can I help you?' it was important how it sounded. He then divided the volunteers and their mentors into groups and gave them four tasks. They were asked to describe a person likely to commit suicide, to say how they would cope with a friend who revealed suicidal feelings, what they would do if they delivered Meals on Wheels to a formerly depressive old man who was now rather cheerful and talking of not seeing them again, and finally how they would react to a 'college room-mate' who had cut his wrists and had a poor relationship with his father, who thought him not manly enough. The Catholic priest talked of 'non-directionally pushing' the room-mate towards help. 'I wouldn't be shocked,' someone said of the friend who felt suicidal. 'I wouldn't belittle his problem,' someone else volunteered. 'I wouldn't give him a loaded gun,' emerged as another unexceptional solution. Physical contact, 'whether male or female', was what a young, bespectacled woman suggested was needed. 'Just give them a hug and make them know they are loved.' Rather ominously, the business man said of the suicidal friend, 'I wouldn't tell him to go to the Samaritans.' No one asked why. Linda, one of the brightest present, said she thought a person likely to commit suicide would seem 'edgy and uptight'. The Very Interesting Person reminded them all that bereavement could include the loss of a pet. Somehow the two-hour evening had seemed a bit disjointed and inconclusive, but perhaps it had been meant to.

A week later they were scheduled to learn about befriending, from a grey-haired man with a grey goatee beard. When taking a telephone call, he said, they should 'read between the lines' and 'give space to the caller'. This was what another member of the training team, helping out by role-playing, described as 'reflective listening'. Because different people use words in different ways, he said, the Samaritan should try to test what the caller was really trying to say. He read a hypothetical resumé of someone's telephone call, about a man who had difficulty keeping his food down, and had been given three months to decide his future at work. It all sounded very confusing. Then he asked for comments on the caller's general state of mind. The lady from the Foreign Office offered what sounded like a most intelligent appraisal, but received little encouragement from the team.

Then up popped the stereotyped lesbian, a caller who had said she found she was more attracted to women than to men and found it hard to face the day. 'Phoning you has made me realize I am not normal,' she had told the Samaritans. Sally, the member of the team posing the 'problem', suggested that a possible response was to say something like, 'You feel you have homosexual leanings and this makes you feel you are not normal?' But she got shot down by the cleric, who pointed out that the caller had never used the word 'homosexual', so neither would he. And then they were plunged into the 'suicide question'. Was it, the male role-player wanted to know, a good idea to ask a caller if they were feeling suicidal? Linda thought that by doing so you might sometimes put the idea of suicide into someone's head. 'Could you catch a headache?' the Samaritan inquired. The priest, who knew the right response, of course, from his previous experience in another branch, said that if someone had rung the Samaritans they were not going to be 'given a headache' by being asked the suicide question. The group were then firmly told that Samaritan policy was *always* to ask the suicide question, because by funking it a Samaritan might end up with a potentially suicidal caller ringing off without having been given the chance of discussing the most urgent reason that had prompted them to ring. The problem was deciding at what stage in the conversation to ask the question, and a number of tapes were played, offering possible variations on an exercise which, it was agreed by all the members of the team, was one which many Samaritans found particularly difficult to deal with.

How might the new volunteers pose the crucial question? Linda suggested asking the caller how they felt about their life, and was emphatically told that this was not the same thing as asking if they felt suicidal. Andrew quite seriously proposed, 'Have you thought about jacking it all in?' Would it be cheating to ask, 'Why did you ring us?' a rather earnest, middle-aged lady wanted to know. Her rhetorical question was greeted by a derisive chorus of 'Yes!' Other euphemisms suggested by the recruits included, 'Have you reached the point of no return?' One was beginning to realize just what they had taken on. How many people, before becoming a Samaritan, *have* ever asked anyone if they were feeling like killing themselves?

Finally, the class were told that one of the most difficult calls they would ever have to deal with was the silent call. 'You don't know whether the caller is a man, a woman, a hoaxer or someone about to commit suicide,' the man with the goatee explained. Then they listened, for what seemed like a very long time indeed, to a tape of a Samaritan trying to coax someone into speaking. It was an eerie experience. 'How do you actually know there is anyone there?' the secretary in the probation service wanted to know, but no one on the team picked up her question. 'Would you ever place a time limit on a silent call, before replacing the receiver?' she persisted, and again, in the general hubbub that had broken the tension of the silent call tape, her question was ignored. In conversation after the session had ended, the training officer said the longest silent call ever taken to his knowledge in his branch had lasted three hours, and had only then been terminated by the volunteer when he was as certain as he could be that there was no one on the other end. What no one asked, or was told, were the reasons for the silent call. One of the training team tried to interest the meeting in an adjournment to 'a local hostelry', but everyone remained glued to their chairs, chatting away like mad.

'It's lovely to see you all again, I think we're all here,' Basil, the trainer with the goatee beard, told the assembled volunteers eight days later. A bank holiday had intervened since their last session. In fact, two of the trainees who had been volunteers before were missing. In this branch, a certain flexibility is exercised in relation to re-training, and former Samaritans preparing to enter the branch are permitted to carry out shift work during the course of their preparation classes, so perhaps they were manning the switchboard. 'I hope you're all refreshed by that super weekend,' Basil went on. Most of it had been swept away by a howling gale.

On the subject of Communication, three versions of a call were played on a tape, after some technical difficulties and waste of time through a lack of proper rehearsal. A woman unable to sleep after taking several drinks and two mogadon tablets was ringing in at three o'clock in the morning. When the volunteers moved into groups to discuss the Samaritan's three different responses to the call they were talking in tones far more subdued that at the start of the course, as though they were now beginning to capture a sense of reality. But in questioning the groups about their response, the Welshman never really drew out any positive aspect of their conversations. Two prime weaknesses were beginning to show up. Individual volunteers were not being called upon, by name, specifically to speak out about their feelings and reactions to what was being taught, and the class, instead of being seated in a semi-circle, or even in a circle with the trainers in the middle, sat in rows with their backs to one another, so that visual and audio communication – the very subject under discussion – was minimal, and sometimes impossible. Even the director sat at the back of the room, and whenever he interjected a remark, necks had to be craned to hear what he had to say.

In order to demonstrate a Samaritan's need for consolation after taking a call, one of the team pretended to take a call while finding it hard to sympathize with the caller. Some may have felt she had earned a pep talk rather than the hug she got. Avoid questions that can be answered by Yes or No, the trainees were told. Open-ended questions that might lead on to a further exploration of someone's problems tended to start with the letter 'w'; why, when, who, what.

The Welshman ended by emphasizing that the Samaritans were not a religious organization, but then got Basil to read the parable of the Good Samaritan. Laughing heartily, he then explained the relevance of the parable to the Samaritans; the Samaritan had not asked if the man battered by thieves had been worthy of help.

Before the next session began, the training officer explained how his team worked behind the scenes. 'Assessment is a continuous process. After each session we get together and we fully debrief the evening. And an essential part of it is to discuss any problems we might have seen or felt from some of the volunteers. Last week, for instance, two of them showed a lot of reticence in speaking about death. "Have you thought about jacking it all in" was a throw-away line, really. We felt sure that it must be a throw-away line, but it's being watched. It does show an attitude that might be slightly less than what we want. I've tried to make it not too obvious that they are being assessed. Our previous training officer was much harder, and the last lot of volunteers were far less responsive. They never entered fully into discussion. You had to drag everything out. It was like standing in front of a sea of porridge. They know they're being assessed, but I've kept it very low key so as not to inhibit them and influence what they do say.

'There is no one I'm seriously concerned about at this stage, but there are four we're looking at specially, with doubts. Two of them because they have told me already they are not going to be able to complete the course, and we feel it is essential that they miss not more than one evening at the very most. I know it's difficult but we have to cram a lot in. And the two who expressed this problem last week with death. It's fairly basic in a suicide situation. It was when they started to talk about death in their groups that two of the girls said, "I don't know that I could cope with talking about death." This was picked up by the mentors. At some stage or other when you're on line you are going to join a person in a situation where maybe they are dying. So the prospect of death must be something with which you can cope. We've had nobody self-select out, but then we're still in the relatively easy part of the course, and I would say that with doubts hovering over four heads out of sixteen we're in an average situation. They're a good bunch, and we'll probably get some good Samaritans from them. Certainly, I should imagine, between twelve and fifteen on the rota.'

Jennifer's comments at this stage were as follows: 'When I was first interviewed, they said to me, "How are you going to cope with all this? It's going to be outside your experience." And I said, "I don't know," and I still don't. I don't think any training in the world will do anything for you, and I think the people training us actually get that feeling too. It's almost as if there's not a lot they can do to prepare us for it. There is, however, a family feeling developing, so that you feel you can depend on other people, and I think that's the most important thing. I'm not very good with people who are really nice to me, who are immediately nice; I rather step back! The important thing they've said is, "You can't actually expect to change anybody." I really do feel that. I'm enjoying the sessions, though sometimes I'd like to go into discussions a bit more deeply. Maybe there is an element of morbid curiosity behind my motives.'

The secretary from the probation service: 'I think it's a very good course. I'm getting a lot out of it. I think it's extremely good. The reservation I've got, if I have one at all, is that I feel a little bit as if I'm in a goldfish bowl, and I'm being assessed by all these mentors, and I feel they're all looking at me, and I have a nasty feeling that at the end they're going to say, "Sorry, you haven't quite made it." It's a bit as if they're all looking at me and waiting for me to say something stupid. Which I could, easily. That's inhibiting. So I daren't always say exactly what I feel in case I get chucked out, and I'd be very sad about that, I really would, because I really want to be a Samaritan. I think the Samaritan policy is fine, I'm very happy with it. I just wonder if I can do it. I wonder if I'm good enough, you see, that's part of my anxiety about being watched by so many people who obviously wonder if I can do it, too. Certainly last week, when they were doing the role-play, I felt very stirred up; the second one, when the woman just put down the phone at the end and said, "I'm going to take my tablets now, thank you for listening," I was very much with it. I was very much being the volunteer and thinking, "I would never know what to say." I'm not sure at the end of the day whether I'm going to be suitable. I can't come to the last two sessions and I wonder if at the end of six I'm going to be able to tell if I'm ready.'[1]

James, the business man: 'I had very few expectations, actually. I find it quite exhausting. I feel pretty nackered at the end of the sessions, obviously one's concentrating pretty hard. And that will no doubt increase as we get more intense. And it's an indication of what one will be feeling when one is doing duties. So it's a good training in that respect. I'm conscious that we're being watched but I don't find that disturbing. I say what I feel. Nothing has arisen yet that I couldn't cope with but obviously I'm apprehensive. But there hasn't been one particular thing yet that I've thought, "Oh God, I wouldn't cope with that!" But I can imagine with the silent call, if I was in that situation I wouldn't know what the hell to do. So that struck me as something I thought would be very difficult. I know people who have committed suicide, acquaintances rather than friends.'

A session on Anger was opened by the training officer and another Samaritan pretending to be having a blazing row,

---

[1] In the event, she did attend the final session.

which most of the class described afterwards as 'embarrassing' or 'frightening'. Rosemary, a calm and self-assured Samaritan who clearly knew what she was doing, addressed each volunteer by name and drew them out individually. Outside the centre she could have been a very efficient and successful schoolmistress. She asked the volunteers to note down the things that made them angry. The room, for once, became almost entirely silent. Someone said that what got her going was seeing a baby seal being bashed on the head. 'I get very angry if a good friend gets hurt,' a smart housewife volunteered. 'I like to get my own way and I feel quite cross when I don't,' said the probation secretary. 'Men who wee in the street,' turned out to be Jennifer's *bête noire*. A second member of the training team, a rather elegant lady who looked like a retired Russian ballet dancer, said *she* could be driven demented by someone continually sniffing. James said he thought a caller with racial prejudice might make *him* feel angry.

'How would you feel if someone rang and said he had raped a child?' the class was asked. 'Very angry,' said the smart housewife. And how would they feel if another Samaritan had felt so angry that he had reported the matter to the police? 'Angry' was what they were told they should feel, because he would have broken his promise of confidentiality.

The evening became really lively when for the first time three trainees volunteered to take a call from one of the trainers. The first role-play concerned a widow who said that her husband had died young of a heart attack. She was angry with the hospital staff. The volunteer on the receiving end of her wrath was the over-confident joker who had suggested the euphemism about 'jacking it in'. He seemed to flounder horribly, but after his ordeal was over Rosemary reassured him. Everyone said how well all the volunteers had taken their calls, but everyone who had not volunteered felt they had had a lucky let-out. At last the course seemed to be beginning to understand just how incredibly difficult it was to take a call from a complete stranger who felt angry, often at the expense of the Samaritan, who in turn was forbidden to offer advice. To soothe any ruffled feathers, Rosemary ended the evening by playing some music not entirely dissociated with a television commercial for wool.

A week later, outside the centre five ten-year-old boys were bending over the pavement, intent and probing, and then they moved away with exclamations of disgust. In the gutter, on her back, lay a pregnant squirrel, hit by a car, gasping and dying. Inside, the trainees were gathering to discuss Pain. The training officer was on holiday, and three of his recruits turned up late. One was the priest, who smartly bagged someone else's chair which the occupier had vacated for an instant, and refused to give it up.

Nicholas, rather a willowy young man who twisted and turned as he spoke, but spoke well, said, 'We are not trying to be super people. Calls are a nerve-wracking experience on both sides. Samaritans are only ordinary people who expose themselves to a whole area of feelings which are unpleasant.' They moved into groups to discuss any painful experiences they may have had in the past. Several could be heard discussing bereavement. 'If you haven't had a painful experience, try to imagine what it would be like,' Nicholas told them. The priest gave a guffaw.

The articulate lady from the Foreign Office reported back that her group thought pain a very isolating experience, that the person experiencing pain probably felt in a unique position and better able to speak to a stranger. A large Samaritan in a white linen track suit warned against offering false optimism. 'I know how you feel', was also offered by the doctor's wife as a recipe for disaster, and this elicited a lively exchange of views; some thought it was perfectly possible to know how other people felt. How else was language to be used? 'If I had not experienced loneliness I would not be a Samaritan,' the cleric, who had a lot to say for himself on this occasion, informed the class.

Nicholas said that one of the most difficult aspects of taking a call was when the caller's pain seemed to be getting worse and the call was getting nowhere. 'Then words do begin to seem fairly pointless.' He said he usually suggested they had got as far as they could, and it might be better to leave the matter for a while. Another volunteer suggested inviting the caller round to the centre. 'Yes,' said the lady in the track suit, 'let them come in, and hold them while they cry.'

The mentors were taking a very verbal role during this session. One young man assured the trainees that the Samaritans were at their best at a point of crisis, and the words would come, he said, 'Believe me.' A young volunteer said she had taken a call the previous day from a woman who said she was going to die, and felt she had failed because the caller rang off. 'It's all right, she rang back,' a colleague reassured her. 'We are blotting paper, to absorb the pain of other people,' Nicholas ended by saying. 'Always remember, they called the Samaritans, not some other organization. We must be prepared to be hurt. Never bottle up the experience. You won't survive if you do.' Outside, when they left, the squirrel was dead.

On a sweltering evening when, for the first time, sunburnt shoulders were in evidence, the trainees were handed an application form for membership, although none of them had yet been accepted as a volunteer. 'I promise implicit obedience to instructions whilst carrying out the work of the organization,' it read. It also committed them to the possibility of having their membership terminated by the director at any time without reasons being given, and released the Samaritans from 'any legal responsibility for injury or loss . . . in carrying out my duties with clients.' It was strange that the word client, privately frowned upon by the director, had, even in 1986, crept back into an official document.

After scrutiny of the legal clause it seemed appropriate that the class should be asked to consider the subject of Loss Adjustment. 'This,' explained the young north-country volunteer, togged out in a yellow track suit, 'is one of the biggest background areas we work in.' The trainees were invited to compile a list of likely lost causes, starting with death itself. The lady from the probation service suggested the inability to walk. Loss of self-respect, and childen leaving home, came from others, and then the probation secretary added, 'If I lost my car for any reason.' Helen, another member of the training team, said that many psychiatrists now believed reactions to loss from any cause were no different to those experienced through bereavement. The attachment of the caller to the lost object, whether their parrot or their purse, was what counted.

One of the mentors, who had never had drama classes in her life, left the room to act the part, on the telephone, of a woman whose eighteen-year-old son had been killed on his motorbike. The blind Samaritan took the call. The class became very subdued as the 'caller' wept copiously down the phone, and the Samaritan gently but firmly questioned her about her feelings. The role-play in fact became almost too painful to listen to; one felt like an intruder on private grief. Afterwards the trainees were clearly impressed, and many expressed serious reservations about their own ability to take such a call and to deal with it effectively. A rallying cry went up from the Samaritans. 'You will, you will, the words will come, your own pauses are valuable, the day I arrive for duty without a gut feeling I shall give up and go home . . .'

'But what would happen if I did it wrong?' asked the young man out of work.

'What is wrong?' came the reply.

Then the class went into pairs, each trainee taking a call from a mentor. The lady from the Foreign Office felt very diffident about her performance, but her mentor assured her she had displayed a kind and sympathetic voice, 'and that's often all you want to hear, someone being nice for a change.' Someone again expressed concern about asking if a caller felt suicidal in case it might encourage suicidal feelings. 'Talking about suicide often has a salutary effect,' he was told. By the end of the evening there was a distinct feeling that the class was suddenly beginning to mature.

The training officer, back from holiday and looking sun-tanned, spent a session on Loneliness and Isolation elsewhere than in the training room, so the training team were sharply called to order by the blind mentor and began eight minutes late. Snippets were played on a tape. A man's voice said, 'It's easier to be a transvestite if you're married.' A woman commented, 'I think loneliness is a state of mind.' 'I daren't tell anyone I'm gay,' someone whined. The trainees were asked to discuss their reactions to what they had heard, but no one made sure they knew what a transvestite was, or, indeed, a 'gay'.

'If you didn't know about loneliness, you wouldn't have come along here to offer to be Samaritans,' a young man called Henry informed the volunteers. He had only been assigned to the course at the last minute and seemed very badly prepared. 'Everyone is going to be in some way lonely,' he limped on. A lot more time was wasted while fact sheets were handed out that could have been distributed on arrival, and then the trainees went into huddles to simulate a call from someone so lonely he wanted to know their name so that he could form a relationship and always ask for the same person when he rang the centre. Really getting into his stride, Henry told the class he was not at all sure the Samaritans offered friendship, though some might contradict him which, he said, they were very welcome to do. The relationship between a Samaritan and a caller was one-way, he said by way of explanation, 'so it wasn't friendship.'

'Now,' said Maureen, a member of the training team who was trying hard not to sound as though she had been postponing the inevitable hour for ever, 'I'm afraid to say we do get some calls from men who ring to make obscene calls, or to masturbate, or generally abuse the person on the other end. But it's better that a person like a Samaritan who is prepared for such a call should take it than an unprepared housewife at home.' Once Henry had managed to disentangle the tape recorder from the xerox machine, a voice boomed across the room, 'Can I wank on your tits?' You could have heard a pin drop, were it not for the whirring of the copier. 'When that happens, you are all at liberty to put the phone down,' Maureen assured her perfectly placid trainees. 'Harder to identify is the person who isn't so overt. It is vital not to encourage the man who just wants to masturbate and not to put off the man who has a real hidden problem, and is seeking help.'

Now Henry and a female Samaritan prepared to enact a variety of sex calls, but at this point the telephone would not work at all. The most sensitive and potentially embarrassing session was rapidly turning into farce. Afterwards, a lively and not always totally coherent young recruit called Jane, who had missed the last two sessions, said she now knew heaps about the Samaritans she had not known before. 'I had a very naïve view, when I think about it. I was actually thinking, "Crumbs, what is the substance of the course going to be like? Is it going to be sort of psychological? Or could it be a test of ourselves drawing on our own experience and our own energies?" That's what it's been, in fact. It's been like a mirror reflection. It's been an opening-out for me. It's made me evaluate myself and think, "Could I be good enough?"

'But the more they go on about it the more I keep thinking, "Crumbs, I don't know if I could hold that sort of level of not letting my own personality botch it up." There is a sort of ideal. There is a thread. I'd never really thought about sex calls before, but when I came for my interview, the lady who was there started talking about it and asked, "How would you handle a telephone masturbator?" and I thought, "Well, there must be some policy Samaritans have about that." When the chap phoned up and said, "I'd like to wank over your tits," my immediate reaction was to laugh. I was shocked in a way, but not threatened. I think we all have to accept that none of us in this entire world is pure. All of us are subject to masturbating and having weird thoughts so we all have something in common with each other.'

A middle-aged spinster now had this to say: 'My views, or attitudes, I hope have changed during the course. I envisaged that Samaritan work would obviously be listening, I knew that was important, but also being able to be practical, and perhaps suggest things they might do, things they might move on to, but I now realize that's not the way this branch works, anyway. It's not a disappointment. The intensity of what is being asked is greater than that. It's much more difficult for me. I would still like to be accepted, but I've no idea if I will be. It's quite an awe-inspiring – quite a frightening – thing, always with the anxiety of thinking, "Shall I say the right thing?" The course has been very valuable, very valuable. One looks forward to coming. I was prepared for this evening, unexpectedly, in a way. Like most women, occasionally I've had that sort of call at home. I have, once or twice, although I'm not down as female in the telephone book. But I feel if it happens in the centre I shall be able to cope much better than if I hadn't had that session tonight.'

The smart housewife: 'I don't think I had great thoughts about what the course was going to be like. I don't think I stopped to think about it very much. I think it's been immensely valuable, it's been an interesting and stimulating mixture between just talking and discussing various ideas and then actually interleafing it with role-plays and telephone calls, and it's beginning to give one a feel of what it might actually be like. As to whether one is better prepared, it's impossible to tell until you actually start on the thing for real. In some ways one is not necessarily reassured because you are now more aware of what some of the difficulties might be. I suppose I was aware there could be obscene calls and there could be sex calls and that sort of thing, and I suppose it was helpful to have some idea how you might lead into it and how you might be involved. I certainly wasn't unaware that such things occurred. But it was certainly useful to discuss how far one should let it go and how one could reasonably end it. Now the course is almost over I'm more keen than before to be a Samaritan. Whether I shall be accepted I can't tell at all. One hopes one will be.'

It was again a sweltering evening, and for the last night of the course the chairs had been rearranged in a semi-circle. The Catholic priest was sporting a green T-shirt with 'J.D's Hamburgers' on the back. Members of the training team presented a resumé of the topics that had been covered in the course, one of whom came up with the *bon mot*: 'Try to hear what the caller means as well as what he says.' The branch chairman, a nice young man who had swopped spectacles for contact lenses in the fifth week and looked even younger than before, explained about fund-raising and other essential activities, and the rota secretary said that although the branch was up to 170 members [the director had said 196], a hard core of thirty were always stepping in to do extra duties, and really a minimum of three duties a month and twelve overnight duties a year would be essential. [Seven overnight duties a year is regarded in most branches as a reasonable commitment.] The new volunteers, he said, should try to vary the times of their shifts, to avoid being telephoned by the same persistent callers and to gain experience of working with a variety of other Samaritans.

Then came the set piece, a demonstration of how an operations room might function on a night when the flying squad had to be called out. There was only one telephone – which whistled and shrieked – and one of the two Samaritans on duty had to go 'ring-ring, ring-ring', like a benevolent uncle playing games at a children's party. A chap called Mike, alias the training officer, rang in. He had taken a bottle of whisky and twenty codeine, and was getting drowsy. The Samaritan on the make-believe telephone rang the poisons unit to seek advice while his female colleague, in soft and rather soapy tones, tried to keep Mike on the phone and *compos mentis*. Hastily scribbled notes flew across the table, and eventually the duty director was contacted at home, who said a flying squad should be sent out. And then the muddle really got under way. A Samaritan was telephoned who had no car, then another was contacted who seemed less than sure of his way around the area, or where anyone lived, and while time for Mike seemed to be slipping away a persistent caller arrived at the door, and was cheerfully supplied with coffee and biscuits. However, all ended happily and in a welter of self-congratulations, the flying squad arrived in time, the duty director quite needlessly left her post and turned up at the centre, and when the performance was over there was a good deal of statutory hugging and kissing, well-earned on this occasion by the training officer: to pretend to be dying from an overdose for half an hour is quite a taxing task.

All that was left was to make sure that every trainee had booked in for an interview in a week's time. 'Arrive ten minutes early,' they were told. They would be interviewed by a deputy director, who might not have been a member of the training team, but who would have a report to go on. If they were rejected, they would be told on the spot; if accepted, they would undergo a preliminary observer duty, a second observer duty during which they would take their first call, and then an overnight duty, when they would be accompanied by only one other Samaritan, and be expected to take fifty per cent of the calls. If all was still well, they would be placed on probation for a three-month period or for a series of ten duties, best taken, they were told, at regular weekly intervals. Then everyone held hands and had a singsong. And then they all went home.

It transpired that one volunteer had dropped out half-way through the course. All but one of the others passed their final selection interviews, but as soon as Jennifer had begun to take up her observation duties she learned that she had been offered a job overseas. For some weeks a question mark hung over the lady from the Foreign Office. The team felt strongly that she needed the Samaritans in order to fill emotional gaps in her own life, and they doubted her ability to cope with demands the work would make on her. But she complained that she had been put off by her mentor, and in order that she should be seen to have received 'the best possible deal from us' her case was referred to the new director. The director confirmed the view of the team, and rejected her. 'She did not seem to have much contact with other people and there was not much warmth there,' the training officer explained. 'In a nutshell, we felt she wanted to be a Samaritan for the wrong reasons.' Out of seventeen potential volunteers, thirteen had joined the rota.

·5·

LONG-TERM BEFRIENDING

Always assuming the lines are not engaged, when a caller telephones a Samaritan centre he or she will hear the phone ring at least twice; this is to avoid the impression that someone has been sitting by it all day ready to spring into action. And the first words they will hear are, 'The Samaritans, can I help you?' The Samaritan, before he or she has picked up the receiver, and no matter how much of an open mind he or she has been taught to try to exercise, will have, stored somewhere in the recesses of their memory, a set of criteria for guidance in any number of possible situations. The lynchpin of those criteria was spelled out by Basil Higginson in the *Samaritan* in 1975, when he wrote, 'The Samaritans are an *emergency service* for the suicidal and despairing – not a long-term support service,' and he went on to quote a dictum of the founder: 'We do not permit our service to those whom we can help to be impeded by those who cannot benefit from it.' The New Testament itself provides a respectable pedigree for hard sayings such as these. Who can always judge, especially on the telephone, whether a caller is likely to benefit from talking to a Samaritan? And how do you terminate the conversation if you decide that a caller who cannot benefit is possibly preventing a suicidal caller from ringing in? There have been occasional surveys of calls that have received the engaged signal, and the numbers are high. Part of a Samaritan's task is trying tactfully to weed out those who cannot be helped by Samaritan methods from those who can in such a way as to leave the lines open while leaving the Samaritan ethos of a caring and compassionate organization intact.

Neither does anyone know how many callers, in desperate need of help, have failed to have their expectations matched by the Samaritans, and have even been propelled into a disastrous course of action as a result. In 1967, shortly before he murdered the playwright Joe Orton and then committed suicide, Kenneth Halliwell went to see the Samaritans. 'He started telling me how ill he was,' the actress Sheila Ballantine reported to Orton's biographer, John Lahr, 'how he was going to have a nervous breakdown. And how awful he felt. He was a bit strange. He'd rung the Samaritans and gone there. He said that was no good, they just make cups of tea.'[1]

Borderlines between feeling desperate or in despair, of contemplating suicide and attempting or committing suicide, of feeling lonely or just fed-up, overlap and are often wafer thin. Endemic loneliness may have little to do with being alone but a great deal to do with an inability to enjoy or even tolerate your own company; depression may represent a passing sense of sadness or a disabling and permanent incapacity to get out of bed; suicidal impulses can range from a wish to make someone feel sorry for you to an overwhelming desire to blank out for ever the pain of existence. The spectrum of what most Samaritans would regard as a genuine Samaritan caller is wide, but leads to little debate. Where Samaritans do often disagree among themselves is in the more nebulous context of persistent callers, particularly of those who treat the Samaritans as an extension of the National Health Service, as part of a welfare state that never shuts up shop and never sends out bills, and whose centres may even be regarded as surrogate massage parlours, albeit of the most rudimentary and voyeuristic kind.

So that while you are certainly not automatically expected to be feeling suicidal to ring the Samaritans, during the course of

---

[1] *The Orton Diaries* (Methuen, 1986). When Halliwell was eleven his mother choked to death in front of him; when he was twenty-three he found his father dead with his head in the gas oven.

any conversation with a caller the volunteer is expected to ask what is known in the movement as the 'suicide question'. 'The way in which it is asked and the point in the conversation at which it is best introduced should – and will – depend very much on how the contact has developed and what the needs of the caller are,' Simon Armson explains. 'There is no stock phrase. I think the sort of phrase, "Do you ever find life is getting to the point where you can't carry on any longer?" is one used quite frequently, rather than, "Are you contemplating committing suicide?" which is pretty harsh and narrow and rather cold and uncaring.' Why a caller feels suicidal – if they do – is far less important than whether he or she is in imminent danger of taking their life, and the criteria used by the Samaritans for determining a caller's state of mind are radically at variance with popular conceptions on the subject of suicide. People often say that someone genuinely intent on suicide would never talk about it, but the Samaritans estimate that at least four out of five people who kill themselves will have given quite definite warning of their intentions. Few dinner parties at which the subject comes up lack, too, the knowledgeable guest who avows that if someone is seriously intent on committing suicide, they will do so whatever happens. The truth is that many people who succeed in killing themselves never make a clear-cut decision; they seem more to gamble with death by playing a kind of Russian roulette, leaving it to others to save them. Almost the most pertinent fact about suicide, in relation to the work of the Samaritans, is that while suicidal feelings are far from permanent, most suicides occur within about three months of the onset of a period of 'improvement', for this is precisely the time when the potential victim is able to summon up enough energy to channel morbid thoughts into physical action. Another source of comfort to society has traditionally been the myth that everyone who commits suicide is mentally ill. A psychotic person – a paranoid schizophrenic, for instance – may be very seriously at risk, but the vast majority of successful suicides are carried out by people temporarily incapable of coping with unhappiness. They constitute a large proportion of the callers prompted to contact the Samaritans in their desperate search for a lifeline.

Depression, in its most virulent form an illness, commonly leads to suicide and masks a large number of calls to the Samaritans. For many people who suffer from depression fail to recognize the symptoms; they do not even know what illness they are suffering from. Guide-lines on the subject produced by one branch aptly describe a truly depressed person as living in a kind of fog or mist, where everything and everyone seems dull and hopeless, and adds the stark warning, 'We can regard depression as a killer.' No amount of love, money or privilege seems to protect a victim of depression; it strikes at royalty, artists and fathers-in-God. Prince Henrik of Denmark is frequently incapacitated through depressive illness; Elgar was almost certainly a paranoid schizophrenic; some years ago a suffragan bishop committed suicide in a London hotel. One reason a depressive may call the Samaritans is because his illness has alienated him from his family; he may have been told to pull himself together, and failed, and he can sense an irritation at his withdrawn condition growing in those he loves, who seem quite unable to help him. Depression is socially unacceptable because many of those who suffer most severely are highly intelligent people who hold responsible or demanding jobs, feel guilty about their 'failings', have been conditioned to put on a stiff upper lip and to set an example to others, and experience great difficulty in admitting to a form of mental rather than physical illness. They suffer from an acute emotional pain in the mind, without apparent cause and with no easily accessible cure. While dispirin will take away a headache, depression remains impervious to drink, sympathy or self-discipline. 'You cannot take the depression away,' the Samaritans tell their volunteers, 'but you can gently explain that this is an illness and the feelings described are the classical symptoms of the illness.' These symptoms often involve an inability to make decisions, and, if the depression is really bad, an almost total incapacity to act. Insomnia, loss of interest in work, a general lack of concentration and a liability to burst into tears at the slightest provocation are all pointers to depression, but not necessarily factors the caller will mention without some gentle probing.

Most people who suffer from depression find it a condition almost impossible to describe. A Samaritan who has experienced severe depression has said you might as well try to tell a man what childbirth is like; you cannot. A caller who is well aware that she suffers from depression, and of her sense of inadequacy that seems to trigger it off, is Kay, twenty-one, highly educated but somehow tangled up in a web of words. 'I rang the Samaritans because of severe depression,' she explains. 'I was having a very bad time on the personal and professional level. I think I've always found it difficult dealing with people. There's usually been one individual in each job I've had a violent personality clash with. I think it's my lack of assertiveness that's been the cause of it, and this lack of assertiveness and lack of ability to just knuckle under and cope with crises of a professional nature has led to this severe depression. I feel I've failed, you see. And this sense of failure has led me to become almost hopeless, to feel hopeless, to feel that there's no future, to feel that I'm just no good in the eyes of society.

'I talk of my problems to certain friends, but there are times when I feel I can't burden them any more. In the past few years they must have come in for quite a bit of earache. They've got problems of their own. What's really going on in my mind, I feel it's impossible to express it. I feel that the patience of friends is limited. They will listen, but the ones who are my best friends tend to be wrapped up in their own problems. There are times when I feel trapped. That's why I went to the Samaritans. The worst spell of depression I've ever had, which I would describe as true depression, was in 1982. The worst time is when you wake up in the morning and you've got to get up and face the day, and there just seems to be a blank wall ahead of you.'

Kay later had the misfortune to set up for herself a situation which was almost bound to end in disappointment; she offered to join the Samaritans. And although her personal unsuitability may have been an extreme example of the sort of potential volunteer who has to be turned down, her sense of rejection, even though it was born of so much unreality, was probably fairly typical.

'I felt that I'd been through the pits, and I just wanted to help other people, because I knew I could overcome it, and I thought, Gosh, if I can overcome what I went through four years ago then I'd like other people to get over their crises. You know, just sort of talk them through it. I think there are some people who can benefit more from going to the Samaritans than others. So I phoned them up. There was an advertising campaign at the time. I filled in a form and then later I went for an interview. When I filled in the form I thought I did it quite well, really, and I got one or two friends to go through it with me. So I went for my interview, and a lot of the interview was going over the things I had written on the form, and a lot about my background, how I coped with depression, how I'd react in certain circumstances. It was a very in-depth interview, actually. And also my attitude towards suicide. That was very important. I was interviewed by a woman, in her late thirties or early forties. I thought it was slightly unnecessary to go over the same ground as was on the form. She was calm and precise. I thought I was on quite an even keel. But looking back, I think I looked an absolute wreck. I think I may have looked like a depressive, for a start. And I think she might have questioned my motivation. She might have seen things I couldn't even dream were visible, you know, such as seeing into somebody's mental state. At the end, I thought it was not too bad. It lasted about an hour, maybe a little less.

'A few weeks later things were going badly for me again. I was very depressed, actually. I'd had a very, very unhappy time with this man over the last six years. There was a bit of a bad scene in April 1985, about two weeks after my interview with the Samaritans. There was a bad scene with the man, and there was also a crisis in my job. Again, a personality-based sort of crisis. So I was feeling very low because of work, and I had a scene with the man, which set me off feeling pretty depressed, and I got home feeling in a very bad state to see I'd got this rejection letter from the Samaritans. Now, there was no reason given. And I found that a bit upsetting. I'd have liked to have known. A possible reason could have been my attitude towards suicide. Because that was one of the main topics of conversation in the interview. I said that I thought suicide was justifiable in some circumstances and I thought it was quite understandable, and the woman said, "Well, what do you mean, why would it be justifiable, under what circumstances?" and I said, "If a person, for example, is terminally ill, or they've got some very severe disability, or if they're old, their friends have died, they've got no family, they've got nothing to live for, they're on the decline, they don't feel like carrying on. I think that's perfectly justifiable," I said. I wouldn't encourage them, but she may have thought from what I said that I might encourage them. But I'll never know, because they never told me why I was rejected. I found that more hurtful than being rejected. I thought of various unflattering reasons to myself. She might have just guessed that I was potentially a depressive person, in the future as well as in the past, because you have to admit whether you've ever been to the Samaritans as a caller. You fill in the form and you have to state that. But that doesn't prejudice your application. I admitted it, of course.'

A major cause of depression, and a reason high on the list of personal disasters that prompts callers to ring the Samaritans, is one form or another of bereavement. The death of an animal can cause similar symptoms to the death of a person; so can the loss of a job or a home. Although as common as the birth rate, death has become a taboo subject in our time, partly because with astonishing advances in medicine our expectations of a long life – perhaps of living for ever – have been increased out of all proportion to our inherent vulnerability to illness and accident, thus exacerbating our disappointment when the Great Reaper does in fact appear, and partly through a universal loss of religious conviction, and thus at least some sort of rationale for pain and suffering. Few people any longer believe in life after death. Old age, too, holds far greater material terrors than in the past, with the prospect of a prolonged and senile decay locked away in a geriatic hospital, abandoned by family and friends.

Society has come to despise old people rather than respect them, to regard them as a drain on national resources, and by some young men, equally the victims of a sense of alienation, as a source of hatred so violent as to lead to rape. Death is no longer celebrated. Few people have watched at a deathbed,[2] or paid their respects to a bereaved family, and few hearses leave these days for the church from the dead person's house; most sneak off from the impersonal side door of a uniform firm of undertakers. No wonder that with death swept under the carpet, expressions of bereavement have become an almost intolerable burden to those who would once have been only too pleased to join in the process. When a recently widowed neighbour comes into view there is a hasty retreat to the other side of the street.

Many of those who call the Samaritans are in a way preparing themselves for bereavement; they may have a husband or wife suffering from a terminal illness, and be wishing that death would interpose, relieving them of the chore of nursing, along with the anguish of watching someone die. Such feelings give rise to anger, guilt and shame. 'To prompt them to talk about their anger,' volunteers are reminded, 'can obviate the ensuing guilt. Perhaps to be assured by another human being that they are not wicked, cruel, callous and thoughtless is the most healing way of all.' Many relationships founder through an inability on the part of the partners to talk in depth, yet many relationships survive non-communication sometimes for fifty years, and much that was never verbalized in life will haunt the surviving partner. Yet those who mourn seldom have anyone to mourn with or to moan at; after the funeral, life is meant to go on as before, and callers often complain that their friends think they should have 'got over it.' The widow is a potent symbol of ill-luck; what has happened to her could so easily happen to you, and the sooner she bucks up and pulls herself together the sooner we shall all be able to ignore reality once more. And of course, coping with bereavement is one of the hardest tasks a Samaritan may be faced with because, as a branch who have

———

[2] Four out of five of those who still die in bed do so in hospital.

supplied an *aide memoire* on the subject to its members very sensibly points out, 'Most of us have suffered some form of bereavement at some time, and we should be aware of our own vulnerability and not gloss over parts that we found particularly painful, as we will then be defending ourselves and not helping our clients.'

The Samaritans recognize the vital importance of giving people time to mourn: 'We must be careful not to "cheer them up",' they say. They are also aware that callers may in some way be asking permission to stop mourning, for to some extent we still cling to the Victorian idea that ever to cease fixing one's thoughts upon the dear departed is unthinkable, and remarriage obscene. A form of first marriage still obscene in the eyes of many people is a permanent homosexual partnership, and if society is bad at dealing with heterosexual bereavement it can hardly be expected to take seriously the destruction by death of a loving relationship it refused to accept when it existed. So in bereavement, homosexuals frequently turn to the Samaritans for support, for they often have nowhere else to go. The family may not have known of the most important person in their life, and the homosexual subculture is notoriously inept at dealing with death, preferring to concentrate on the illusory 'gaiety' of the passing scene. 'Bereaved homosexuals can be the most difficult to help,' one branch informs its volunteers. 'Their isolation can often become so acute that their thoughts turn to suicide. We must help them to mourn, to accept their grief.'

It should come as no surprise that a large number of callers will actually be clinically neurotic or psychotic, nor come as any surprise that as a consequence, a common misconception about the Samaritans has grown up to the effect that they are ill-equipped do-gooders dabbling in amateur psychiatry. In no circumstances does an individual Samaritan comment on a caller's psychological state of mind or offer psychiatric advice, but in deciding how best to steer a conversation, and whether to regard a caller as temporarily distressed or in need of expert medical help (which might be made available if a caller were invited to visit the centre for further befriending), it is thought advisable for Samaritans to be provided with some outline understanding of the most commonly defined psychological problems. In preparing guide-lines for the members of the country's busiest branch, central London, the director, John Eldrid, makes a very general distinction between people who can be said to be in touch with reality and those who are not. What is most noticeable about callers out of touch with reality, he says, is that the volunteer will find it very difficult to recognize some of their feelings and ideas. 'The caller who speaks in detail about being followed by the police, and sexual attacks through the use of radar, does seem to be, at the least, a bit unusual. Those who have these experiences seem quite unaware of any personal identity or sense of disintegration.'

Mr Eldrid specifically draws his members' attention to characteristics of the manic depressive – mood changes that swing from very excessive excitement to utter and complete feelings of despair – and schizophrenics, who 'are most likely to be very withdrawn and to be living in a world of their own.' He is careful to warn of similarities between those who are depressive and those who are schizophrenic, but cites as examples of schizophrenic behaviour callers who speak of voices giving them special directions, 'which may involve them in wanting to take special responsibilities in political or religious activities, or suicide. Sometimes the voices may be very condemning and threatening, and accuse them of all kinds of strange sexual behaviour.' Evelyn Waugh's *The Ordeal of Gilbert Pinfold*[3] is an autobiographical account of just such an experience. Mr Eldrid has gone on to warn Samaritans of the dangers a psychotic caller may present. 'It is not always easy,' he says, 'to recognize how very disturbed they really are. Many people who feel persecuted and paranoid can be very convincing indeed, and it is always important to recognize that those who are out of touch with reality seem very quick to pick up your weak points, and sometimes you may feel very threatened by their attitudes.'

In trying to encourage a caller with a severe psychological

[3] Chapman & Hall, 1957.

problem to accept on-going befriending John Eldrid says it is important to recognize that although we can say mentally ill people have no apparent insight into their state of unreality, there does seem to be, more often than not, some hidden awareness that they may need support and psychiatric help. 'It is possible that when the caller feels more secure and has trust in the Samaritans he or she will accept some professional help. This is especially true of those suffering from depression. Befriending will help to combat the awful feeling of isolation and loneliness of the depressed. I would suggest that it is essential for befriending contacts to be maintained on a daily and nightly basis together with the making of every effort to arrange psychiatric medical help. As always, a lot of care, patience and tact is required.'

A branch in the North East has a deputy director responsible for 'on-going befriending', a service they have extended on a permanent basis to a local psychiatric hospital. 'We have two or three volunteers who go to the hospital regularly,' she explains. They speak to all the patients who want to speak to them, and we play exactly the same role there as we do in the centre. The nurses are very short of time, and time is the essential thing we are able to offer. Some of our callers are regular inmates of the hospital, in and out, in and out, and they like to see the volunteers every week. There are no special gifts involved, just the ability to listen. Our volunteers involved in the scheme are of course approved by the hospital. Every time we speak to a caller we're really befriending them, but those we officially 'befriend' are people who need that little bit more, who may be going through a particular crisis when we offer them extra support. But it doesn't mean we automatically agree to befriend someone. Some people think we are a branch of Age Concern. We don't just go out to sit with people who need a visitor. We like to use our befrienders for people who are going through a crisis. They may have been accused of shoplifting, and be very distressed.[4] If a volunteer feels that a caller may possibly benefit

[4] Isabel Barnett, the television entertainer, who was also a magistrate, committed suicide when accused of shoplifting.

from befriending they will discuss it with their day leader, and if the leader agrees, they come to me and we discuss it. We try to match the caller to a suitable volunteer. No volunteer should ever promise off their own bat that a befriender will be sent out in an emergency. If we couldn't find someone that would leave the caller in a dreadful mess.'

Not every caller who ends up being befriended is mentally ill, and as the general secretary says, 'Branches define the operation differently. One branch will say they are currently befriending 100 people and another six, and when you poke around they're both befriending perhaps twenty or twenty-five. Befriending is usually undertaken if the branch thinks a caller is at continuing risk of suicide and would be helped by an on-going relationship with one or a pair of Samaritans. The volunteer would then give this person quite a lot of time outside the centre. To avoid the danger of dependence, the volunteer is supported by a leader.'

A personal experience of befriending, not entirely successful, is recalled by a leader in Scotland. 'I did it once, for a woman, and it was very difficult. She was a very clingy lady, and at the end of the time I felt that she actually didn't need the befriending but it was quite hard to get rid of her. She lived alone, and she had had a dreadful upbringing, but she had managed to get a degree, and to bring up two boys, and she had a secretarial training, but she couldn't get a job. And she found this completely demoralizing. Also, she couldn't make relationships, and this, I think, was basically the problem. She had married the first man she thought would marry her. And I think she felt she had found a kindred spirit in me, which was probably true, she had. She was very keen on dancing, and music, and all the things that I enjoy, and so it could have developed into a friendship, but she was very clinging, so in the end I had to sort of distance myself. I could see that the longer it went on the more difficult it was going to be to get out of. She would never phone unless I was on duty, and I said, "There are other people to talk to," but I have a feeling in a way that we didn't do her much good because she wanted more than we could actually offer. I mean, she actually wanted a long, on-going friendship.

'Not all branches will refer people to other organizations equipped to give long-term assistance. But a lot of branches will. If, for instance, a caller is alcoholic we will refer them, if we feel they are in need of help that we cannot give, to Alcoholics Anonymous, gays to Gay Switchboard and transvestites to the Beaumont Society. And of course for people who are afraid they have got Aids, there is the Terrence Higgins Trust.[5] We are very aware of all the other agencies we can turn to to help the caller.'

Other reasons for seeing a caller outside the centre were given by a leader whose special responsibility is to make such decisions. 'A caller might not have a telephone at home, and in order to ring the centre she is crammed into a phonebox, with her children outside in the street.' Some long-term befriending is conducted by means of a weekly visit by the volunteer to the caller's home; but if a caller wishes to preserve the anonymity of their own home, the meeting place may be a café. No Samaritan reveals their surname, address or telephone number to the caller without their director's permission, for no befriender can guarantee to be available at home twenty-four hours a day, and the person being befriended needs to be reminded that in an emergency, help will always be available at the centre. One of the tasks of a befriender is to try to steer the caller away from feeling he or she is just a person with problems, to try and encourage them to see themselves as part of the community. There are no hard and fast rules about the length of time befriending may last, but something like three months seems to be a generally accepted maximum. 'Make it a happy ending, not a rejection,' volunteers are advised. 'Discuss ending the befriending with a caller; don't let it peter out. Summarize what has happened in the course of the befriending.' Above all, they are told to remind the caller that the Samaritans are always there.

[5] BM A.I.D.S., London WCIN 3XX.

From the earliest days, long-term befriending has been seen as essential for certain callers. Basil Higginson warned that 'One of the great weaknesses – indeed, dangers – of our work is that depressed people are often allowed to telephone once, or make one visit to the centre, and then go out and kill them-selves,' and in 1975 he was drawing attention to the vital necessity for every client's form and continuation sheet to be assessed as soon as possible by a director or leader, 'one with considerable experience as a Samaritan . . . to see if necessary further interviews and perhaps referral (with the client's con-sent) has been offered – especially if the enquiries on the report form about suicide and consent to follow up have not been filled in by the volunteer.' And with disarming honesty he went on to point out that 'this lack of competent assessment has been justly criticized by responsible friends of the Samaritans.' He quoted some tragic examples of deaths that had followed negligent assessment of callers' problems at a basic level: the case, for example, of a thirty-five-year-old widow who called at a centre, where the volunteer failed to ask how her husband had died, or encourage her to express her anger at his death and her loss, but assured her instead that time would heal her feelings. Six weeks later, she took an overdose. And of a man of forty-five suffering from depression: 'He was worried about his declining business. The Samaritan talked about business today and reminded him that many others were in the same boat. John perked up and said he would "get by". The Samaritan said, "I'm sure you will." John went home and shot himself at the bottom of his garden within an hour.'

One form of befriending which gives rise to controversy among Samaritans themselves concerns the degree of attention and length of time that should be lavished on persistent callers; younger, more impatient volunteers particularly seem to wish that the Samaritans would stay at the grass roots level of being available in a crisis. 'This is what we're good at,' a social worker in his thirties, contemplating resignation after five years, firmly believes. 'Far too much time is wasted, in my opinion, dishing out tea and sympathy to casual callers who don't really need us or benefit from an emergency service.' Nevertheless the Samaritans do put themselves out for a hefty proportion of callers who are so lonely or inadequate they feel the need to telephone their local centre at regular intervals, or call in, perhaps only for a cup of coffee and a chat. There is a universal awareness that the befriending of such people must never interfere with emergency work, yet a persistent caller has only to be on the telephone for a couple of minutes to block an emergency line. Once a caller has been marked down as a regular, he or she is often allocated a specific length of call, or stay. Such decisions are necessarily taken on their merits. One particularly busy branch has as a regular visitor a young man who is schizophrenic, who wanders in, leaves his money lying around, makes a cup of tea, talks to anyone who may be available, usually on topics of no relevance to his mental or physical state (like many schizophrenics, he is intelligent, totally unemployable and often sleeps rough), and then drifts off again. The centre at least provides one point of reference in his otherwise tragically dislocated life.

The regular or persistent caller comes in a variety of guises. A deputy director at one of the London branches, where regular callers are inevitably more numerous than in small country branches, said, 'I would say a regular caller is someone who has been calling maybe half a dozen times. I think a lot of them are just lonely. A lot need some sort of reassurance. Some of them become like alcoholics – telephonics, if you like – and they can't stop ringing. There are others who have the need to make a phone call quite literally to wind up the person on the other end, the so-called fantasy or hysterical caller. They ring us because they know we will never put the phone down. If you get a caller with a very bizarre but nevertheless believable problem it is very easy to get caught up in the whole presentation. I know, because it's happened to me. And you think, "I must go on listening. If it's true, it's horrendous." We are always trained to go for feelings rather than what the "presenting problem" is. But with hysterical or fantasy callers, they can wind you up to such a point that you totally forget about feelings and start trying to resolve the problem, whatever it is, although we are not there to give advice. And they know they are doing this.

'So far as some of the persistent callers are concerned, there simply are people who don't develop at all. They will talk through a problem with one volunteer, and then do exactly the same with another. Because we don't offer advice or solutions, people sometimes get quite angry. If they get really angry and frustrated, they will put the phone down. If you have a call where you have been talking through the problem and trying to discuss how they feel there comes a point, sometimes, when the caller himself will say, "Thank you very much, I think we've talked enough, I've got a lot to think about but I will ring you again, thank you and goodbye." At other times you have to make the first move to end the call. You can say to them, after you've been talking for an hour, say, and sometimes they go on much longer than that, "I think possibly we're beginning to go over the same ground again. Wouldn't it be a good idea now just to have a break and for you to think about what we've said and then, if you want to ring us again, do so?" That's one way. There are a lot of other ways of doing it. The thing is, you mustn't make the caller feel you are rejecting them. But there is a point where you actually don't do any good by going on talking for hours and hours and hours.

'I can think of perhaps four or five people I've spoken to in the last year who didn't ring again. But one never knows if one has actually helped them, or whether you haven't helped them and they think it just wasn't worth ringing again, or if they ring another branch. You would know if they had rung your branch again but spoken to a different volunteer because we have a system of recording calls. But the real problem is when you have a caller who gives different volunteers a different name. It's generally the callers who are afraid that if they keep ringing under the same name they're going to be turned away or rejected in some way. After every call you fill in the log book with the time, and their suicidal factor, from 3 to x. Three is absolutely suicidal at that moment, 2 and 1 are lesser degrees of that. Nought is not suicidal and x means you have failed to ascertain. You generally make notes on a piece of paper while you're talking, and if you're so busy you haven't time to log it there and then you do so as soon as you are free. Then we have a card system on which we write down the essential points of the story; how suicidal they were and what were the factors that were making them suicidal – bereavement, isolation, depression, whether they live alone, whether they're employed or sick and things like that. And they're given a number. In my branch it's the year and then a number after that. They don't know this, though I'm sure some callers suspect we do. The card is really to help the leaders to ensure continuity.'

The question of maintaining and eventually destroying caller records is a sensitive one. Definitive advice was approved by the executive committee in 1985 in the following terms: 'Records must contain the minimum of information which might indicate the identity of a caller. They should be kept for the minimum length of time compatible with our care for the caller.' Simon Armson explains: 'If there hasn't been a contact for six months then the record is destroyed, and it's up to branches to work through their records and to destroy on that basis. If this had not been done properly it is something the Visitors would pick up. Of course, it may cause problems over the compiling of statistics, because if someone contacts a branch in the month, let us say, after their records have been destroyed, they will go into the statistics for individual callers twice that year, but that's a small price to pay for ensuring that we're doing all we can to protect the confidential information that is kept.'

'Not all regular callers are manipulative or unable to be helped,' one branch reminds its volunteers in a set of standing orders. 'The branch has frequently helped callers over a period of time by applying a consistent policy.' When carrying out instructions drawn up for dealing with persistent callers, it reminds Samaritans to be 'as gentle as possible, and only as firm as necessary', to be alert to a deterioration in a regular caller's situation, and always to ask about suicide.

An amusing anecdote about a persistent caller was recounted by a volunteer in a seaside town. 'We have one woman who is only allowed to call once a day, but she uses fifty different names. Fortunately she has quite a strong German accent. She got the director the other day, and she'd already rung twice, so he was very firm. This caller is agoraphobic, lives on the ninth floor of a block of flats, and she is always telling us she wants to put an end to it all and throw herself off. Some days she is worse than others, and she has long tales of woe, about people next door playing their radios and so on. She nearly always rings at midday, and she would talk for an hour if you let her. Well, she rang me up one day and said, "He's going to kill me, he's going to kill me!" So I asked who was going to kill her and she said, "My husband. He's just paid one phone bill and now another one's come in!' So I told her, "If you call after one o'clock it's a lot cheaper!" Now she tends only to be on the phone for about half an hour.'

The relationship between a Samaritan volunteer and a caller is unique in one specific way if in no other, as cinema-goers who recall Rita Tushingham rushing up a garden path and shouting at the lady of the house, 'Rape!' will readily realize. 'No, not today, thank you,' came the response. Few of us listen to a word that anyone says, either because what is said falls outside our expectations or comprehension, or because we are quite simply waiting for a pause in the 'conversation' to express our own beliefs, ignorance, prejudice or witticism. Learning to listen is perhaps the hardest task the Samaritan faces, and not solely on account of the persistent urge we have to talk. Most of us think about four times as fast as an average person speaks, so that a person listening has three-quarters of a minute of spare thinking time for each listening minute. It is like being left with a kind of blank space we feel we need to fill, and usually we do it by thinking about our own concerns. Once you do that you have ceased to listen, and once you begin to comprehend the social attitudes to silence you begin to realize how unnaturally listening comes to most of us. 'Have you nothing to say for yourself?' we petulantly enquire of the silent child, and monks and nuns who enter silent orders we look upon as the most extraordinary eccentrics. In fact, what the Samaritans list as 'barriers to good listening' are almost endless. They warn their volunteers against taking up a defensive attitude if they hear mention such emotive words as 'should', 'must', 'police' or 'unions', and they remind them that often we jump to the conclusion that either the subject or the speaker is going to be boring and make no sense. 'When we listen to ideas that are too complex and complicated there is a danger we will shut off,' they are told. And again, 'Sometimes we concentrate on the problem and not the person. Detail and fact about an incident become more important than what people are saying about themselves.'

If at the best of times listening takes practice and a determined effort of the will, how much harder is it for a Samaritan to cope with a call from someone who for whatever reason refuses or declines to speak? The silent call is every volunteer's nightmare. In a piece of unconscious humour, the members of one branch are reminded not to assume that every silent call is a sex call: 'On the contrary, heavy breathing may denote considerable distress and not sexual desire.' There seems, not surprisingly, to be little solid research into the genesis of the silent caller, but just as there are people who find it hard to stop talking so there are people who find it almost impossible to articulate their thoughts and feelings, more than ever when under stress. They may be content merely to hear a sympathetic voice on the other end of the line. Volunteers are encouraged to join in the atmosphere of silence by not talking continuously themselves, and by reassuring the caller that no matter how long they wish to remain on the line, the Samaritan will not replace the receiver. Giving the caller the volunteer's name and asking for theirs is a personal touch which sometimes elicits a response, but above all, the volunteer is enjoined not to hurry, to make it plain that they have all the time in the world, and to allow variable amounts of time between their own remarks. Anything between ten and thirty-five seconds is regarded as reasonable, and it is not until you time the second hand of your watch slowly ticking away that you realize just how long thirty-five seconds can seem.

Even though every silent call is not a sex call, the fact remains

that people with sexual problems constitute a very large proportion of callers to the Samaritans; their problems may be
something physical, albeit with psychological origins, like premature ejaculation or impotence, or something emotional, like
an inability to come to terms with being homosexual. Whatever
the 'presenting problem' may appear to be, Samaritans are told
not to exhibit any attitude of shock or disapproval, although
certain forms of sexual behaviour, taboo in our society, such as
bestiality, incest or sexual relations with a child, may be
difficult for the average Samaritan, being an average sort of
person, to sympathize with. For some people, even such sexual
activities as fellatio, sado-masochism, lesbianism and heterosexual buggery (still illegal in the United Kingdom but commonly adopted in Roman Catholic countries as a form of
contraception) are difficult to comprehend. 'Callers coming to
the Samaritans with sexual difficulties will in the majority feel
very guilty about them,' John Eldrid has explained to his
volunteers in central London. 'So it is essential for us to be
accepting and not in any way condemning or shockable.' And
he has gone on to warn that, 'Even if you do not express your
shock or condemnation verbally, your negative feelings will be
communicated to the caller, so one of the best preparations for
Samaritan befriending is to come to terms with our own
psychosexual make-up. Most of us are going to have hang-ups
of one kind or another, but it makes all the difference if you are
aware of them and have insight into your reactions.'

As a priest, Eldrid is in a useful position to admit that it is not
easy for Samaritans neither to condemn nor condone a caller's
actions, 'because we are all contaminated with perverted moral
and theological ideas about sex. At the same time,' he says, 'we
have to realize that some guilt feelings are healthy, and in fact, if
you are not capable of feeling guilt, you are sick.' He also sees
clear similarities in the sexual field – as in so many others
('There but for the grace of God go I') – between the volunteer
and the caller: 'The majority of us, whether Samaritans or
callers, can afford to improve our emotional and sexual relations,' he says. He might have added that some volunteers

need to give attention to their vocabulary; one noted in the log-book, 'Could have been a sex caller but he did not expand.'

For all the absurd pretence that we live in some sort of permanent permissive orgy, agony columns in newspapers and phone-in programmes on the radio are daily flooded with letters and calls from people unable to express or talk about their sexual difficulties at home or with friends, difficulties and desires that often seem to stem from an inner loneliness and anxiety, fed by outrageous demands by the advertising industry for women to be glamorous and for men to be masculine, and by prejudiced and ignorant educationalists intent on forcing children from infancy to enact polarized gender roles to the exclusion of a development of their full human potential. 'Sex is really about relationships,' John Eldrid is at pains to point out, and this is why he believes it is a great help to create, within the Samaritans, the kind of atmosphere where a caller feels they can speak about their sexual difficulties. 'The majority of callers will agree that just to speak about them is a tremendous relief. I think it is essential for Samaritans to recognize that what we are offering are not solutions to problems – although we can arrange counselling and other professional help as required – but the presence of another human being. This is a positive step towards making life more worth living.'

However easy (or difficult) a Samaritan may find it to be confronted with another person's sexual hang-up, most well-selected and well-trained Samaritans will recognize that no matter how bizarre or unpalatable someone's 'sexual difficulty' may seem to them, for the caller it could well constitute such a source of anxiety as to present a serious threat of suicide. Yet there is a division of opinion as to how to deal with one category of caller presenting a sexual problem, the man known throughout the Samaritan movement as the telephone masturbator, whose calls are variously labelled M-calls or TM-calls. Unless the frequency of such calls were often made light of, many female volunteers would find it even more difficult than they do to absorb into their work as Samaritans the kind of experience that can send an innocent housewife, chosen at random from the telephone directory, flying beneath the kitchen table for cover, or even to the police for protection.

One reason given by some volunteers for the frequency of obscene telephone calls to the Samaritans is because the caller knows, in theory at any rate, that a Samaritan, unlike a random victim, will not slam down the telephone; also, a Samaritan centre is manned twenty-four hours a day, and by a large proportion of women. In point of fact, once a volunteer is satisfied that a caller is intent only on trying to sustain a conversation with a woman long enough to masturbate and then to ring off she is nowadays at liberty to terminate the call after explaining that she is not there to be used in that way, yet leaving the door open for the caller to ring back or visit the centre if he really wishes to discuss his situation.

One director in the Eastern Region says: 'It is mostly the women who have to cope, but male volunteers have taken M-calls. I've taken many, both homosexual and heterosexual. I've got a fairly light voice, and there have been occasions when I've been mistaken for a woman. And sometimes when I say, "Do you realize that I'm a man?" the caller has rung off. But on one occasion he said, "Well, it doesn't matter." We've occasionally had women ringing up wanting to masturbate. Why not? I haven't spoken to any, but I have spoken to quite a few men.'

There is a standing joke that whenever a newly trained female volunteer takes her first call, it is always an M-call. An attractive volunteer of thirty-four, now with seven years' experience, recalls her first call, and it was a sex call 'that went on for an hour and a half. It was very explicit, and most of it was certainly an eye-opener to me!' Many of what are known as click-calls, when the emergency line is answered and someone just rings off, are potential M-callers waiting until the phone is answered by a woman. A Samaritan in Surrey remembers that at her branch, 'We had a wonderful girl, a very pretty girl from Australia, who's left us, unfortunately, and gone back to Australia. When I was being trained she gave a demonstration in the class, and she just said outright to the other Samaritan in the role-play,

"Are you masturbating?" I'm reasonably unshockable and I must say I now find it much easier to use plain language to people, but it was the kind of thing I would have found very difficult to say at that time. Now, thank goodness, we are permitted to say, "This is an emergency service and I'm afraid I can't help you but if you have a real problem you are welcome to come in and discuss it with the director," and then to ring off. If you give way to them all the time the phones are just blocked with these calls. And all they want is for you to talk until they've got what they want. Then they hang up. I think it should not be encouraged. They obviously have a problem but we're not equipped to deal with it, really. We're not experts in sexual problems and inadequate people, but you have to be frightfully careful that somebody hasn't got a real problem.

'I had a chap who rang me three times. He would take twenty minutes to get talking, and his story was that he was having incest with his mother, and it was usually pretty much the same story; his mother had come back from the pub, and it had always started that day or the day before, and then I discovered he'd been calling quite three months before, and then he started describing what was happening and he was thoroughly enjoying himself. And I suddenly realized he was having himself a fine old time. It was basically a sex call. Some of them are very clever, they've worked out their story. I haven't had nearly so many of these calls lately, but when I first joined there seemed to be an awful lot of them, and I found that you started being cautious. Instead of listening really sympathetically you were making judgements all the time and you were being careful. You don't want to be made a fool of, although you're supposed to be prepared to be made a fool of, but you do have to acquire a kind of sixth sense, and it therefore means that if you've had two or three of these manipulative calls, when somebody serious calls you tend to be careful and cautious, which is very bad for the real caller.

'But you have to take every call as potentially serious. After a while, of course, you get to know certain voices – although one man kept changing his voice. We've had him for years. He's aggressive and there's nothing we can do for him. It's always difficult to assess if you've helped someone. Just occasionally somebody says "Thank you for listening, I feel better now," or you feel that they've let off a lot of steam, or they've cried, and you always leave the door open for them to call you back. To have someone ring who is clearly suicidal, and you don't know, when they ring off, if they are going to kill themselves, that's very distressing. That's why it's good to have somebody else there, to have a back-up, someone to talk to. My morning bath is my great time for thinking. I suddenly think in the bath, I didn't handle that one right. You can't get it right all the time, anyway.'

The difficulty in sorting out the manipulative callers unable or unwilling to achieve sexual stimulation in proximity to a real person, but intent on using a Samaritan as a voyeuristic vehicle, from the genuine caller too nervous, perhaps, to articulate at first the matter he really wants to talk about, lies at the core of 'TM Procedure'. A branch in Wales has been told that 'some indicators to help you to do this' include whether the caller expresses strong interest in the Samaritan's personality, in the colour of her eyes or her underwear, whether he speaks of his sexual problems in graphic detail, and in particular whether he tries to explore the Samaritan's own sexuality. Talk of fetishes, like spanking, and fantasies (about 'the woman upstairs') are all regarded as clear indications that the caller will soon lose interest if an offer of real help is extended; he has no desire to shed his voyeuristic impulses, and the volunteers are warned that 'by providing him with a telephone prostitute (i.e. you) you are doing nothing for his isolation. We merely satisfy temporarily a symptom of the problem, while at the same time reinforcing the need for inadequate relief.' But in terminating a call with such a person, the branch members are reminded never to be angry, sarcastic, clever or indulgent: 'These are totally inappropriate responses to any Samaritan call.'

In 1973, an experiment was launched, at the central London branch, and taken up for a time in a number of other branches, to see if in fact positive assistance could usefully be offered to men initially wanting to masturbate on the telephone. In order to carry it out, female volunteers were required to engage in prolonged conversation with M-callers. The result of this was a composite Samaritan called Brenda, in reality a group of ladies all using one pseudonym, to whom certain M-callers (those believed capable of benefiting from befriending) were transferred. Not surprisingly, although less widely applied in the movement today, Brenda's role became a controversial one, both inside the Samaritans and outside. As one of their number wrote in justification in the *Samaritan* when reporting on the scheme in 1978, by which time some 5,000 'Brenda calls' had been dealt with (an average of twenty a week), 'They are willing to help some clients masturbate *as part of a real befriending relationship.*' (The italics were the volunteer's own.) It was as a result of this experiment that in 1976 Chad Varah wrote his booklet, *Telephone Masturbators And How to Befriend Them.* Opposition to dealing with Brenda calls in other branches came not entirely from hang-ups or over anxiety, Dr Varah wrote, but mostly from imagining that all Brenda callers were tarred with the same brush, 'that they are people who haven't a real problem at all but are just doing it for kicks.'

Until recently, although the numbers have since declined, half a dozen branches ran a Brenda scheme, all based on principles originally laid down by the central London branch, although in Birmingham, for instance, the lady is known as Sandra. A very attractive, single Samaritan in her thirties, with four years' experience as a Brenda volunteer, explains how the system operates in her branch, and how she copes, as a Samaritan, with calls from men on whom she would slam down the telephone if they rang her at home:

'Originally it was really a way of identifying sex calls, when the branch was getting about 250 to 300 a week, and they were tying up the emergency lines. And it was found they weren't in fact 300 individual callers, just a few who were ringing in with different names, some of them several times a day.

'The Brenda system has changed quite dramatically since it

was started. Nowadays we befriend one type of caller, and one type of caller only, or one type of problem , if you want to put it that way – addictive telephone masturbators. And addictive is the operative word. The caller we befriend is not someone who might make obscene phone calls a few times, over perhaps a few months, because he got some sort of pleasure out of it. They are men who are actually addicted; it is their only form of sexual gratification. And a person selected for befriending must actually perceive this addiction as a problem, and want to do something about stopping it. In other words, he is chosen because he will respond to befriending. Somebody who rings up and asks direct questions, about the colour of your knickers, or something of that sort, and will not move on from that topic, hangs up if he's not getting what he wants, because obviously we don't respond to questions like that.

'It's not only the Samaritans who get calls from men wanting sexual gratification with a woman they've never even seen. If you ask anybody who runs a telephone service of any sort, they will tell you they get their fair share of obscene telephone calls. Telephone operators get them all the time, apparently. Very often there is a difficulty in relating to women, and therefore it is less threatening to relate to an unknown voice than to a physical presence standing next to you. The caller suitable for befriending by Brenda will actually move away from the topic of knickers and start talking about his feelings. He may begin to talk about the fact that he hasn't got a girlfriend, that he's very lonely, that he lives alone and feels depressed about this. By talking about these sorts of feelings you are not denying him the opportunity to talk about his feelings about sexuality at all, but he will be a candidate for befriending because he is able to respond to what the Samaritans have to offer. It may take him some time to reach this stage. He may ask what colour your knickers are and hang up and ring up and ring up, and it might be six months later that he begins to respond to befriending. The volunteer would then say something like, "I can see that this is worrying you. We have a volunteer called Brenda, who understands this problem, who may be able to offer more support. Would you like to contact her?" You then explain when she is on duty.

'In my branch one of the Brenda team is on duty four to six hours a week. At present we have eight Brendas, doing a two-hour duty once a fortnight. This is a commitment in addition to their normal duties. A leader may recognize in a volunteer that they are particularly helpful with telephone masturbators and suggest they might consider joining the Brenda scheme. We work very closely together and hold regular meetings. We are befriending approximately thirty to forty men at present, but they're not all ringing currently. Probably a dozen ring on a regular basis. If we decide that a caller is befriendable by Brenda we will give him a telephone number, tell him when we're here, and explain that there is more than one Brenda but that we all work together in a team. So every time he rings he doesn't have to start a fresh conversation. He starts from where he left off, so it's on-going befriending. We keep notes, and he knows that.

'On the whole, a Brenda caller is in his twenties and single. Very many have never had a successful sexual relationship, and certainly at the time of befriending are unable to have a sexual relationship. Success is difficult to measure. As with the majority of Samaritan callers, usually they stop ringing, and one hopes that when a regular caller stops ringing it's because the situation in their life has changed for the better and they don't need us any more. Very, very occasionally someone will actually say, "Thanks, I feel better. Goodbye." But very occasionally. Some tail off in a way, remaining in contact, but although they stop ringing Brenda they go into face-to-face befriending in the centre on a regular basis. The aim with Brenda is quite tough. It is to get the men to stop making obscene telephone calls to anyone. The first stage is actually to contain the addiction, which means that we may allow them to masturbate. Not necessarily. But we may. It's for a limited time, and with conditions. But it's not just a case of sitting there, listening to someone masturbating. It's a very controlled and structured on-going befriending situation, with definite aims and periods set, and if those goals aren't reached, the contract, if you like, begins to change. The idea, I suppose, is that if it is an addiction then it's like alcoholism, you can't make anybody stop. That person has got to reach the point of controlling the addiction themselves. Some go cold turkey, and some wean themselves off it. We work on the assumption that they want to be weaned off the addiction. If after a period of time it appeared there was no change, the situation would be reassessed. It's always a two-way thing. We never make decisions without involving the caller. And after six months they *must* come and visit the centre, and have a face-to-face interview with a leader. People get emotive over the whole issue because I suspect – in fact, I know – that a lot of people are not aware of the structure of it. Because the majority of volunteers get "what colour are your knickers?" calls they think we actually sit and respond to that. And we don't. If the caller needs to masturbate on the telephone, what we are doing is saying, "If you can't stop it, fine, but you do it with our knowledge, so you will not be deceiving us. You're not actually lying. If you are unable not to, it must be on our terms." The aim, if somebody does masturbate on the telephone, is to restrain their fantasy within a loving relationship. We would not listen to a lot of obscenity. We would not allow that. They are addicted to telephone masturbating because they cannot form relationships, and not only with women. With men as well. They tend to be quite lacking in the skills of relationships. The aim, within the fantasy, is for them to relate to a woman as a human being with feelings. We ask him to set a scene, and it has to be normal; no whips. And we ask, "What does she look like?" that sort of thing. And the only help we would give, if help is the right word, is simply to interject with things like, "How does she feel? Does she like you?" As a real person, we are aiding a fantasy within a loving relationship. Our aim is to help them to see women as whole human beings with feelings, not as objects to relieve your feelings on but as someone whose feelings and thoughts have to be accommodated.

'Very often these men had unhappiness in their childhood. Often their parents were divorced during their adolescence.

They lack what they perceive as love from their mother. They have feelings of rejection. Very many are suicidal, and many have attempted suicide. Most, if not all, suffer from depression, whether they are suicidal or not. Many are unemployed as well, which makes their isolation even stronger. They have very few friends. Maybe they've had a bad sexual experience. Many haven't had a sexual experience at all. Some simply cannot masturbate alone, so that their addiction to telephone masturbating is actually their only form of sexual release.[6] Sometimes part of what we do, in fact, is to help them find their imagination, to learn to fantasize. In the beginning they are unable to create images in their own head. We would never ever take on as a Brenda caller someone who was in a successful sexual relationship, because telephone masturbating for them would be an extra.

'Some of our Brenda volunteers are married, and their husbands know what they are doing, and accept it. I know of one Brenda volunteer who was a virgin, and actually had had no sexual experience herself. But that doesn't preclude befriending telephone masturbators because you may not have been bereaved yourself but that doesn't mean you can't befriend someone who has. I think if there was difficulty in a relationship, the volunteer wouldn't volunteer. Apart from the usual qualities any Samaritan requires, in a Brenda there needs to be a certain amount of toughness, and a certain amount of directness, because one way in which Brenda befriending is different from normal Samaritan befriending is that we are directive. We do actually make boundaries and set goals, and we try to keep within them with the caller. An ability to stick to the contract with the caller is very important because, like all people who are desperate, Brenda callers can be very persuasive in their desperation. It's important not to give into that persuasiveness. You couldn't do the job unless you had an empathy for the predicament of the man. But it's funny, if I get an

[6] For a sympathetic exposition of masturbation as a component of human sexual experience the reader is referred to chapter four of *The Psychology of Sex* by Oswald Schwarz (Penguin, 1949).

obscene phone call at home, my reaction is as me and I put the phone down, but in the centre I have my Samaritan hat on, and in a way I'm role-playing. A Brenda volunteer couldn't do it unless she recognized the distress created by the problem.

'I'm sure every woman in the country has had an obscene phone call. If men were honest, and you took a survey, you'd find that almost every man at some point in their life has done it once, even if it was just to see what it was like. Very few men get addicted. It's the addiction which is the peg to hang the coat on. There are always other problems. It's never only a sexual problem. Conversations that we have are very rarely sexual conversations. It's very much about their feelings of despair, distress, suicide, loneliness and fear. It's no different, in a way, from the befriending we normally do except that the caller may at some point need to masturbate during the telephone call. We know all about it before they do it. They don't masturbate without actually saying that that's what they're going to do. That's part of the contract. We expect honesty, and in return we're honest with them. If we have doubts we will express them. That's what I mean when I say we are very much more directive, and we may actually say, "I don't think you're being honest, and therefore I don't think this befriending is at all helpful." And if they wanted to masturbate on their own terms – perhaps, say, by having fantasies about bondage or something – we would just say, "I'm not prepared to be here while that goes on, I find it offensive and unpleasant." It would not be within the context of a loving relationship, because although some successful relations depend on bondage, in this case there would be no actual woman in front of them. They would not be relating to another human being, just a bit of anatomy, and they would just be talking about leather or rubber or whatever. All we would be doing, I feel, is perpetuating something that is not going to help them to form a relationship.

'You can't join the Samaritans and two months later become a Brenda. You need to have been a Samaritan at least a year. But the length of training is extremely flexible. A new volunteer will be on duty with an experienced Brenda for just as long as she feels she needs support. Our Brendas range in age from their sixties downwards. They are simply women able to empathize with the problem. It has nothing to do with age or type or whether you're married or single. We have had at least one caller who got married. But not to a Brenda! It is certainly a controversial issue. Some professional sex therapists believe it's unhelpful actually to allow somebody to masturbate. Others believe that in a controlled, weaning-off process it is actually helpful. So the professionals are divided about it, and about the handling of sex calls in general. It is such an emotive subject. The Samaritans put themselves on the line over the two most controversial issues that we have in life, death and sex, and we all have our own hang-ups and concerns about both subjects. Then we actually fling ourselves up front, which means we're bound to have our differences. Death and sex create the most hang-ups in the most people, so by definition they are very emotive subjects. Quite frankly, I don't know how positive the results are, how beneficial it all is, but in a way I think that's quite healthy, because it means at least I have no axe to grind.'

There is another type of caller other than the 'sex caller' who for many years has been a source of contention within the movement – the third-party caller, someone who telephones the Samaritans to say, perhaps, that they are worried because a neighbour seems very depressed, or has been talking of committing suicide. The problem about acting on a third-party call is the possibility that the caller is only trying to make trouble, or is a natural busybody. In 1974, the Lincoln branch received a telephone call from a hotel manager about a guest he was worried about; a volunteer went round, found the guest had taken barbiturates, and arranged for him to be admitted to hospital, where he recovered, and there now seems to be a fairly standard procedure that is followed in most branches. The caller is asked for their name and telephone number, and for that of the person they are telephoning about, and where there definitely seems to be a risk of suicide, the volunteer will contact the person at risk provided the caller allows their name to be used by way of introduction. The caller is also asked to advise his neighbour that the Samaritans will be ringing, so that a call from the centre does not come as a complete surprise. 'The rules are a bit hazy,' one leader confessed. 'The other day a woman telephoned to say she was very concerned about her neighbour, whose wife had died about three months previously. She said she had tried to befriend him in her own way but that he was becoming more and more introverted, and she had been in to see him that evening and had found him with a bottle of aspirin and a bottle of whisky. She had talked to him, but she didn't really know where to go from there, and so she rang the Samaritans to see if we could do anything.

'An important point to remember is that the woman who rang us needed support while we were making up our minds what to do about her neighbour. In any situation like that, the leader is always contacted. And we always say to the caller, "I don't know if we can take action, we'll see, but we will come back to you and let you know whether we are doing anything or not. And we always ask if we can use their name. Obviously we prefer to, because it's not very nice to arrive at somebody's front door and say, "Somebody tells us that . . ." If they won't let us use their name, we might just say, "A neighbour is worried about you." What we never do is pass on messages.'

There is one potential category of caller who has always been less than enthusiastic about contacting the Samaritans – always assuming they have any need to do so; the non-European immigrant and their British descendants. An article in the *Samaritan* in 1977 asked why this is so. It is still being asked, and no certain answers have been supplied, even by branches in towns where the non-European ethnic communities have expanded rapidly, in some cases overtaking in numbers the indigenous British. Asians, Africans and West Indians are in fact unlikely to respond to the sort of publicity currently emanating from the Samaritans, if indeed they ever encounter it; and they are unlikely, for historical reasons, to entertain any perception of white English people as altruistic helpers. As immigration policies of successive governments have consistently failed to make provision for any kind of cultural assimilation, it seems inevitable that for emotional support in times of stress, members of immigrant populations will continue to turn not to the Samaritans but to one another.

·6·

BEFRIENDING
IN THE OPEN

A cynic searching for a common denominator among Samaritan centres might conclude, such is the degree of independence and diversity they display, that their need to be self-financing is all they share. They exist in as many different environmental situations as can be found throughout the length and breadth of the British Isles, and the key to their effectiveness lies in their ability to blend in with the background of local people likely to call in person. Very few seem remotely ostentatious; many give an almost claustrophobic impression of cramped and slightly chaotic conditions. Some seem constructed entirely of staircases. Volunteers with initiative furnish the waiting rooms with cheerful posters and *Country Life*; those without create a funeral parlour atmosphere with plastic flowers. The majority of Samaritan centres are to be found in former private houses, which usually convert quite easily, for the basic ingredients of any centre are a minimum of two interview rooms, an operations room where volunteers man the telephones, an office and a kitchen. The operations room should, but does not always, contain a library, funded by the branch itself. Very unusually, Weybridge boasts a custom-built centre, originally opened in 1969 on land loaned free of charge and then repossessed, so that twelve years later the branch had to start hunting for a suitable site for premises all over again. Eventually a new centre was erected at a cost of £26,000, consisting of two small interview rooms, a small operations room, a large office and a kitchen.

The volunteers regard the place as 'comfortable, warm, and tastefully furnished and decorated.' Modest and appropriate, the building may look a bit like a scout hut, but there can have been few suitable existing buildings available at the time for the price, and clearly it was functional from the start.

Another method of acquiring rather grander premises than the average two-storey terrace house is for a centre, where such facilities exist, to apply for a grant from the Urban Programme, intended 'to relieve the stress of Inner Urban Deprivation'.[1] Today, the Sunderland branch enjoys a beautifully renovated and elegant early nineteenth century house because they took the plunge, and a considerable risk, in applying for a grant, and the result is a centre that would leave volunteers from central London, used to knocking on broom cupboard doors to find a square inch of privacy, gasping with amazement. Sunderland began 'with £1,000 to our name' and received a grant of £80,000. But as the director at the time humorously points out, 'You must be prepared to gamble. It is much more likely that help will appear if you are in debt than if you are timorously considering your project. A bank must be persuaded to offer a loan to launch the scheme while you are juggling with your Urban Aid application. As we all know, banks don't want to lend you money unless you can prove that you don't need it, and the only security you will have is the building, which you must be prepared to sell if your plans go awry. If you can find a donor to pay your bank interest for a year you will have a breathing space. This was our position in early 1983.'

Under the scheme, capital grants are allocated for purchase, repair and equipment, and revenue grants exist to meet increased running costs, which may include telephones. On top of their £80,000 capital grant, Sunderland received a revenue grant of £5,000 for four years. Sunderland did well, and the results are a reception area callers can walk straight into without having to hang around outside the door, and a ray that detects

[1] At the time of writing, some thirty authorities were operating an Urban Programme.

their presence and rings a bell upstairs. Here the rooms are strikingly cool and welcoming, with plenty of space for training new volunteers and holding branch meetings. But as their former director explains, 'It is essential to present a very good case which reflects the Urban Programme's aims of relieving stress within the deprived area. It's quite clear we relieve social services of a great deal of work. People who come to us may also need their help, but for others it is quite sufficient to come to us. And if we didn't operate the service that we do, social services couldn't possibly cope. We also applied to the metropolitan council for a grant for a chair-lift, so that disabled volunteers could get to the first floor for duties and to the basement for training. In a town with an urban scheme there is usually an official at the civic centre whose job it is to advise you how to put forward your case.'

The size of accommodation needed (but not always obtained), the numbers of volunteers milling about and the general ambience of a centre will to a large extent reflect the size and nature of the area it is designed to serve. When the Shetland branch opened in 1985, it did so with just twenty-six volunteers; the branch covers seventeen islands and a population of 22,500, traditionally employed in crofting, fishing and knitting. One of the Shetlands' claims to fame is a profusion of no less than 750 species of wild flowers. 'It might be difficult to imagine that a place like this would need the services of Samaritans,' said one of the first volunteers. 'But behind this beauty lie problems of all descriptions, some brought about by the isolation of the islands. Many problems came with the oil boom at Sullom Voe Oil Terminal, the largest in Europe, and the very fact that it is a close-knit community can in itself create its own special problems. The main problems seem to be alcoholism, depression and loneliness.'

At the other end of the social spectrum from the Shetlands lies the first branch ever founded, now known as central London, where, with 380 volunteers, a rota secretary has to be employed full-time to ensure that, if necessary, ten telephones could be manned day and night and enough volunteers still remain available to interview an erratic stream of callers. The branch estimates that thirty-seven per cent of all callers are suicidal. They depend to a large extent on volunteers who are nurses and actors, and therefore liable to have free time during the day, always the most difficult period to cover in any branch. Because of the itinerant nature of London's population, its central branch attracts between 150 and 200 callers every year with nowhere to sleep at night except on Samaritan premises. Like all centres, London receives its share of regular callers; it also takes two calls every hour from people who have never contacted them before, a total of 13,000 new callers a year out of an annual tally of 80,000 incidents. Obviously not every telephone is ringing all the time; during the day six calls could be in progress simultaneously, and at night perhaps eight or nine. London may well be the most hectic centre but there are others not far behind; Birmingham, for instance, takes care of around 11,000 new callers every year out of a total of 40,000 calls, and Manchester deals with approximately 17,500 first-time calls out of a total of over 43,000.

The constant flux in London's population affects not just the incessant through-flow of callers but the stable rota of volunteers, many of whom move away because of a change of job, and almost all of whom leave London on retirement. The current director in Bournemouth was once a volunteer in London. Between 400 and 500 potential new Samaritans volunteer in London every year, and about 100 are taken on. On a day-to-day basis, the centre is run by a team of twenty-four leaders, who inevitably carry a larger than average load of responsibility for administration; the full-time director, who believes that because of the ceaseless change-over of personnel in the centre there is a great advantage in having at least one permanent figure around, undertakes no administration at all but keeps a watching brief on every aspect of training and befriending. In recent years, London has become a far more violent city than it used to be, and inevitably some of this violence has overflowed into the Samaritan premises, although in fact any Samaritan centre has always been vulnerable to violence, for people with dependency needs which the Samaritans are unable to meet are always liable to turn their aggression on to people they see as failed benefactors. Two men started smashing up St Stephen Walbrook not long after it had first opened its doors to Samaritan callers, and the staff on duty felt obliged to act against their principles and call in the police for protection. There is no recorded case of a suicide actually being committed on Samaritan premises, but distressed callers seeking attention, sympathy or help may well overdose and then pass out in a centre, an occasion that calls for considerable discretion; the last thing the Samaritans want are wailing police or ambulance sirens outside their door. John Eldrid says he has been attacked about five times in thirty years. 'There is a problem,' he says, 'because the Samaritans don't want to keep ringing the police, so we are pretty strict about admitting callers we regard as manipulative and difficult. Volunteers are told that if someone has been barred, then they are barred, and if they let that person in or don't obey instructions they are probably out as well. We bar someone if we feel they are not befriendable.' The central London branch has a long history of befriending, for resources in the capital in terms of psychiatric consultants, clinical psychologists and psychotherapists to whom callers can readily be referred exist in greater profusion than elsewhere. At least 300 callers are being befriended by central London at any time.

The central London branch covers Camden, the City of London, Hackney, Islington, Kensington & Chelsea, Tower Hamlets and Westminster, encompassing a population of about 990,000. But it is practically impossible to arrive at any 'success rate' to be deduced from an apparent recent reduction in the suicide rate in London in relation to an enormous expenditure of time, energy and money, partly because the statistics relating to the capital's population are so confused. In the decade between 1971 and 1981, the overall population of London decreased by 234,900 and the numbers of people living in the City of London, Kensington & Chelsea and Westminster have continued to fall, whereas some recent growth in population in the boroughs of Camden, Hackney, Islington and Tower

Hamlets has been recorded. It has to be remembered too that non-residential workers who enter the area by day and leave by night help to make population statistics for London socially meaningless; non-residential workers may well spend a third of their life in the area without qualifying as residents. But for what it is worth, there were 146 suicides recorded in central London in 1980 and 124 in 1983.

As you enter the railway station an advertisement on a hoarding tells you the town offers a warm welcome to industry, and there follows an invitation to telephone for information. The hoarding is attached to a derelict building without a single window intact. The Samaritan centre looked after 10,982 callers last year, and in one month their numbers of volunteers have risen from ninety-six to 120, but they say they could do with 150. These are figures the director, a Samaritan for seventeen years, who has lived for nearly as long with another man, reels off without a pause for thought. His welcome is warm and friendly. The reason they need yet more volunteers? 'Our callers are up 2,200 on last year. The economic climate has something to do with it, but sex problems are on the increase. Women are now more aggressive, and men can't cope so well.' The branch was founded nineteen years ago. 'It's become a sausage machine,' the director says. 'This is a very transient town. Sixty per cent of our volunteers are not even locals. And you have to live here a long time to be accepted.'

A blind piano tuner, who has been a Samaritan for eleven years, arrives to meet a young man he is befriending, a bisexual fantasist with an identity crisis, so lonely and desperate for affection that he has even tried to have an affair with his blind befriender. 'The situation got completely out of hand!' says the volunteer, who takes his caller upstairs to the attic, the only unoccupied space available, weaving his way with confidence through an obstacle course of tables and chairs. In the operations room, it is Evelyn's first day on duty. She is a shop manager with Finefare, married to a professional footballer, with two young children. They came to the town because her husband got a transfer, liked it and decided to stay. 'I wasn't frightened when I came in this morning,' she says, 'but I *was* rather apprehensive.' She had spent the first half of her first shift familiarizing herself with paperwork, and listening in while another volunteer dealt with a phone call. Suddenly the phone rang again, and the volunteer told her to answer it. Sure enough, at 11.30 in the morning she had a sex caller on the line. She said afterwards, 'I ignored his request to talk about sex and tried to turn the problem back on to the caller. He got a bit fed up and put the phone down.' The director said he thought Evelyn had dealt with the call beautifully. 'She sounded very warm and calm.'

In a university city, with its statutory Dunn & Co, its Pizzaland, empty icecream cornets blowing down the street and its dingy pubs run by disinterested young bartenders and dispossessed Irish landladies, the Samaritan centre lies closer to the bus and railway stations than the city centre, in a poky house off a one-way system, where all is muddle, and even the volunteer who opened the door had forgotten that her regional representative was calling. The branch costs £10,000 a year to run, £1 for every caller, one-tenth of whom last year put through a silent call. Family problems led the field in the list of reasons prompting calls, with depression running second and unemployment at the bottom of the list, although unemployment in the area is high. The regional representative had said he thought this was rather an inward-looking branch, not much involved with matters outside their own region. 'This is partly because they are short of volunteers,' he explained, 'and they are very much concerned with manning their rota, so they never get around to offering a paper at a conference, or putting on a workshop somewhere. I also think some branches just tend to imagine that if they're doing what they can for their own callers, they don't really need to get involved with the movement in a wider sense, and it's a great pity if they think that. You can learn so much by becoming involved at an inter-regional level. If a branch does cut itself off and become inward-looking it impoverishes the region as well as the branch. You've got to be aware of how each unit fits into the whole.'

In the operations room, furnished with a battered sofa and looking pretty grubby, one of the volunteers on duty, a middle-aged lady with unkempt hair and slacks she might have been better advised not to wear, was sorting through a stack of record cards. Suddenly she clasped her hand to her mouth to half-stifle a scream. 'Oh, my God, he *did* die!' Later, after she had put her arm round her colleague to comfort her, a much younger volunteer, of twenty-two, explained what had happened. 'It was someone she had been out to visit on an emergency. She'd talked to him a couple of times afterwards, and she thought he was OK, she thought she'd pulled him through. But he's died. We're not sure whether he had a heart attack or committed suicide. So she's sort of half blaming herself. It was an unfortunate way for her to find out. But this does tend to happen. I suppose ideally a leader or someone should have telephoned her at home and told her the man had died, rather than let her come on duty and find out like that. We try to keep in touch with each other and keep tabs on cases, but you can't know every single thing that happens immediately, we haven't got that close a communication.'

Fifty-nine calls a day are being taken at a branch in the North-West, by a membership of 120. A volunteer is on the telephone, in a cubicle; the second telephone is off the hook, because the only other volunteer on duty is interviewing someone. There is provision for a third line, but no purpose in installing it when even two telephones cannot always be covered. Downstairs, a preparation class is in progress. An experienced volunteer is telling a trainee, apprehensive about violence, that she once went to the aid of a woman being assaulted by her husband, and was told by the woman to mind her own business. Back in the duty room, the telephone rings again. A mountainous lady, her face half hidden by enormous glasses, heaves herself out of a chair to answer it. Quickly she replaces the receiver and sits down at a table to write her report.

'He just said something rude, and rang off,' she explains. 'It won't surprise me if he rings back.' Without support from their local borough and a couple of trust funds, who contributed, between them, £6,500, the branch would have been hard pressed last year to raise enough money to keep going. A Catholic Women's League coffee morning produced a sprightly £105.40, and a rotary club a surprising £100, but a local Business and Professional Women's Club only managed to spare £3.

At the other end of England, the Samaritans function in a tiny compact house tucked away in a neat street near the station, the bus routes and the shopping centre. Trains rattle past the windows, and in summer they bring day trippers longing for a sight of the sea. The branch paid off their mortage five years ago, on premises that look as if they might once have belonged to a veterinary surgeon, or perhaps a boot mender. The town itself sprawls along the coast, a combination of imposing Victorian villas and dull, peeling boarding-houses painted canary-yellow, which merge into a modern glass and concrete shopping jungle and a seafront given over to amusement arcades, children's empty playgrounds, listless pubs and a fish restaurant charging exorbitant prices. When the tide goes out the sea becomes a memory on the horizon. One grandiloquent hotel clings to the edge of a cliff, and old-age pensioners knit in the shelters while they wait to comment on new faces as the season gets under way. Plenty of people live here, but as so often in ugly overspill towns, one wonders why. There is nothing to go down to the Esplanade for except to get away from the shopping centre.

The Samaritan centre itself is spotlessly clean if sparsely furnished. In the kitchen at the back volunteers congregate with coffee mugs. In the operations room, a thin young married woman, with a job in the mornings so that she is free for afternoon shifts, waits nervously for the phone to ring. On the wall hangs a map of the town, with the homes of all the volunteers marked with pins and categorized by gender. The volunteer is still on probation. Her first call had been from a woman with a rubber fetish. 'It's not at all what I thought it would be like,' she says. 'Better, really.' How had she coped with the rubber lady? 'Terrible!' The branch is in the process of changing over directors. The director-designate, a quietly spoken, serious woman of fifty, smokes heavily. She has only been a Samaritan five years, and became a leader after only one. 'It's daunting, isn't it?' she keeps reminding herself. She and the volunteer who first interviewed her swap reminiscences. 'She was lovely', the new director recalls. 'I was terribly nervous and she really put me at my ease.' The out-going director recalls his interview. He was twenty-five at the time, and he says the interview lasted five minutes. 'Not very good,' he comments. 'My interviews last at least an hour.' There seems to be little activity, but days are recalled when visitors have been sitting on the stairs. The branch has 106 volunteers and last year they dealt with 12,000 calls. They are finding it increasingly difficult to cover afternoon shifts, despite so many people being out of work – not that people out of work are necessarily best qualified to be Samaritans. 'I suppose,' says the director, 'the unemployed are just too dispirited. And don't forget, there are so many more voluntary agencies now than there were fifteen years ago, all competing for unpaid help, and we require a very full commitment.'

The idea that all Samaritan activity, apart from controlled befriending, is confined to the centres is rapidly becoming an old-fashioned one. Tentative experiments with broadcasting have been carried out in one branch, invited by their local radio station to supply a volunteer to join a clergyman and a doctor on a Sunday evening phone-in. 'I have mixed feelings about the programme,' one of the leaders confessed, 'but our director is terrific. The problem is, you are more or less forced to give some sort of advice or comment, but Bill is very good at making comments which are not actually constructive advice. He will throw the question or problem back to the person who rings in, offering food for thought, and leaves the solid advice to the other people on the panel. But you have to say something quickly on the air, you can't play for time. The programme does act as free publicity for us, and we know that people who have rung into the programme have become callers, so in that way it works very well.' At a national level, in 1984 the Samaritans were invited to take part in Christmas Line, a co-operative venture run by Capital Radio, London Weekend Television and Thames Television with a view to filling the gap in emergency services caused by a general closing down of facilities over the Christmas period. The Samaritans provided three volunteers for each shift.

But co-operation in agony radio shows is small fry by comparison with the rapidly accelerating scale of what is now known as 'befriending in the open', a major departure which began as a public relations exercise carried out on market squares and has spread to hospitals and prisons. Many Samaritans, impatient with what they regard as the excessive stress laid upon anonymity when befriending on the telephone, see this new development in technique as a blueprint for the future. 'I love our centre', a volunteer from King's Lynn wrote in the *Samaritan* in 1985. 'It's warm, inviting, situated in just the right part of town. We have about 10,000 contacts a year. The population we serve is around 222,000. The branch has a marvellous group of friends. We need £10,000 a year. The suicide rate here has been falling. It sounds all right – well, comfortable, anyway. I had this feeling, though, niggling away; should we not be reaching out and working where it's actually happening?' In co-operation with the area social services officer, the branch, with twenty-six per cent of its callers aged under twenty, is now involved in a project called the Samaritan Youth Counselling Support Group.

The branch involved with their local radio station is also 'working where it's actually happening', both in prison and in hospital. 'For many years we've been giving talks in the local women's prison,' a deputy director explained. 'We used to meet the pre-release group in the youth detention centre, and then we suggested to the governor the possibility of befriending on a one-to-one basis, because the girls couldn't really talk when they were in a group. We always had to have a prison warder with us, and it was very difficult. A year ago the governor agreed, so we selected some pretty experienced volunteers, and I had to send details of their names and addresses and where they were born. If a girl feels that she wants to talk to a Samaritan she has to apply to the probation service, and I think at first this put the girls off, because they felt it might affect their parole. But once the first girl had actually done it and applied and realized it was totally confidential her befriending went on for several months, and she felt so much better afterwards that she spread the word, and I think that so far we've had about half a dozen. It's a slow trickle, but the ones we've had very much needed to talk. We were quite impressed because we were given a room to ourselves. The only problem came when the prison was having a blitz on drugs. We have to be very careful. We're not allowed to take anything out. We're not allowed to post letters or anything like that. Sometimes volunteers want to send a card, which is all right, but we have to be very careful that we stick to prison rules.

'Problems in prison are very much the same as outside. Depression is the most obvious problem, and the girls can be suicidal. They suffer from isolation and loneliness and the feeling there is no one they can talk to. And of course they have family problems. A lot of girls have left children behind. The youngest we have befriended was a fifteen-year-old, in for robbery with violence. Some of them, at fourteen and fifteen, have been living rough for a couple of years. They've no stable background at all. It helps them to be able to talk about the whole experience of the crime. I think they've become more honest as the befriending's gone on. They start off being very guarded, and quite quickly realize it doesn't matter to a Samaritan, you can say what you like, so you might just as well tell the truth. But you have to gain their trust first. You can't actually condone what sometimes they are telling you they've done: that would be dishonest on our part. You just try to take a very objective approach. We concentrate on their feelings more than on the actual crime they've committed.'

The major pioneering work of befriending in prison has been carried out in a former market town, now an ever-expanding multi-racial industrial zone, which contains, almost exactly opposite the Samaritan centre, the grim redbrick county gaol. A volunteer who works in local government, joined the Samaritans at the age of twenty and became director of his branch when he was twenty-four, explains the philosophy behind his activities on the other side of the wall.

'Although fifteen suicides a year are reported in prisons, we believe there are many more that are not reported.[2] We hear from other prisoners, "Oh, did you know, so-and-so topped himself last night?" And nothing appears in the press or in any reports. It's often put down to an accident or an accidental overdose.

'I was director when we first made contact with the prison. Part of my duties, I thought, was to make more contact with the community. We were still very much an enclosed sort of branch, waiting for people to come to us, and I thought it was time to start getting into the community and getting known. So I made a direct approach to the governor, and that's how it started. I've personally been inside the prison about a dozen times. It is reportedly the most overcrowded prison in the country, with three men to every cell, and about one hour's exercise a day – and not even that if there's a prison dispute on, which seems to be a fairly regular occurrence, with some sort of work-to-rule or industrial action, or there's a security clamp-down. There's always a problem of some sort.

'We don't get much feedback from the staff. The educational department, who are slightly separate, are more open in their feelings than the warders, and they feel frustrated at having their activities curtailed. Prisoners complain about the short amount of recreational time. Conditions are bad. They don't

[2] According to a Home Office working group on suicide prevention which reported in 1986, the risk of suicide in prison was four times greater than the rate outside.

have much opportunity to talk problems over with people. Even though there are people around, there is no privacy. Ours is a transit prison, and holds prisoners on short sentences. The longest they are there is from nine to twelve months. They have a remand centre as well. So whenever we go in we see a new set of faces.

'The governor was very enthusiastic, but he said everything would really depend on his education officer. We prefer working under the education department to the probation service. The probation service wanted us to liaise with them over individuals, which we were not happy to do. We have to make do with a classroom, so if we get a dozen prisoners, which is all we can manage at one time, then we see them as a group, identify those who need individual attention, and then sort of pluck them out somehow or other so that the next week when we go in we have already allocated a volunteer to a prisoner. The group of volunteers comes to about twelve as well. We always have to wait to be called, but we chase up the invitations. Linked to the education department we're also linked to school terms, and we have to finish at a certain time, and so we try to see individual prisoners on visiting orders, and also correspond with them. That way we continue the contact without actually going in on a formal basis. We go in as a visitor, basically.

'We are on our third governor in three years. The present one is more accessible in the sense that he encourages officials to come to the centre to hear what our role is, so they are not suspicious of our motives. And since this new governor took over they have been more ready to come out and talk to us. The education department, prison visitors, the probation service and the chaplains have all come to the centre to discuss various ways we can improve liaison. But last year we were promised better facilities and nothing has materialized.

'The problems we deal with range from finance and housing to personal relationships, with wife, girlfriend or boyfriend. Relationships often deteriorate while men are in prison and they can't get out to deal with them. Most of those we talk to have a drug addiction problem, and they worry about getting back on to drugs when they leave prison. There's not much concern about going back to crime because they all say they won't. What worries them more are the chances of getting a job when they have a record.'

Eight days after the Samaritan gave this interview, a thirty-seven-year-old burglar, given a seven-year sentence at the Crown Court, was discovered hanged at the prison. He had been found with jewellery valued at £1,000 and had asked for 164 offences to be considered. As his death was reported in *The Times*, presumably it will constitute part of the official statistics on suicides in prison in 1986.

Perhaps the most impressive experiment in befriending in the open has been carried out at Addenbrookes Hospital, Cambridge, where the consultant in the accident and emergency unit conducted a discussion about its origins and effects with the director of the Cambridge Samaritans, who says her membership is currently down to 99 – 'lower than it's ever been since I've been here, and that's nine years'. They really need 160 members. A team of eight volunteers visit the accident and emergency unit, visiting in pairs for three hours once a week.

Director: It's a very token appearance. We had gained some previous experience of befriending in the open from a caravan in town centres, and at fairs. There is a danger, in open befriending, of a loss of anonymity, but that's something you have to accept. If you were paranoid about anonymity there wouldn't be any befriending in the open at all. When we visit the hospital we wear a badge with our Christian name and 'Samaritan' on it. Last night, for example, I came on duty with one other Samaritan at half past seven. It was very busy. We usually wander around first and see what's happening. There had been a traffic accident. Two people had been involved, and they were in different areas of the department. There were a lot of children around, several with eye injuries. Most of the children had come in with parents. If you bring one child you have to bring the rest of the family, very often. I think I spoke first to a girl who was on her own. You have to be sensitive to family groups and to what is happening within that group. They may be befriending each other, they may not need you.

People who have been in a traffic accident may have given a statement to the police, and explained to the medical people where they hurt, but they haven't been able to talk about the accident. They need to do this, and we have the time, the doctors haven't. One gentleman went over his accident several times, repeating, 'I don't know why it happened . . .'
Consultant: One of the problems about psychological shock is that it's very similar to grief. Sometimes there is a feeling of guilt, and they don't see it as a medical problem. They are preoccupied with insurance claims. You go through the stunned phase, where you don't accept what's happened, then there is the anger phase, then there is the sorrow or depressed phase, then there is the recovery. Days two and three after an accident are much worse than day one, both physically and mentally. So for someone who may be on an emotional high, having survived an accident, to meet up with a Samaritan here may prove very valuable in the days ahead, when he or she is feeling depressed and suffering severe reaction.
Director: People need to talk after a visit to a hospital for all sorts of reasons. Last week we had a child brought in, who had fallen from a window. The whole family came in. They were all obviously very upset. The child came in still just about alive, and a nurse asked one of the Samaritans on duty to take tea in to the family, and she stayed with them most of the evening. The child died, and the family have stayed in touch with us, and put a thank-you in the paper, thanking the hospital staff and the Samaritans for all they did, which was very touching.

We've had several opportunities of talking with people who have attempted suicide, because not all are suffering from a drug overdose. Some have cut their arms. And we make sure they know where to come if they want to contact us again in the future. Sometimes someone is here with a minor injury, and you get to talk to them and find they have much larger emotional problems. A man who had left home and been walking the streets turned up at the unit with blisters on his feet. He was also suicidal. He had left home on the Sunday evening and he arrived here mid-evening the next Friday. He'd been walking the streets and living rough. One of his sons had been killed in a road accident last year. He had had heart by-pass surgery last November.

I had an aversion to hospitals, and when we started this experiment I thought, Crumbs, I'll never cope with it, but there isn't the pressure on you once you're here. When the sight of blood and the smell of hospitals is not connected with your own family, and when you're not expected to do anything medical, you can just be a Samaritan and do exactly what you're trained to do. The gory sights haven't affected me. I was hooked from the first night I came.

Consultant: The most impressive comment picked up by the nurses when the Samaritans first suggested coming here was when one of them said, 'We can sit and listen for two hours.' That actually had a few jaws dropping, because at times we are literally with a patient for a matter of seconds. Accident departments are geared to the management of physical injury, but the emotional after-effects of a road accident may take months to heal. I think developments over the next decade will be in dealing with psychological injury, and counselling won't be done by doctors. We are trained scientists who carry out highly sophisticated procedures to exclude serious disease, but the caring element, at present, is someone else's problem.

I am sure the Samaritans would not want to get into psychiatric assessment, but there is plenty of scope for people who will treat the psyche by being charitable, kind and caring. I see the Samaritans having a role simply because I now understand how they operate. A voluntary first-aider can be a professional by having a high standard of expertise, and the Samaritan system allows checks and controls. Until we became involved with the Samaritans we thought they were a rather nebulous group who answered telephones, and that was their own public image, because they were rather secretive about what they did. I would like to see the scheme extended. The Americans are more advanced. They now realize that you need to counsel rescue workers who work under stress. I go to about 170 traffic accidents a year, and I have never come to terms with pronouncing a child dead. I don't think in the health service we take enough note of stress. I'm very worried about the rescue services in Bradford. There is an immense psychological stress still on the police and firemen who were there.[3]

A vivid and revolting example of the type of trauma our rescue services are faced with, and so seldom helped to come to terms with, was presented by a report in *The Times* on 24 July 1986 following a crash on the M4 motorway in which a grossly overcrowded van crossed the central crash barrier, killing a total of thirteen people, four of them members of one family travelling in the opposite direction. 'Those who arrived at the scene of the crash were sickened by the sight,' two *Times* staff writers reported, and a fire officer was quoted as saying, 'The carnage was absolutely staggering. When I returned home I could not sleep and could only hear the screams of a woman who was dying by the side of the decimated van.' He said that he and his men were sickened and left numb by their experience of the accident. Of 400 police officers who attended the Bradford

[3] On 11 May 1985, fifty-six people died in a fire at the Valley Football Ground in Bradford. The Bradford branch publicized their services in a local newspaper, and one of the nurses who attended the fire telephoned to say she could not get the sound of the screams out of her head and was unable to sleep. A young policewoman, similarly affected, was immediately befriended. When the Townsend Thoresen ferry *The Herald of Free Enterprise* capsized outside Zeebrugge harbour on 6 March 1987, the Folkestone and Canterbury branches jointly set up a temporary caravan centre in Dover to befriend in the open relatives and friends of the dead and missing passengers. They were assured of the availability of continued support if this was wanted and many were given the address and telephone number of their local Samaritan branch.

football stadium fire, all were offered counselling, fifty were thought to be in need of such help, and thirty-four took up the offer; they were counselled by an occupational psychologist in Leeds. Feelings of guilt for having failed to save more lives, and for themselves surviving, appear to have been the salient feature of their continuing waking nightmare. One problem about police officers traditionally putting on a brave, macho image of indifference to suffering, and in the past declining to unburden themselves of their own true feelings, has been for them to acquire a very real hardened crust of indifference to the sufferings and anguish of other people. Another result is that 1.5 million police working days are lost on average each year through illness – in a service necessarily staffed by men and women who enjoy outstanding physical fitness.

Another branch who have taken up the challenge of befriending in their local hospital's accident centre has found both male and female volunteers equally in demand. A deputy director recalls: 'A male volunteer of sixty, on his first night in casualty, had to feed a baby and change its nappy. He was suddenly pushed into this role, so he did it, and I was relating this story to one of our female volunteers, who said, "I would give it up tomorrow if I thought I had to do that, I hate babies." On the other hand, when someone comes in who has been raped, then obviously a woman volunteer is needed.

'We are there to comfort relatives, and also just to talk to people who are waiting, and have got nothing better to do. There's nothing more boring than waiting in an accident centre. It's an excellent way of giving out information. It's very good propaganda. It gives us an opportunity to say, "Here we are, we're not just shut away in our centre, we actually come out sometimes." People with minor injuries sometimes have a long wait and they don't see emergency cases coming in by ambulance, and we can help staff by explaining to the patients why they've got to wait, and sometimes by going into the treatment rooms and then reassuring relatives who have been waiting a long time for news. It took the nursing staff a few weeks to realize how they could use the Samaritans, and now nursing staff actually say, "Thank God you're here, we're waiting for you, somebody's been raped, or somebody's overdosed," and they can't spend two hours listening to someone talk. I used to be a nurse myself, and I remember patients who were being prepared for major surgery, who knew they might not come out of it, and I knew they really wanted someone to sit with them and put everything right the night before. There was no time, as a nurse, to do any of that.

'We don't very often get an opportunity to see people who have overdosed when they are coming round. Mostly we are there when they come in. They don't do so many stomach wash-outs now. It's not medically necessary. It was felt it was often done as a punitive gesture. Very often, now, they're left to sleep it off. In quiet moments we talk to the staff, and I think that's one of the most valuable bits of our work. When I was a student nurse and worked in casualty I constantly heard it said, when a repeated overdoser was brought in, "Oh, for God's sake, why can't they do it properly?" I don't think for one moment they actually meant it, I think it was just sheer pressure of work. They were always overloaded with work, as they are now. But I must say, since we've been befriending in casualty they are much more enlightened. I think they realize there is a need for greater care for these people, but they just can't provide it.'

EMOTIONAL TIME
AND SPACE

Every other year, when Samaritan Week gets under way, provincial journalists, no doubt primed by someone in the local Samaritan centre, and certainly grateful for a peg on which to hang a 'human interest story', trot out with faithful regularity heart-stopping features about the Samaritans suddenly being inundated with ten-year-old callers, and tales about primary school children contemplating suicide are invariably passed off as international scoops. The truth is, children have been calling the Samaritans for a very long time indeed. In 1973 a vice-chairman was writing in the *Samaritan*, 'An increasing number of young people under the age of eighteen and down to the tender age of eight are telephoning the branches and this has caused some concern, particularly about the way in which they should be befriended.' He went on to say there were a few golden rules which must be observed, and the first was that every child should be treated in the same way as an adult. What these 'golden rules' could therefore lead to is a traumatic testing of the basic criteria of Samaritan conduct, a situation in which a child turns up at a centre at night, is taken in and befriended by the volunteers on duty, and possibly given a bed, while the child's parents are going frantic with worry, the police are out searching for him and no one at the Samaritans is prepared to contact anyone even to say the child is safe unless the child gives permission.

This is only one reason why some volunteers find the

befriending of child callers a confusing, even on occasions distasteful, part of their duties. In the first place, not every adult finds it easy to establish a rapport with children. Many of us actively dislike children, feeling envious of their freedom and lack of responsibility and of what we see as their sexual licence, threatened by their contempt for, or at least their challenge of, authority, and irritated by what we regard as their lack of a logical perception of grown-up values and judgements. The desire to give advice and instructions to children is almost overwhelming, and the concept of consulting with children is alien to our entire educational and parental system. If you cannot persuade a child to obey you by verbal threats or coercion, then a beating should do the trick: this has been the philosophy for moulding one generation into the footsteps of another for centuries. These habits and attitudes are hard to break, even assuming we wish to break them. Many Samaritans are themselves parents, have sometimes felt tempted to throttle their own children when nerves have become frayed, and yet have fought hard to fend off the worst fears a parent can imagine, of their child being run over or kidnapped. There is no situation ever likely to confront a Samaritan in which the movement's practices and principles are more likely to clash with their own emotional reactions than when confronted with a caller who also happens to be a child.

Even back in 1973, no fewer than one caller in four was under the age of twenty – the majority of them fortunately teenagers rather than children. Basil Higginson listed their reasons for contacting the Samaritans as depression, loneliness, 'boy or girlfriend', pregnancy, drugs and examinations, but the real cause of distress, he said, 'is nearly always family or other personal relationships'. Of the child callers, categorized by him as aged between eight and twelve, he said they sometimes spoke immediately and directly of tensions and quarrels at home, and he did not believe that the increase of child and teenage calls indicated a dramatic breakdown of family life in Britain. 'Rather, it suggests that "The Samaritans" is now a household word . . . and that people – especially the young who have grown up with the telephone – are more accustomed to dialling for help.' Samaritans who are themselves all too acutely aware of their own short-comings as parents, of the quarrels and tensions in their own family life, may easily feel an instinctive impulse to advise a child to return home rather than admit that any home – and by extension, their own – might be an undesirable place to which to return.

Strange as it may seem, just as there is no statutory law against trespassing, and squatters cannot automatically be evicted by the police when you return from holiday and find they have taken over your house, there is no legal obligation to return a child to its parents or legal custodians, even if the police have been notified of its absence, and no Samaritan could be prosecuted for kidnapping a child unless the child was held in a centre against its will. 'It is very easy to think that the first thing a child should do is to go and discuss his problem with parents or schoolteachers,' the vice-chairman, who was also a solicitor, wrote in 1973, 'but very rarely is this the case when he has a deep-rooted anxiety about home, school or sexual difficulty. The last person he wishes to discuss this with is a parent, schoolteacher or family doctor.' Young clients, he went on, must be offered complete and utter confidentiality, 'and it is about this point I believe that there is most anxiety. All volunteers must remember when listening to a child, either on the telephone or face to face, that their own anxiety at the thought of a child having run away from school, home, children's hostel or some other establishment must never be shown. Their instinctive reaction to tell him to go back and that everything will then be "quite all right" is about the worst thing that could be done.'

Of course, not every child caller has run away from home or a hostel. Some merely telephone out of devilment, perhaps to say something shocking to find out how the Samaritans will react, and a good deal of giggling in the background may indicate a crowded phone booth. But just as no one writes graffiti on a lavatory wall without wishing to have it read – and to get it off their chest – so no one telephones the Samaritans without a serious reason of some sort, even if part of the reason is not immediately apparent to the caller or acknowledged by them. It takes time and trouble to discover a Samaritan phone number. It costs money to make a phone call. The expenditure of any effort and cash is never made without good cause. Yet the inherent seriousness of child callers (we take children less than seriously in almost every aspect of their lives) has, by their own admission, been difficult for a good many Samaritans to accept. In 1976, by which time some 3,000 new callers annually were aged under fifteen, a member of the Leicester branch, who was also a schoolteacher, sent a questionnaire on the subject of young callers to every branch in the country. From one director he elicited this response: 'Far too much fuss is made about young clients. I propose in this branch to do nothing special about young callers.' In Hampshire every secondary school had agreed to display a Samaritan poster, whereas a group of Norwich headmasters retorted that, 'Children shouldn't need Samaritans while at school.' At this time, three boys and girls under sixteen were committing suicide in England and Wales every month. The director of the Norwich branch, however, replying to the questionnaire, wrote, 'Some volunteers immediately think, "Oh, here is some poor child," and so are apt to talk down to them in a patronizing sort of way.' From Wigan it was learned, 'We feel that a lot of adults do not really listen to children without imposing their own mores.' The Liverpool branch reported, 'There is always the tendency to forget how deeply sensitive the young are; and perhaps we tend to have an underlying belief that the teenager is "sure to grow out of it", whatever "it" may be.'

In a pamphlet titled *Young Callers and the Samaritans*, John Eldrid lists a selection of case histories illustrating the reasons a number of teenagers between the ages of twelve and sixteen contacted the Samaritans. A boy of fifteen was fed up with being nagged all day by his parents over the clothes he wore. A girl of fifteen with a newly acquired stepmother no longer felt wanted at home. Another girl of fifteen had been in love with a man in his twenties. She killed herself. Because, he said, no one spoke to him at home, a boy of fifteen was pretending to be seventeen in order to join the army. An academically brilliant sixteen-year-old public-school boy was developing alarming symptoms of schizophrenia. A girl of twelve, bored at school, hating her older sister and aware that her mother was having a lesbian affair, was reluctant to return home at night. A girl of fifteen had broken off with her boyfriend; she killed herself with an overdose of sleeping pills.

Eldrid writes, 'It is a great mistake to think that the adolescent may not be as seriously ill or depressed as a much older person, or to disregard the importance of a suicide attempt.' But, he writes, 'Few teenagers want to die in the suicide attempts. This is much more an expression of anger born out of feelings of emotional frustration; a protest, if you like, against the environment in which they find themselves enclosed, an expression of the emotional hopelessness of their situation. There may be a feeling that they can stand no more emotional pain; a natural emotional weariness makes sleep a most attractive answer.' In offering advice on first encountering a young caller, he reminds the Samaritans that they need to recognize that the typical young caller has little or no experience of being accepted by older people. If they had, he says, they might not have needed to contact the Samaritans in the first place. 'So this will be one of the barriers which prevent the young caller opening up to the volunteer. Like all of us, the young caller wants to be taken seriously, yet it is all too easy for us to dismiss early teenage worries too lightly.' Like most of us in a crisis, 'the young caller will forget what they intended to present and end up with rather a confused presentation. This is very likely to involve a certain amount of laughing, giggling and general lack of seriousness, so beware of dismissing such encounters as hoaxes.'

Currently, says Eldrid, about 500 fifteen to sixteen-year-olds are in touch with the central London branch, 'and we are not going to give information about them to the police or anyone else unless we have their permission. If these kids run away and they know there's confidentiality, that is a great attraction, I think. And it's more than likely that if they stay with us and talk with us they will open up negotiations with the home they've run away from. If an eight-year-old turned up on the doorstep one would have to talk round the situation. We have no right to inform on callers. I have met eight-year-olds who were very much on the ball. And for an eight-year-old to go to the Samaritans requires a certain amount of sophistication.'

'Try not to get over-anxious about police enquiries,' the Samaritans are told. 'If the police telephone or call about a particular caller and ask directly if you are in touch, the answer is NO.' And if a young caller asks to telephone his parents, volunteers are particularly warned – whether a Samaritan or the caller telephones the parents – not to mention the Samaritans. 'If you mention Samaritans then it is very likely that the parents will tell the police and you will be visited.' Again, 'As we do keep summary forms, it is probably best if we omit or disguise references to actual criminal offences,' Samaritans are advised. They are further cautioned that in point of fact 'The only circumstances in which we are legally bound to contact the police is when we are present at the scene of a crime and see a body.' On the whole parents do not appear to make the first contact, 'and some do not wish to contact their child at all.' And social workers, one learns from John Eldrid's pamphlet, 'seldom seem to contact the Samaritans about runaways.' Accept their enquiries as you do from the police, volunteers are told. 'Children under care orders are not of immediate interest to social workers.' He makes the point that it is natural for parents to feel guilty if their child turns to the Samaritans for help. 'The parents will often show their feelings of guilt, failure and sadness in rigid, angry reaction.' He goes on: 'The be-friending and supporting of the parents is never likely to be easy and for the most part few parents will allow us to get close to them, but we should always try and keep the lines of com-munication open for them. On many occasions we will need considerable patience, because many parents will have little or no insight into how they are causing problems for their child. This kind of reaction is not so surprising since concern for children as individuals is still in the early stages of development in our society.'

Speaking about the befriending of children, a leader in the Midlands confirmed from her own experience all the general principles upheld by the movement as a whole. 'I think the youngest caller I've encountered personally was about fourteen,' she said. 'They're becoming more frequent partly because we're getting better known, and, for a child, confidentiality is really important. I think the youngest we've actually had in the branch was eight. There aren't that many organizations that deal specifically with young people, are there? For a young person to talk to anybody is quite a difficult thing to do. It can be very hard, especially if we get the parents of a young caller ringing in. Then we might try to get permission from the young person to tell his parents he was safe. We are under no moral obligation to return a runaway child to its home. Any caller who contacts us, no matter what their age, is assured of complete confidentiality. Even if we knew the parents were worried stiff, if the child refused permission to disclose his whereabouts we would respect his wishes. If children come to us knowing we are an agency that deals with suicide and related problems, then it's got to be pretty serious before they actually pluck up the courage to get in touch with us. And when they do, all our practices and principles apply to them as they would to anyone else.

'Yet although we treat child callers in the same way as everybody else, one is a bit taken aback. It's important to remember that young people don't always have the words – adults don't either – to explain how they are feeling. We still ask the suicide question, but it's how you ask it that is quite a different matter. Young people don't understand what death is. They don't have an idea of the permanence of death. They think of it as going to sleep. They've heard about grandfather "passing away". They ring up about various things, exams, not knowing how their bodies work, feeling they might be gay. Of course, we don't know if they're gay, we can't give them a test. But I think it depends on their age. If, say, they are ten or eleven and they've got a best friend and they're worried about that, that's a different matter to being seventeen or eighteen.'

The youthful age of callers is only one of the cultural shocks the Samaritans have in store. Equally surprising, at first encounter, is the lower age limit for volunteers, nationally a mere seventeen, although individual branches are free to decide on a higher minimum age if they wish. At one time Cambridge, reputed to be run entirely by the wives of dons, refused to recruit anybody under the age of thirty. Someone with radical and firmly held beliefs both on young callers and youthful volunteers is Nick Ellerby, appointed honorary youth officer in 1985 at the age of twenty-six, and a year later director of the branch he joined when he was only seventeen. He has an almost passionate obsession with trying to eliminate concepts of age in relation to ability. At Hull University he read psychology, with a special option on child and adolescent suicide, and he has worked for or among young people ever since, in schools and with young offenders.

'At seventeen I had a lot of doubts about joining the Samaritans,' he recalls, 'but things were different in those days. The branch at that time was taking quite a risk. I don't think they'd had any volunteers under the age of twenty-four. They had to put up with a lot, really, things like my impatience with other volunteers! But the average age now is much lower than it was ten years ago. I know in my own branch that's the case.

'Last year, when we had a very strong drive for new volunteers, there was a tremendous response from seventeen and eighteen-year-olds – some younger. This may be the beginning of a different response to unemployment, as quite a number of young volunteers are unemployed. Also perhaps there is a change in attitude towards doing voluntary work; it's no longer seen as something you're going to waste your time at. By class, too, the Samaritans are a more representative cross-section of society than they were. More working-class people join.

'When I first became a Samaritan one of my biggest fears was my age. I felt very inadequate. I thought, what happens if I get a call from a lady of thirty-eight with two kids? Here am I, seventeen. Some people do ask how old you are. What I used to say was, "I'm seventeen, is that of concern to you?" If they found it was important, either we worked through it or perhaps we found another volunteer. On the one hand, I do see that older people have an experience of life, and can use it. But on the other hand, you are, at seventeen, to a certain extent more open.

'Twenty-five per cent of our callers are under the age of twenty-five. Last year, between 8,000 and 9,000 were under sixteen. But statistics are dodgy. Many branches don't include testing calls, and some branches only log a call statistically if it goes on longer than fifteen minutes. A testing call is one the Samaritans find difficult to deal with. They think the person is not being serious. But a testing call is not a hoax, it's somebody who has heard about the Samaritans and quite understandably doesn't believe what they've heard. You talk to schools, and you say, "Here's an organization made up of people who are non-judgemental, non-parental and totally accepting of you as a person. They won't judge what you do, they will just accept you, and whatever you've done or thought, or want to do, that is completely confidential." And they don't believe it. I wouldn't have believed it. I would have wanted to find out, even if I didn't have a problem, and what better way to find out than to ring up and actually test them. Invent a story. Sometimes, when you do a role-play in school they pick that up and feed it back to the branch. Some young callers touch on the thing they really want to talk about but see how the Samaritans are going to react first. Others will pick up the phone and dial and when you say, "The Samaritans, can I help you?" they'll shout, "Fuck off," and put the phone down. Or call you a stupid bag, or something. Sometimes you see volunteers getting upset at this, frustrated, but we need to remember back to how it was when we were younger, how we found it very difficult to put into words how someone could help us. Young people often find it difficult to communicate on a feelings level. And so I suppose part of my job as youth officer is to say to the Samaritans, This is difficult to cope with, but if you look at why it's happening it's a very natural thing for young people to ring and not say anything, because the fact that we are there is the important thing.

'I think for Samaritans there is a big difficulty about respect for young people. Maybe we weren't respected, or we didn't feel we were when we were young. But when we join the Samaritans we try to move away from the general view of society that a youngster is unable to make his own decisions: "I'm older so I know better". In a way it's easy to look after children because we think they're more vulnerable and therefore we don't need to give them much time to make their own decisions. If anything, with a young person a Samaritan has got to give so much more time. Training for dealing with children varies tremendously from branch to branch. In workshops, we say, "If anything, you need more discipline as a person, because it's not the problem that's affecting you, it's the age of the person. And you can justify it by saying things like, "A nine-year-old can't make his own decisions." But a nine-year-old has already made some decisions if he gets in contact with you. I suppose part of my role is just reminding Samaritans all the time that age should not change the quality of care. That for young callers the quality of care should be increased, because a young caller has less power than any other group. There are fewer people willing to believe you. There are fewer people around you feel you can trust. And that's going to get worse.

'I think this generation is going to find it more difficult to find people to trust and to share with, and there are going to be more secrets. And I suppose I see the Samaritans as providing something that no one else provides; nowhere else can you go where you are promised a safe place and to be given emotional time and space. That is just so incredibly important. I think the difference between a Samaritan and someone else is time. Because you can get people to advise you and do things for you in every other walk of life.

'As far as young volunteers are concerned, they may not have experience but they have care and acceptance. The problem is one of getting hung up on age. I know personally fourteen-year-olds who I would feel comfortable talking with, who would give me time and would care. And there are a lot of fourteen-year-olds I wouldn't want to talk to in any way whatsoever. But there are a lot of sixty-year-olds I wouldn't want to talk to either. And there are sixty-year-olds who would give me time and space. So I think it's wrong for the Samaritans, of all organizations, whose principles and practices are there regardless of age, to get hung up with age. If the person has the right attitudes, despite their age, then we should count that as being something very positive. Whether young volunteers stay depends on how much they're used. I was used fairly quickly. I'm sure that where antagonism exists between old and young volunteers, it is both ways. You get young people who are not tolerant of older volunteers, and you get some older volunteers who aren't tolerant of young ones. The Samaritans is an organization in which everything takes time. Evolution rather than revolution. And I think we've got a long way to go. There are still young volunteers who look at still younger volunteers in an odd light. It's the age thing again. They think, "I'm thirty-two and the seventeen-year-old seems to be doing quite a good job, and that upsets me a bit."'

A volunteer of fifty-two in one of the London branches, who interviews a lot of potential new recruits, said the youngest she had interviewed personally was twenty. 'My basic attitude to all volunteers is that they have something special to offer. Young people have their freshness, their spontaneity, their natural friendliness. They are closer to the up and down feelings of teenagers. I have no experience of the pressures of young people today. In my own personal life it was totally different when I was a young girl. Young people today have so much more choice and therefore so many more pressures put upon them. I've seen my own nieces and nephews be of tremendous value to older people in their community. They can be very sensitive. Just because they're young I don't think it matters that they haven't experienced all of life. They have a much more open, accepting way than we had. And I think life is tougher for them, actually.'

Her comments were echoed by another middle-aged volunteer, from Surrey. 'We've had one or two young people in our branch who have been absolutely wonderful. I couldn't have done it at their age, not in a million years. They are so patient, and they are so wonderfully compassionate. I was much too taken up with my own concerns at that age. I could never have done it. I'm fascinated. I certainly had a very protected childhood and upbringing, and I didn't know how the rest of the world lived at all. We've got a couple of nineteen and twenty-year-olds in my branch, men and women. I'm thinking particularly of a couple of young men we've had. One is still doing his "A" levels. We had one young man for three or four years who was particularly good with the young callers. As you know, the main thing is listening – and getting people to talk. Some people ring up and don't draw breath for an hour! Our young volunteers are much more patient with these gasbags than I am!'

By 1972, the particular needs of certain young callers and the understanding aptitudes of certain young volunteers were drawn together by the formation of the Festival branch, formally recognized two years later, an *ad hoc* selection of volunteers, about half of whom are drawn from centres throughout the country, 'with a sympathetic attitude towards the pop music world and the type of people who attend pop festivals.' The Festival branch got their first real taste of the work that lay ahead when they attended the Reading Pop Festival in 1973. Since then they have appeared, among many other places, at Wembley, Knebworth, Stonehenge, Glastonbury, Alexandra Palace and Trafalgar Square. It is a form of befriending in the open with a vengeance, a very public and visible presence, with a large tent proclaiming 'The Samaritans', from which are distributed leaflets that read, 'It's not always fun for everybody; if that's the way it is with you, look out for THE SAMARITANS.' And there are volunteers wandering around, not actually going up to people and offering their services but making contact in a very definite way. A volunteer normally based in London reported on the branch's baptism, and nothing, in essence, has changed very much since then: 'Though we were equipped for Samaritan work of the most general nature,' he wrote, 'the type of client we encountered, being predictably younger than average, that's to say, exclusively in the fourteen to thirty years age group, gave the emphasis of the problems presented a distinct "slant". Given that young people in any case have problems associated with their age – those which for lack of a better phrase we term "the problems of adolescence" – we found that the specific circumstances of the festival, the carnival atmosphere, the excitement of the music, camping out, and the like, coupled with the ready availability of drugs and alcohol, led to us caring mainly for people who were drug users of one category or another. Naturally enough we also encountered crises provoked by other factors, disillusionment with the festival, anxiety about brief, personal and intimate relationships, depression, no money and so on. A high percentage of our clients were, however, "stoned", and not particularly enjoying the experience.'

He went on to say that the 'state of chaos which reigns at events like Reading puts a special strain on the Samaritans on duty. The very nature of the event produces relatively large numbers of potentially disturbed clients who may have very serious problems indeed. All the familiar background details of being on duty are also absent and the fact that nearly every client is a new client who is asking for immediate attention can make a turn of duty a very wearing affair.' Despite the 'state of chaos' he concluded by saying the Reading Festival was by far the best organized of the regular festivals, but two major concerns cropped up. 'Unfortunately the promised financial assistance never materialized from the promoters. The other depressing aspect of the event was the large quantity of alcohol consumed, especially by young people not old enough to be out of a schoolroom.'

At a pop festival lasting three days, the Festival branch, manned by perhaps twenty-five volunteers, may befriend some ninety young people, usually far more young men and boys than young women and girls. Problems relating to drugs, including alcohol, and emotional situations of one sort or another will account for about sixty per cent of the reasons for Samaritans being consulted. General enquiries about Samaritan services will account for perhaps fifteen per cent of contacts, and then there is a rapid falling off to some five per cent who might be complaining of loneliness, and three or four per cent with medical or legal problems.

A member of the Festival branch attached at other times to a centre in a university city, which is also an area of high unemployment, works in the local supplementary benefits office, and therefore sees something of the practical difficulties facing potential Samaritan callers in the course of her everyday life. She was accepted as a Samaritan three years ago, when she was twenty-two. She looks alarmingly vulnerable but completely relaxed. The cramped little room at the centre where she talked, with its crumpled divan bed and unwashed tea-making equipment, seemed strangely reminiscent of a student's bedsitter.

'Although this is a university city, I wouldn't say we get a particularly high number of students as callers,' she said. 'In fact, we don't get very many students at all. I think they have their own help lines within the university. We tend to get more students as volunteers than as callers, and quite a lot of volunteers from the local Roman Catholic theological college, just outside the city, but they tend to leave when they've passed their exams, and they also create problems for the rota when they go on holiday.

'I know I was very young when I became a volunteer but I think I've always been an old woman at heart! When I was interviewed I never felt I was being questioned about my age. Not at all. I think that half the people on my training course were about my age. There weren't a lot of people who seemed a lot older than me, although of course we have got volunteers in the branch of seventy. I don't feel as if I'm too young to be a Samaritan. Callers who meet me face to face don't seem to react in any way on account of my age. And of course a lot of people round about my age like to talk to someone of their own age. We get a lot of people who are gay, and have problems at home with their families. There's a great range of problems. We've just lost a steel works in the town, for a start.

'The boredom of unemployment is a great problem for people. They become depressed because of it. They've no motivation. I think if people had work there wouldn't be half so much depression. We'll always have people who are unhappy, but there wouldn't be so many. I'm a fairly happy person. I would say so, yes. You have to be able to take the depressing part of the work and care about it and then forget about it. You can't take it home with you or you'll worry yourself silly. You can get too involved. No one that I've ever befriended has ever died, that I know of. But you can't know, you see. You might just lose contact with them, and you don't know if it's because they've died or they don't want to be befriended any more because they're all right now. You never know how high your success rate is.

'Outside the Samaritans I haven't known anybody who has killed themselves, but apparently my grandfather committed suicide. I didn't know him, but I think I knew how it affected my family, because he disappeared, and they found him in a river, about four days later. My mother's told me about it, and I think I must have taken that in. It must have made an impression on me when I was young, hearing about that. I don't know whether it contributed to me ending up being a Samaritan. I think I just had a feeling I could help people who felt depressed, maybe because I'm the sort of person who gets depressed myself, at times. But if I feel depressed I just think there's somebody worse off than myself. I have friends I can talk to. A lot of people who end up phoning the Samaritans don't have anyone they can turn to.

'I think everything I heard when we were trained came as something I would have expected Samaritans to be involved with apart from the sex calls. The telephone masturbators. When we heard the tape of a mock-up call, I thought, "Oh, heck, can I cope with this?" But the tape was highly exaggerated, to make you realize what you would be up against, so that when you actually got one it wouldn't be as bad as you expected. Though some of them are pretty bad. I thought, "I can't cope with somebody saying things like that to me, I will feel as if I am being used like a prostitute over the phone." Then I went away and thought, well, all the other things I've heard about I can cope with, I must just try to cope with the M-calls too and not take it all too much to heart, and think to myself, he's just a caller, he doesn't know who I am, he just wants someone to get his frustration out on, I suppose. When it actually happened it wasn't anywhere near as bad as I expected it to be. I just took it in my stride.

'And I've had to take a lot of testing calls from teenagers. It tends to be a bit of a joke. You know, let's phone the Samaritans, Mum's out, we've got nothing to do. Our practice is to encourage them to phone again. You don't say, "Don't be a silly little boy, go away," you try to be nice to them and encourage them to phone again in case in the future they really do have a problem. You don't say, "Oh, get lost you silly little child, I'm busy," you say, "What's your name? Have you really got a problem or are you just having a bit of fun?" and they usually admit it and put the phone down.'

John Eldrid summed up his views on young volunteers by saying, 'If they've got a reasonably good life going for them outside the centre they are not very likely to succumb to other people's depression. A lot depends on whether they are using the Samaritans as a kind of escape. Obviously one tries to check this out. My son joined the Samaritans at seventeen, in the Festival branch, and it certainly never had any adverse effect on him. I think a lot depends on the person's own lifestyle. But of course if a young person is befriending someone, and gets quite close to them, and they kill themselves, then obviously this will be quite traumatic and the volunteer will need a lot of support.'

While the Samaritans in the United Kingdom have no plans to lower their minimum age for volunteers to sixteen, as the Samaritans have done in Boston, Massachusetts, where volunteers between sixteen and twenty, recruited specifically to befriend other 'teenagers', have been named, all too predictably, Samariteens, it *is* possible to serve as a Samaritan while still at school. Lucinda, who is now nineteen, applied to the central London branch to train as a volunteer when she was only sixteen, and was told they preferred not to consider recruits below the age of about nineteen (although central London have in the past accepted volunteers of seventeen). So a year later she contacted her local branch, and became a volunteer at the age of eighteen, while she was still a schoolgirl. After one year as a Samaritan, she spoke about her limited and youthful experience.

'I didn't know a great deal about the Samaritans before I read Monica Dickens's book at the age of sixteen.[1] That really did make me very fascinated about the whole idea. I read it actually simply because I like reading Monica Dickens's fiction. From quite a young age I'd been interested in voluntary work, cubs and things like that, and I think I was looking for something I could do, without quite knowing what. I wrote to the central London branch. I was terrified of ringing them up because I didn't want to be treated as a caller. They put me off temporarily, until a friend, interested in being a social worker, suggested we both contact our local branch. We made separate appointments. We didn't like to reveal the fact that we knew one another, we thought it might look as though we weren't serious.

'At the start I was totally unprepared for the sex calls. I didn't know they existed or ever happened. Or not to the extent they do happen. I may have been asked at my interview if it would bother me, but I didn't realize how much it would affect me. Or at least, how often it would occur. I think I just assumed it would be every now and again, like you get at home. After a year, I would say the sex calls are basically boring, because you feel you really want to be there for other people. I know a lot of Samaritans come off the phone after taking a sex call and they say, "Oh, how disgusting, why can't they just leave us alone," but inside I feel sympathy for people who have to make calls like this. I must admit I feel very upset about them. Invariably they are unemployed, between about fifteen and twenty-five, perhaps a little older, usually sitting at home doing nothing. I

[1] *The Listeners* (Heinemann, 1970).

find it very difficult just to write these people off as being boring or revolting, they've got many more problems than we realize. At the beginning I was very shocked and very upset, and found it very difficult to cope with. After a while you build up some sort of immunity. Often they slam the phone down when you try to talk about anything else.

'I didn't mention joining the Samaritans to my parents at all. I told them some time during the training course, when I knew that I did want to go through with it. I think they'd have liked to have been told earlier, but I didn't tell them because I didn't know how serious I was about it. You really don't know what you're facing at the beginning, and I really didn't know what my parents' reaction would be. They know I have a certain number of sex calls to deal with, but to be honest, I don't know what their reaction is. I don't discuss the Samaritans very much with them. And I never told any teachers at school that I was a Samaritan. The school itself didn't know.

'The first call I took was from a regular caller who calls us all the time, a bit of a madman, actually. But I didn't know that at the time, so I tried to be very serious and helpful. Someone soon rescued me by putting a note in front of me telling me what to do. Being supported like that I found a very great help. The general response to me, from other Samaritans, being so young, has been absolutely fine. I find sometimes if a caller comes to the door I tend to be pushed into the background a bit, because they feel that somebody older ought to be doing the interviews, but not always, I have done plenty of interviews. Once a lady at the door saw me and asked if she could speak to an older woman. It didn't bother me. Sometimes if a young person comes to the door I'll be asked to see them on the assumption they will relate better to me, but I'm not sure that's actually true. I think if I was a caller I might prefer to talk to somebody older. But generally it doesn't seem to matter.

'My positive lack of experience of life is irrelevant because I'm not there to give advice, whether it's about something I know about or not. But being a Samaritan has certainly made me much more aware of what goes on in the world. How many people out there are unemployed, unhappy, lonely. But I don't think it's changed my attitude to people, except for my sympathy towards people who make sex calls. Before, like any member of the public, I would have looked on them as being wicked and vile and disgusting, whereas now I know their problem goes much deeper than that.

'I'm not sure Samaritans should stay in the movement thirty years. I can see a situation where I could get very stale. In the way you can build up an immunity to sex callers, I think after a certain number of years you might find you didn't react to anything. So I don't think I could be a Samaritan for thirty years. But I wouldn't leave now. I feel a great sense of responsibility, now I've been trained, and the drop-out rate is so high. In my branch we've got eighty volunteers and we really need 110. I like night duties best because I feel I'm doing much more positive work at night. You get some very sad stories at night. I have been upset sometimes and rung other Samaritans to talk about it. I find it difficult talking to very lonely callers, people who are very, very lonely, and have very little to look forward to. People who have been bereaved call at night because they can't sleep, and they tend to go on for a very long time.

'I often speak to callers of my own age who have such terrible lives compared to what I've got. When I was worrying about my school exams and waking up in the morning in a terrible state I went down to the centre, and spoke to a girl of nineteen whose mother had committed suicide, and she'd had two miscarriages, and then I thought, what am I worrying about? I don't look forward to going to the centre. I'm not a born Samaritan who wants to submerge themselves in every aspect of the Samaritans. I couldn't do that. But I certainly have no immediate plans to leave. Ten people started on my training course, six got through and now there are four. And one of those is on leave of absence. So after only one year there are just three active volunteers left out of my intake. And I'm one of them!'

PUBLIC PERCEPTIONS

In 1985, Audience Selection conducted a survey among 1,532 people to try to discover something about the public's perception of the Samaritans. Asked initially to name just one charity, 287 people came up with Cancer Research. Five people – the same number to whom the National Trust immediately sprang to mind – named the Samaritans. Eventually a total of 728 people – forty-eight per cent of the sample – named Cancer Research as a charity known to them, forty-two per cent Oxfam and thirty-one per cent Save the Children. Even the Royal National Institute for the Deaf rustled up six per cent. On four per cent, representing a total of sixty-four mentions altogether, and on equal pegging with the National Wildlife Fund, came the Samaritans. Asked how desperate they thought the Samaritans were for money from the general public in comparison to the others, ten per cent said they thought the Samaritans were extremely desperate, fifteen per cent said very desperate and fourteen per cent did not know. To the question, 'Do you personally think the Samaritans are a deserving charity to give money to in comparison with other charities?' twenty-eight per cent said they thought they were very deserving, forty-seven per cent only fairly deserving, ten per cent not very deserving and five per cent not deserving at all.

The previous year, a National Opinion Poll had revealed 'a lot of uncertainty' as to whether local government or even Westminster funded the Samaritans, an organization seen largely as only providing a telephone service. It was found that 'virtually everyone had heard of the Samaritans' but that about one in ten aged between fifteen and seventeen, and one in six over the age of seventy or currently unemployed, could not say what the Samaritans did. Some confusion with the Voluntary Euthanasia Society seems to have existed for two per cent, who believed that the Samaritans would tell you how to kill yourself if you wanted them to, but a major muddle revolved around the question of befriending; thirty per cent said the Samaritans went out to people who had cut their wrists or taken an overdose, twenty-three per cent did not know whether this was so or not, and forty-seven per cent maintained that the Samaritans never went out on such occasions. Perhaps rather more alarmingly, ten per cent of those in the sample of 1,896 people over fifteen thought the Samaritans decorated old people's homes, and twenty-three per cent thought they took bread and soup to down-and-outs. Asked why some people might be put off calling the Samaritans, thirty-five per cent mentioned a concern about confidentiality, more perhaps a reflection upon a world that practices deception as a matter of course than upon the reliability of the Samaritans themselves.

So when it comes to attaining public awareness of its existence and purpose, what has Cancer Research – or Oxfam or Save the Children, or even Mencap or the Salvation Army, for that matter – got that the Samaritans have not? Fund-raising and public relations are intimately linked – it is on the strength of the projection, by whatever method, of a charity's image that income from the public depends – and for four and a half years (she left in 1986) Barbara Lynch, a professional fund-raiser, took on the task of producing, for what is known as the National Appeal, an annual income of £1.75 millions. Her job inevitably necessitated some very clear-headed thinking about the related topics of advertising and press relations. Reflecting on her experience of the Samaritans as an outsider, she said: 'I think it's quite difficult for the Samaritans to raise funds because of the sort of charity it is. People tend to want to give money to something very specific, and the money the Samaritans spend tends to be on what other charities hide under overheads. Take the case of the phone bill. No other charity would advertise the fact that they spent £275,000 a year on telephones. Children's charities, for example, can actually portray the victims they help, and that of course is something the Samaritans can't do. When we talk in terms of statistics we find it very hard to put a human face on them. People like to buy something specific with their money, whereas we want them to give towards a service, and it often isn't specific enough.

'I don't think the general public gives nearly as much to the Samaritans as it could, but big companies are pretty generous, and charitable trusts are particularly generous. I think the image of the organization as far as the public is concerned – and research has proved this – is of rather an old-fashioned, possibly government-funded, set-up. They can't see why it has any need for money. They think, "Samaritans are volunteers, people ring *them* up." People react emotionally to charity. Not very many react rationally. When we give to a charity we give because we are giving to people less fortunate than we are, and we want them to be victims. There is still a very strong feeling in this country that if you are depressed, and certainly depressed enough to kill yourself, it's because you're weak, and that by funding a service that helps people like that you're perhaps not doing the individuals themselves very much good.

'People don't want to know about despair. It's something we tend to experience individually, and although that could be said of cancer, cancer is now a much more open subject than it used to be. We all know someone who's had cancer, or died of it. But there's been a tremendous turn around. Not so many years ago people wouldn't even mention the word. There was a fear that if you talked about cancer, somehow you'd get it. And perhaps that attitude still exists with depression. It is probably something people want to forget about rather than do something that will help. And of course, we can't promise, as we can with cancer research, that if you give us money we might be able to make things go away. There isn't an overall cure for unhappiness. There isn't going to be a drug for it.

'People see the Samaritans as an extension of the welfare service. Very much so. They think of the Samaritans as they do the Citizens Advice Bureaux. Lots of people think the Samaritans give a wonderful service, but while very few people actually think the volunteers are paid, they certainly think the Samaritans are funded by the government. And the other problem is that the Samaritans themselves don't like fund-raising very much. They're always very worried that if they do go out and fund-raise they will be giving away the fact that they are Samaritans. And anyway, I think the sort of people who make good Samaritans don't make good fund-raisers, because the fund-raiser's mentality is a bit like the salesman's, it's quite pushy, whereas volunteers are selected for their ability to be passive. And so in many ways we deselect potentially good fund-raisers when we're recruiting Samaritans. There are many charities whose primary aim is fund-raising. I'm thinking of War on Want and Help the Aged. Mainly they raise money and then they spend it to alleviate the problem. That's not how the Samaritans see themselves. They see themselves as providing a service which is essentially run by volunteers, and the fact that there are costs is something they have only recently begun to realize. I imagine most branches would be very relieved to draft on to the branch committee an outsider with expertise in fund-raising.'

The £1.75 millions raised every year from an office in the same building as the central London branch goes towards paying telephone bills, national publicity, financing the general office at Slough and paying the salaries of full-time staff. Because central London's running costs are exceptionally high and the branch could never be expected to become self-financing, fifty per cent of the national appeal is allocated to central London. A government grant currently set (and fixed for a three-year period) at £131,500 is made by the Department of Health and Social Security. Every branch has to raise locally enough to meet their domestic expenses, and they presently send seven and a half per cent of their income to Slough as a contribution to the cost of the services the general office provides, like running conferences and arranging inspections by Visitors, and to supplying grants, currently amounting to £71,000, to the regions. There is a recommendation that a certain proportion of funds raised locally should be spent on publicity, and branches are asked to resist approaching national firms with local offices due to be canvassed by the appeals director. If a branch incurs high costs it is because it is receiving a lot of calls, which will mean it is situated in a densely populated area where in fact fund-raising ought to be relatively easy. Those branches that find it hardest to meet their target are usually in rural areas, and particularly depressed rural areas, where potential supporters are scattered.

Barbara Lynch's job was to approach major companies and charitable trusts, to organize concerts, balls and highly publicized auctions, and to try to inculcate in branches an understanding that fund-raising needs to be high on their agenda. 'What the national fund-raiser has to do,' she says, 'is act as an interpreter between the Samaritans, who have their own language and their own customs and beliefs, and the outside world, which wants thumb-nail sketches of the organization in terms they can understand. I don't think the Samaritans in general understood the need for money at first, but they're getting much, much better about this now. I think over the last four years they have come to realize you can't have total privacy if you want people to give you money. They tended to want absolute secrecy about their organization. They didn't want to speak to journalists, whereas now they do, but they want to speak to them at length so that they can really explain what they are doing. And I think that has been greatly helped by the national appeal, because I couldn't do things quietly, in a vacuum, if I was going to raise the money they needed. I think they have realized that. And I also think the Samaritans are unique. The only other charities that have similar problems are the mental health charities, but they don't have the same problems that we have about actually portraying sufferers. There isn't the same stigma attached to mental disability as there is to depression.'

In one year, Miss Lynch doubled the income from the national appeal. But like so many outsiders working conscientiously for an organization traditionally deeply suspicious of the 'media', she has sometimes wondered whose side she was meant to be on. The answer, of course, as with any good press officer, is both. 'The branches,' she says, 'resent what they see as a growing professionalism in the Samaritans. It's a dirty word to them, professionalism. They want things done well but they don't like the idea of professionals, whose motives they suspect, working for them. In some ways, the fund-raising is no different than for any other charity, but the organization can be quite difficult to get through to! A major problem which other charities don't have is this idea of appointing people to posts like branch director for a maximum of three years. I've had to try and indoctrinate Samaritans into the rules of fund-raising, and as soon as I get one lot sorted out, they change. There are a whole lot of new faces at the top and you have to start all over again. There doesn't seem to be any hand-over in the branches at all. That's frustrating. I understand the idea behind rotation, you can get people who stay in jobs too long, but continuity is desperately important when you're building for the future, which is what we're trying to do. The Samaritans are still going to expand, and they're going to need more and more money.'

In April 1984 clashes occurred which presented a nice example of a public relations exercise requiring expert handling on behalf of a jittery client. Permission had previously been granted to the Samaritans by the Bank of England, custodians, apparently, of the nation's image of its currency as well as its expenditure, to feature a crumpled £5 note in press advertisements; a stark headline 'Suicide Notes' was backed up with copy stating that it cost £2.66 a minute to run the Samaritans, and asking readers to 'spare a few minutes'. Because the Samaritans wanted to make use of the same motif as the central feature of a national fund-raising campaign, aimed at raising £150,000, by adapting it to a poster, they were obliged to resubmit the idea to the Bank of England, who now refused permission, on the grounds that 'designs which might be seen by the public as lowering the dignity or prestige of the currency will not be permitted.' All Barbara Lynch's instincts as a professional were to capitalize on misfortune, for she, like her colleagues in Fleet Street, had been trained to spot a good story when she saw one. 'From a fund-raising point of view, it was a wonderful thing to have happened, because it got a lot of attention, and a lot of sympathy, and also some money.' Prompted by a press release sent out by Barbara Lynch, the *Guardian* ran a front-page story; there were editorials and the inevitable follow-up radio and television interviews. 'We got a tremendous amount of publicity, far beyond what we could have afforded. It was a very fortuitous thing to have happened, but the organization was slightly anxious about it because it seemed to be the Samaritans making a fuss. It was not something I would have courted, but when it came it was useful.'

Alerted by the findings of the National Opinion Poll, which had highlighted widely divergent perceptions of the role of the Samaritans, and in particular the failure of the public to recognize them as a charity, a public relations agency was hired and Saatchi & Saatchi were commissioned to dramatize the Samaritans' public image. One result was a poster that won three campaign press awards. It featured a photograph (using a model, of course) of a girl with straggly hair, aged perhaps eighteen, with tears discernible on her cheeks, a telephone receiver to her ear and a couple of bottles of pills, some red, some white, strewn on a table in front of her. Utilized in different contexts, the photograph has appeared with a variety of captions. One reads, 'The only thing holding her back is a thin piece of cord with you on the end of it.' The award-winning poster carried a lot of advertising copy, designed to attract new volunteers, and the words 'I'm about to kill myself. Can you talk me out of it?' made up a double-column headline. It won the *Guardian* silver award for the best-written advertisement, but no doubt its merits had been judged by *Guardian* staff who were not themselves Samaritans. Its apparent flouting of Samaritan practice by seeming to suggest pat answers to specific problems aroused the indignation of *Samaritan* readers. A member of the Winchester branch wrote to the magazine to complain that the nature of the copy 'seemed to be quite alien to anything a Samaritan would say to a distressed and suicidal caller.' He went on, 'For potential volunteers, at whom the poster is directed, to be led to think this is how we respond to callers, or worse still for any potential caller to believe this is the kind of response they may receive, seems to me appalling and likely to do incalculable harm.' He hoped the poster would be withdrawn, as it was 'totally inappropriate.'

Another volunteer, also 'appalled' by the poster, was the recruitment officer from the branch in Hove, who wrote to say, 'I'm afraid that if anything this poster, with its melodramatic headline, is more likely to scare away than to encourage potential applicants.' The burden of her complaint, like that of her colleague's from Winchester, was that, whereas the Samaritans are trained not to supply ready-made and specific responses, as though every problem had a 'correct' answer, the advertisement did just that. She thought that, 'would you like to tell me about it?' should have been included as an option in every issue raised.

These complaints bring sharply into focus the possibly irreconcilable dichotomy between the intimate knowledge of its own mode of operation possessed and prized by a non-professional organization (in the case of the Samaritans, one dealing in highly sensitive areas of human activity) and the necessity an advertising agency considers essential to translate that private understanding into an instantly assimilated message. These problems scarcely exist when it comes to selling food. No matter how disgusting someone's sausages may be, the aim of the manufacturer is to sell them, and if a television commercial succeeds in that endeavour, the agency can say and do whatever it pleases. But the truth is, a literal telephone conversation between a volunteer and a caller would make pretty disastrous advertising copy, and Samaritans individually are bound to react sensitively to translations of their almost sacred principles and practices into the language of the vulgar mob. Of course, Saatchi & Saatchi's copy must have been approved by the executive committee, so perhaps it is even more pertinent to note that the mixed reception to this attempt to modernize and clarify the Samaritans' image may reflect a divergence of attitudes within the movement, between the hierarchy and the shop floor.

Perhaps also the Samaritans have become too accustomed to the never changing format of their own magazine. One of the *Samaritan's* purposes is to act as a sounding board for complaints and as a forum for the exchange of news and ideas, and these functions it performs openly and usefully. But no one could ever accuse it of sensationalism. After fourteen years the layout and contents remain utterly predictable, a perfectly preserved fossilized memento of 1972. As a mirror-image of the movement, it seems quite out of tune with any professed attempt to enliven the Samaritans' public persona or conception of themselves. The quality of the movement's throw-away leaflets, too, can sometimes be indifferent. There is a dreadful air of unreality about leaflets designed as strip cartoons with characters called Mandy, told to scram because she's boring and a creep, and Scott, 'who has never had a girlfriend.' By comparison, a headline like 'Why you should think more seriously about killing yourself' over a clearly laid-out poster aimed at potential callers jolts one with a pleasant, professional shock.

When it comes to receiving beneficial publicity, the Samaritans are inevitably in the fortunate position of being able to see it generate almost at will. Women's magazines, the women's pages of national newspapers and a good many feature radio programmes soak up articles and interviews concerned with Samaritan activity, and the assistant general secretary, one of whose tasks is to handle public relations, happens to possess a natural and unaffected flair for talking to reporters and responding to interviews. But there is always a danger, as there is in any organization which does not employ a full-time press officer with experience as a journalist, that certain stories initiated outside the office, with potentially damaging consequences, will tend to acquire an unquenchable life and momentum of their own. Because of what many Samaritans see

as a high-handed and insensitive approach adopted by some
directors to the whole question of the care and sacking of
volunteers, the movement is particularly vulnerable to former
Samaritans airing their grievances in public. This happened
when, on 30 July 1986, the *Guardian* published an account by
an anonymous Samaritan of her reactions to the voluntary work
she undertook, those reactions being mainly a sense of total
inadequacy in relation to the depth of some of the misery and
despair she tried to relieve. It proved too much of an irritant for
one former Samaritan, who unleashed in the letters column a
fairly extreme mixture of disillusionment, bitterness and criticism, based to a large extent on the way in which she claimed she
had been cold-shouldered when herself in serious need of
emotional support.

'I am sure now,' the *Guardian's* disaffected correspondent
wrote from Harrow, without in any serious way attempting to
substantiate her devastating charge, 'that the good done by the
Samaritans is counterbalanced, or perhaps outweighed, by the
damage to both volunteer and client.' She went on to say she
had written a much milder letter than she had intended. Mild,
too, was Simon Armson's reaction when challenged in a radio
interview to confront these unpalatable accusations. His more
forthright view of the matter, expressed off the air, was that the
former Samaritan would have been quite entitled to express her
opinions in the movement's own magazine, but that she had
been remiss to do so in a national newspaper. However, the fact
that theoretically the *Samaritan's* print run of 13,500 circulates
mainly among Samaritans is no guarantee that copies will not
fall into the hands of journalists, just as parish magazines
may do. Publication is publication. And in any case, there seems
no valid reason in principle why criticism of the Samaritans
should not be voiced in the correspondence column of a national
newspaper. Presumably criticism expressed in a feature or
leading article would be taken on board. This is no more than a
natural hazard faced by any organization striving to do good in a
world which enjoys seeing people with a 'moral' line to plug –
clergymen, politicians, Samaritans – come to grief.

The way in which individual Samaritans take care of their organization's reputation outside the centre where they function as volunteers is always another potential source of damaging publicity, and no more startling *cause célèbre* has hit the headlines since the Samaritans were founded than the case, in 1983, of the writer Charlotte Hough, at that time working at the Canterbury branch. Mrs Hough had homes in Canterbury and in London, where, quite unconnected with her Samaritan duties in Canterbury, she befriended a lonely old lady, Miss Annetta Harding. Mrs Hough recalls: 'Miss Harding had already determined to end her own life, and now, four years later, blind and ailing, she named the day. Unable to dissuade her, I offered to be with her, and I calmed her fears of resuscitation by assuring her, in all good faith, that she could not survive, considering the massive dose of drugs she had arranged to take. But I also promised that if necessary I would apply the plastic bag that Miss Harding had laid ready. In the event, Miss Harding, happy and serene, slipped into a deep coma and remained just breathing, probably dying but possibly not. After two and a half hours I realized there was no alternative but to keep my promise, which at the time I made it seemed like nothing more than soothing words. After it was all over I yielded to the Canterbury Samaritans's suggestion that I tell them this story, and as a result I was charged with murder.'

An anonymous tip-off had already been made by a man to the *Standard*, who alerted the police. The press had a field day, and for two reasons. They managed to associate Mrs Hough, essentially an author of children's books, with a book about murder ('Crime Writer Charged with Murder' could hardly have been a more damaging headline), and they identified her as a Samaritan, without in any way attempting to differentiate between her duties as a volunteer in Canterbury and her private life in London, the implication being that assisting someone to commit suicide, if that was what Mrs Hough had done, might be something a Samaritan would do *as* a Samaritan. Here was a classic public relations scenario concerning a clash between public and private conduct.

In fact, a three-day trial at the Old Bailey was largely taken up with semantics as to whether the old lady had died from the effects of the pills she had voluntarily swallowed or from the effects of having the bag placed over her head by Mrs Hough (or both), and eventually Mrs Hough was advised to change her plea of not guilty to murder to one of guilty to attempted murder, as a result of which she was sentenced to nine months in prison – but not before the judge had somewhat fatuously told her, 'I have no desire to punish you but I must deter others less altruistic than yourself.'

The *Sunday Times* made the point that Charlotte Hough's only crime had been compassion, and that the case served to underline once more the need for better legislation governing voluntary euthanasia, and the dangers of being without it. Meanwhile, the Samaritans were faced with the question whether Mrs Hough's private conduct in agreeing to stay with someone while they died, never mind assisting them to die (which is what the jury decided by their verdict that she had done), had so prejudiced her credibility as a Samaritan that it was not possible for her to continue serving as a probationary volunteer. She says, 'I was taken off the list immediately, without my knowledge and without being given any explanation.'

Undoubtedly the last lingering recollections left with the public was of a connection between Charlotte Hough's 'attempted murder' and her membership of the Samaritans. It was a public relations exercise impossible to win, and the long-term effect impossible to assess, although, as Miss Harding had been a member of what was at that time calling itself Exit, the case my possibly have accounted for the two per cent discovered by NOP in their survey the following year who seemed to be confusing the modes of operation of the Samaritans with those of the Voluntary Euthanasia Society.

Mrs Hough served her sentence, and was released to resume her vivacious and creative life. The one consolation for every organization when things go wrong from a public relations point of view is that round every corner lurks another banana skin lying in wait for another hapless victim, and that ultimately all newspapers are written, printed and distributed to wrap up the fish and chips.

·9·

NOT LIKE
AN ORDINARY DEATH

Attitudes towards suicide have altered radically over the centuries, and have differed fundamentally between different races and cultures. People have been condemned to death for attempting to commit suicide and ostracized for failing to do so. Shifts in reaction to suicide may have had something to do with differing views about death itself. Epicurus, who did not believe in any sort of afterlife, saw no evil in death whatsoever. Sir Thomas More, who was to become a saint, departed from his medieval roots so far as to commend euthanasia. One modern definition of suicide, quoted in James Rachels's *The End of Life: Euthanasia and Morality*,[1] suggests that a person commits suicide if he intentionally brings about his own death, others do not coerce him, and death is caused by conditions arranged by the person for the purpose of bringing about his death. Such a definition may serve as a useful departure point for discussion, but it fails to take account of the successful suicide of someone who in effect has been playing Russian roulette, whether with a revolver or with drugs. Just to confuse the issue even further, it is worth bearing in mind that the Church of Rome condemns suicide, yet in order to qualify for martyrdom it is necessary to seek death.

In the second half of the twentieth century the Samaritans almost certainly reflect society's current feelings, that while

[1] Oxford University Press, 1986.

those driven by despair to suicide, or indeed those who take their own lives quite deliberately, in cold blood, so to speak, are not automatically condemned to hell fire, suicide nevertheless is somehow 'wrong' and ought, at almost all costs, to be avoided and prevented. It is a kind of instinctive reaction. Beating people is wrong; suicide is wrong. Of course, some people enjoy being beaten, and some people who kill themselves do so with the clearest possible desire to die and intention to succeed. Yet they still leave an uncomfortable feeling behind. Even when someone who we know to have been in excruciating pain with no hope of recovery from an incurable illness ends their life with dignity in a rational frame of mind we feel guilty that they should have been brought to such a lonely and dramatic course of action. We feel that death ought to be taken out of our hands, that, in a perfect world, after which we all still hanker, death would come naturally and peacefully, preferably in our sleep.

Whatever their personal views on suicide, in the course of their duties Samaritans are only likely to encounter those people driven to thoughts of suicide by depression and who are still anxious to discuss their feelings, however obliquely, with another person. Someone like Captain Oates, whose 'heroic' death, intended to save the lives of his companions, was suicide in the strictest sense, is unlikely to telephone the Samaritans before walking into the snow, not because of the lack of a phone box but because he has quite deliberately determined to end his life and has no desire or need to be deflected. Someone like Dylan Thomas, who drank himself to death, might possibly ring the Samaritans from time to time, but he is very unlikely to do so because such a person's suicide by stealth is a way of killing yourself by self-deception. While in his cups, and probably not while sober, he would never admit that in the long run his actions were going to prove as lethal as if he were to inject himself with an overdose of morphia. Wilfred Owen's determined and morally quite unnecessary return to the front in 1918, after telling his mother of his need to go back and be with the soldiers he had known and who were now dead, was an act of suicide in the event, and one he would not have wished to be talked out of nor one that anyone regards with other than a sense of the loss to literature which resulted from his death.

The historical role-call of those who, for whatever reason and by whatever means, have committed suicide amounts to an exclusive volume of *Who Was Who*. Dora Carrington, Cato, Thomas Chatterton, Cleopatra, Hart Crane, Mark Gertler, Van Gogh, Tony Hancock, Hannibal, Ernest Hemingway, Judas Iscariot, Arthur Koestler, Malcolm Lowry, Jan Masalyk, David Munrow, Sylvia Plath, Seneca, Socrates, Alan Turing, Virginia Woolf – these are but a fraction of the best or most tormented minds ever born who ended their lives by their own hands. Statistics about suicide only began to be kept in 1860, but in many periods of history suicide has seemed to be so common as to be almost universal. In ancient Greece a man who wished to end his life could calmly seek permission from the senate. 'If your existence is hateful to you, die,' they were told. 'If you are overwhelmed by fate, drink the hemlock. If you are bowed with grief, abandon life.' The magistrates even conveniently kept a supply of poison for those who pleaded their case successfully. 'It is very provoking that people must always be hanging or drowning themselves or going mad,' was the tetchy Horace Walpole's verdict on the close of the seventeenth century. In the Middle Ages, as A. Alvarez has noted in his classic study of suicide,[2] men were preoccupied with death to the point of obsession, 'But for them it was an entrance to the afterlife; consequently, life itself seemed unimportant, devalued. The modern preoccupation – which began in the nineteenth century and has steadily intensified since – is with death without an afterlife. Thus how you die no longer decides how you will spend eternity; instead, it sums up and somehow passes judgement on how you have lived.'

Writing in 1971, Alvarez maintained that suicide was still suspect, but he thought that in the last eighty years a change of tone had taken place. 'The suicide prejudice continues,' he said, 'but the religious principles by which it was once dignified

[2] *The Savage God* (Penguin, 1974).

now seem altogether less self-evident. As a result, the note of righteous denunciation has been modified. What was once a mortal sin has now become a private vice, another "dirty little secret", something shameful to be avoided and tidied away, unmentionable and faintly salacious, less self-slaughter than self-abuse.' How true is this fifteen years on? Alvarez's current analogy with 'self-abuse' seems ironic, for as long ago as 1838 a French 'expert', one M. Jean Esquirol, was pronouncing masturbation to be a cause of suicide, a scaremongering tactic taken up in England fourteen years later by Sir William Ellis, superintendant of Hanwell Asylum, who decreed that the 'habit of solitary vice' gave rise not only to suicide but to asthma and epilepsy as well. What these hypocritical oafs (they had, after all, presumably masturbated when boys themselves without coming to any harm) were trying to establish was that all suicides were mad, and if masturbation could be established as a cause of both madness and suicide it might be possible to frighten people out of a habit at that time mistakenly thought to be prescribed in the Bible by Onan's rudimentary attempts at contraception. At least their cock-eyed theories were some sort of advance on previously held notions that all suicides were the outcome of wilful wickedness. Those who had succeeded were sometimes placed in a cask and thrown into the river; others were buried at the crossroads with a stone over their face and a stake through their heart. In some instances they were parcelled off to a school of anatomy. As recently as the middle of the nineteenth century, people who failed in a suicide attempt were hanged.

Today, suicides may well be 'forgiven' under the guise of being 'understood' if the person killing himself has established a heroic or romantic role before his death, an echo perhaps of the Romantic movement itself, inhabited by people like Byron and Keats, who dreamed of suicide morning, noon and night, thus in many cases very probably preventing them from committing the act itself. When, in 1986, a young and very handsome police officer, who had been paralysed six years previously after tackling two gunmen, committed suicide, the caption to a photograph of his funeral in a national newspaper read, 'Hero's farewell'. The feelings of his family were not recorded. He had been at risk because of his appalling loss of independence. Others who seem particularly to be at risk are men and women with above average intelligence to whom the intellectually perceived horrors of life outweigh the simple pleasures, and also creative artists, people who tend to experience everything around them with a heightened expectation and hence, no matter how successful or famous they may appear in other people's eyes, often regard their creative endeavours, and hence themselves, as a failure. For them, possession of creative powers is their *raison d'être*, and any loss of these powers can never be compensated for by the normal trimmings of old age, by cultivating a garden, playing bowls, enjoying grandchildren or just sitting around chatting.

Irrespective of innate intelligence, people engaged in certain professions have always been regarded as more prone than others to commit suicide. Statistics compiled some years ago purported to show a wide cross-section of professional men and women in England and Wales to be outstanding suicide risks. They included doctors, solicitors, teachers, civil servants, bank clerks, insurance agents and commercial travellers. The stress of daily contact with death and disease, together with the ready availability of medical knowledge and lethal drugs, might have accounted for the successful suicide bids among the doctors; stress again, and perhaps the temptation to embezzlement, could have accounted for solicitors taking their own lives; teachers, of course, are always prone to charges of paederasty; perhaps the civil servants felt frustrated by a lack of public recognition of their role in government, and by a general antagonism towards them if they happened to work in the Inland Revenue; bank clerks, too, may have been tempted to place their hand in the till, bearing in mind how notoriously underpaid they were compared to bank managers; insurance agents perhaps succumbed to depression dolling out cheques to the bereaved, and commercial travellers doubtless pined for their loved ones in lonely hotel bedrooms. It will come as no surprise to discover that the highest rates of suicide among tradesmen at this time reclined among innkeepers, surrounded as they would have been by alcohol. Shopkeepers, farmers, garage proprietors, dock workers, cotton spinners, boiler makers, tailors, electricians and bankers were others whom the statisticians found to have an unusual disposition to suicide, and that must have taken care of almost everyone – washerwomen excepted. The truth of the matter is that since the publication in 1897 of Emile Durkheim's seminal work *Suicide: A Study in Sociology*[3] suicide has become a subject of intensive research resulting in far more theories than scientific results, each new conclusion tending either to refute some other conclusion or obstinately declining to yield up any objective cause. As Alvarez has caustically commented, the Samaritans, in their practical way, probably do more in a month to prevent suicide than the scientists manage in a decade, but it is interesting to note that in his generous appraisal of the work of the Samaritans he felt constrained to insert the word 'probably'.

Just as there is no single cause of crime, there is no single cause of suicide; and just as crime statistics fluctuate, often for no apparent reason, so do those for suicide. Sometimes they seem measurable in a meaningful way against other sociological factors. Sometimes there appears to be no recognizable cause whatsoever. The British are generally regarded as unflappable and tolerant, and this may in part account for the relatively low suicide rate in England and Wales of 8.2 per 100,000 of the population. But how does one account for the astonishing, and over the years seemingly consistent, rate of 40.3 in Hungary? Not surely by national characteristics alone, nor by depression caused by living under a communist regime; the rate for Poland is only 12.1. We have long been told that the Swedes went in for suicide in a big way because they lived in such a materialistic society (President Eisenhower began this extraordinary rumour), yet as Alvarez has pointed out, the suicide rate in Sweden (at present 19.7) has remained about the same since

[3] Routledge, 1952.

1910, long before the welfare state had been invented. Switzer-land, with all its affluence, and, like Sweden, its traditional neutrality, has a rate of 23.9. Do mountains induce suicidal impulses? Or cuckoo-clocks? Mediterranean nations who tend to let their hair down and shout and shriek a lot seldom, if ever, kill themselves, it seems. The suicide rate for Greece, 2.8, is the lowest recorded for any country, and Spain only admits to 3.9, but Spain's figures may well be massaged on behalf of the Church. So may Northern Ireland's, whose rate, despite the tensions under which the people have lived for so long, is mysteriously just half that for England and Wales. Some variations in the suicide rate between different countries can possibly be accounted for by the adoption of different proce-dures for recording the causes of deaths, for there are even countries where suicide is presumed in the absence of evidence to the contrary.

Thanks to the cult of hara-kiri we have come to believe that the Japanese commit suicide at a word of command from their Emperor, but the rate in Japan is 17.9, far lower than that for both East and West Germany, Austria, Denmark and Finland. However, it probably is true to say the Japanese are an imitative race, and well-publicized suicides in that country, by a school-boy unhappy with his exam results, for instance, tend to set off fairly spectacular chains of similar suicides. In 1986 Yukiko Okada, an eighteen-year-old pop singer, killed herself after being jilted by an actor, as a result of which twenty-eight teenagers committed suicide, five of them in one day. But this is not an exclusively Japanese phenomenon. Following the suicide in London in 1770 of the seventeen-year-old genius Thomas Chatterton, Alfred de Vigny's play *Chatterton*, written at the height of the Romantic movement, was credited, between 1830–40, with doubling the annual suicide rate in France.[4]

[4]The largest mass suicide ever recorded occurred on 18 November 1978 when 910 followers of the San Franciscan leader of the People's Temple Cult, Jim Jones, took cyanide at a gathering in Guyana. Seven women, all members of one of the 183,345 religious organizations currently registered in Japan, committed suicide together in 1986 when their cult leader died.

We know that at present more men than women kill themselves, but we do not know why. Perhaps it is because men are
more aggressive and less resilient (women tend, on the whole, to
cope with widowhood better than men). But the ratio of men to
women who take their own lives varies widely across the world.
In Poland it is five to one, in Finland and Iceland four to one, in
Norther Ireland it is almost equal. And these variations in ratio
do not remain static; they seem to shift around like the grinding
of the continents. In 1901 it was discovered that in England and
Wales the ratio of men to women committing suicide was 3–1.
Forty-four years later, that ratio had been reduced to 2–1. By
1974 the gap had narrowed to fewer than three men taking their
own life to two women. But since 1983 the ratio has returned to
2–1. Within these national shifts there are further puzzling
phenomena. In Newcastle, for example, a relatively prosperous
northern city, the suicide rate is almost twice the national
average, the rate for women being slightly above that for men
(at a national level, 10.7 suicides are male and 6.5 are female). In
fact, in Newcastle the rate for women is nearly three times the
national average. But in Cumbria, the rate for women is only
2.5. The range of the male/female ratio varies from 4.4 in
Cumbria to 0.4 in South Tyneside, which means that in Cumbria forty-four men kill themselves each year for every ten
women; in South Tyneside the number is only four. But the
general experience of more male suicides to female among the
adult population holds very steady where children and teenagers are concerned. Both in the United Kingdom and in the
United States, something like three times as many boys commit
suicide as girls. So much for the myth of girls killing themselves
every day because they have been jilted by their faithless
boyfriends; in adolescence, most boys tend to retain the sensitivity they so tragically feel compelled to discard in later life.
And other, more disturbing, relationships between adults and
children appear to coincide. For someone who has survived a
suicide attempt there is a much greater risk of succeeding a
second time, and on 18 July 1986 *The Times* carried a report of
an inquest on a boy of six who it was believed had died from a

deliberate overdose of paracetamol, having been successfully treated for a similar overdose just fourteen days before. Incredible though it may seem, this child's death must almost certainly have been suicide; how many children of six, having undergone the distress of being revived, would carelessly have run the risk of hospital treatment again?

The only time when the number of suicides can be guaranteed to fall seems to be when a nation goes to war, for a country on a war-time footing can usually find a useful slot for the outsider. Many a maverick entrepreneur has dreaded the signing of the armistice. It is also confidently asserted that an excessive consumption of alcohol helps to increase the risk of suicide, but presumably it is also true to say that the more times you cross the road the more likely you are to be knocked down by a car. Often when a prominent politican or entertainer commits suicide we are educated by a hastily researched article in the press, explaining the causes, and the dangers he or she had run. The suicide in 1986 of Ted Moult, who was a farmer as well as a 'television personality', elicited the information in *The Times* that farming had headed the suicide list in the 1930s but that today the league table for suicides from all causes was led by hairdressers, followed by deck hands, general labourers, domestic staff and general managers. One marvels there are enough domestic staff left to find their way into any statistics. A hasty juggling act, however, revealed that 'when the figures are sorted into job-related categories a different picture emerges,' and sure enough, doctors were back at the top of the pile, followed by dentists, farmers and farm workers, pharmacists and therapists, judges and lawyers.

On a global scale, there are said to be 1,000 suicides a day, about a dozen of them occurring in England. Bad weather has been blamed for high suicide rates in the past, and one would not be surprised to discover the Samaritans rushed off their feet at Christmas, when the compulsory celebration of happiness hits particularly hard those who are alone and feel more excluded than ever. In fact, however, in the northern hemisphere suicides reach a peak in the spring, surely because the seasonal rebirth in nature serves as a reminder of the lack of a future an already depressed person may be feeling. For them, as Eliot has said, April is indeed the cruellest month, 'breeding lilacs out of the dead land.'[5] Again, although the Samaritans often report a preponderance of very lonely and severely depressed people calling them at night – as one might expect – the majority of suicides occur during the daytime, most commonly in the late morning and early afternoon. This may in fact be the time of day (the morning certainly) when most people have the most energy.

Explanations for changes in the methods used to commit suicide, and variations in the methods used as between different categories of people, seem far easier to offer than explanations for variations in suicide rates between countries or fluctuations in the numbers of suicides between the sexes. Not so long ago, suicide was almost synonymous in most people's minds with someone putting their head in the gas oven. With the introduction of North Sea gas, substantially free of carbon monoxide, that relatively simple, nearly always lethal, method had to be abandoned. Coincidentally, barbiturates became readily available, and they simply took the place of gas. In 1984, 4,315 suicides were recorded in England and Wales; it was estimated that in the same year some 100,000 people were admitted to hospital suffering from a drug overdose, and just over half the numbers of suicides for women are achieved by overdosing. But on the whole, people tend to choose a method of killing themselves that is readily to hand. A farmer is almost certain to have a gun. The chances are, he will use it, and so would other people if firearms in this country were freely available; in some American states the numbers of suicides by means of firearms is ninety per cent. People in high-rise flats are more likely to jump from a great height than people who live in bungalows, although of course anyone can climb over the top of a suspension bridge if they wish. On the other hand, only car owners will gas themselves in the garage or deliberately crash on the M1. On

[5] *The Waste Land* (New York, 1922).

the whole, men favour hanging. Twice as many women as men drown themselves. Fear of pain and possible injury rather than death does not seem to deter; in 1983, 263 people threw themselves under trains but only 212 were killed.

It has to be emphasized that no one knows exactly how many people commit suicide for the simple reason that not every suicide can be proven. Almost every hanging is self-evidently suicide, but not every overdose or drowning, and many coroners are extremely reluctant to bring in a verdict of suicide if the evidence can possibly be stretched to justify a verdict of death by misadventure. A coroner's court is seldom a scene of levity at the best of times; those who have been bereaved and are compelled to attend, often in the knowledge that a post mortem has been carried out on someone they loved, are often protected from the further anguish of a suicide verdict unless the evidence is overwhelming, even though the coroner has no doubt in his own mind that suicide has occurred. Dr Douglas Chambers sits as coroner for the Inner North District of Greater London, and his courtroom any day is fairly typical of coroners' courts throughout the country, with public benches taken up by two elderly ladies, a middle-aged couple, a small girl and two well-dressed men who turn out to be a pathologist and a surgeon waiting to give evidence. There is a police officer to swear in the witnesses; two press reporters disinterestedly scribble at a table below the coroner's chair, and ugly strip lighting harshly illuminates a scene of quietly and efficiently conducted gloom. Dr Chambers has some very definite and forthright views on suicide. 'It is a subject,' he says, 'more full of loopholes than any other. For example, the law insists on a standard of proof for suicide that is effectively the proof in homicide, because you are in fact trying a person after their death for committing what was a capital offence. So when relatives don't like a verdict of suicide, and the judges are concerned with an appeal, they are much given to telling coroners how stupid they are. Now, we're not stupid. You know damn well when a man's done himself in. But if he hasn't done it in a way approved by their lordships we dare not say so. So coroners are often reluctant to bring in a verdict of suicide because of the possibility of an appeal. Nobody wants to be taken apart by the divisional court. I would certainly agree with the assertion that there are more suicides than are recorded. Roughly speaking, in my area I return a verdict of suicide in about one-third of the cases where I am quite convinced it is suicide.

'I've done two inquests today and neither are going to figure in the suicide statistics. There was a chap dragged out of the Thames, rotting, so there's no diet left and we can't even establish a cause of death. It may just have been alcohol. But he'd lost his job, he'd been drinking too heavily, he hadn't any money, and he ends up in the river. No witnesses to his going in, and a cause of death that is unascertainable. Open verdict. The other was a chap, drink again, no previous threats, lots of history of illness, on blood pressure tablets, for some reason takes ten times the level of the drug prescribed. He was married and really his troubles were all due to drink. He's a chap with drink who's taken an overdose of tablets. If you return suicide in these circumstances the judges will just turn round and say, "Look, we would hold that his judgement was so clouded by alcohol that he couldn't know what he was doing, and thus could not hold the intent." So I said it was misadventure. That's an accident, so it goes down as an accidental death. Which it may well be. I don't believe it for one minute, but that's just a gut feeling. I've been challenged on this, but there's no doubt about it, all overdoses are suicidal. To be honest, the system is bizarre in the extreme, and that's a mild comment.'

With limited means at their disposal, it is, however, the prevention of suicide whenever possible rather than arguments about the number of suicides that take place in which the Samaritans are interested. They do not act entirely without personal experience. 'The suicide rate among volunteers is very high,' says David Evans. 'Certainly higher than the average for the population. It doesn't necessarily mean they are all very disturbed. It could mean they are more sensitive, and more aware, and a lot of people who tend to get depressed are people who are very good at giving support to others. I don't say you have to be suicidal to be a Samaritan but it isn't a bar. Any person can be suicidal, given the right situation and circumstances. Suicides are not a peculiar group of people. Suicide is endemic in the human condition. It is the one thing we have. We can do it.'

In May 1982 a volunteer in the Canterbury branch committed suicide. 'Those of you who have experienced a similar unhappy experience will understand the feelings of incredulity, guilt, shock, grief and anger which affected every volunteer in varying degrees,' one of his friends wrote in the *Samaritan* a few months later. She said that the kind of questions being asked were, 'Why didn't somebody notice?' 'Why didn't he talk to me?' 'What's the use of calling ourselves Samaritans if this sort of thing happens in our midst?' Many were trying to come to terms with their own feelings of failure at not 'interpreting the signs which, in retrospect, were so obvious.' She ended her article by saying, 'Some of us feel he will not have died in vain if as a result we all become more sensitive and caring Samaritans, in so far as we ask those who come to us in a crisis about suicide. But even in our branch this is still not being done on every occasion. How many more people have to take their own lives before we all ask that vital question which always opens up the possibility of talking about suicidal feelings?'

On Good Friday in 1984 a former director of a Samaritan branch (he was also a former parish priest) slit his throat. He had frequently spoken of his wish to die, and was discovered by his son, a volunteer at central London, who commented afterwards, 'He was not the first Samaritan to kill himself and it is unfortunately unlikely that he will be the last.' And he went on to echo the words of the general secretary: 'Those of us who kill ourselves do not do it because we are Samaritans, nor are the rest of us to blame, although inevitably it sometimes seems like that at the time. It is just that those whose nature is sensitive and caring are more likely to become Samaritans, and because of their nature they are more at risk from depression. This does not make them bad Samaritans when they are not depressed. One of the many supportive letters my mother received was from a former client who said my father had saved his life by giving him love, and empathizing with him in his depression.'

A questionnaire presented at a regional conference in 1986 produced some fairly startling results. Out of 181 volunteers from branches throughout the South West who were asked if they had at any time felt suicidal, twenty-one men and fifty-three women said they had. All but one of the men said it would have helped if someone had asked them, but only thirty-two of the women thought it would. Three of the men admitted they had made a suicide attempt, as opposed to twenty of the women. In percentage terms, 40.9 had felt suicidal, of whom 12.7 had attempted suicide. There is no reason to believe that such a questionnaire would not produce similar results in other regions, and they certainly seem to indicate that Samaritans are far more vulnerable to suicide than the population as a whole. They also illuminate most interestingly the disparity between successful male and female suicides. Two and a half times more female Samaritans than male had felt suicidal, while nationally, twice as many men as women commit suicide, suggesting perhaps that women somehow get on top of their problems more successfully than men. Again, far fewer women than men thought they needed to talk about their problems, a further indication, perhaps, of their superior ability to cope.

When on duty, Samaritan volunteers have at their elbow a check-list of signs that indicate a person may be in danger of committing suicide. Some people of course give no hint at all, committing suicide almost on the spur of the moment. A teenager, on the other hand, although many act on impulse, may well start giving away treasured possessions. If everyone who suffered from depression, bereavement, addiction to the bottle, loneliness, financial worries and insomnia committed suicide there would hardly be anyone left alive, but any suicidal indicators taken in conjunction with a call to the Samaritans, in itself a cry for help, need to be taken seriously. If people want to die badly enough they will succeed; an entire cargo of slaves managed to strangle themselves in the hold of a Spanish galleon despite the fact that space was so limited they were compelled to hang themselves squatting. But a great many suicides succeed almost by chance, and enough people who recover from a suicide attempt eventually express a preference for being alive rather than dead to make a continual attempt to save life worth while. In many ways it is the failed suicide who suffers more than anyone, having 'failed' in life and again in ending it. There is a feeling they have somehow come back from the dead, a ghoulish thought in itself, and often they themselves feel they have come back to face not sympathy but judgement. What many were seeking, usually through overdosing or gassing, was a temporary escape from intolerable pressures, a way of being dead without dying, the bliss of a long, deep sleep without emotional pain. Their first conscious realization on recovering may well be that after all nothing has really changed, that the emotional pain will recur, that because the attempt was a failure it needs to be repeated successfully; and many people who survive a suicide attempt will tell you that after falling at the first hurdle, the worst is somehow over and after that it feels much, much easier. Young people who have not yet learned to cope with anger and frustration, who have no experience of adult freedom by which to judge what they sense to be the ensnared, claustrophobic and pointless world of the adolescent, are particularly prone to carry out what John Eldrid has described as 'an aggressive act against Mother-Father'. However, he says, 'the rejected boy or girl remains deeply emotionally involved with the parent. If this love and affection over the years is not accepted, they feel despair leading to depression. Behind depression there is lot of anger. Freud would say when you attack yourself you are attacking the bad parent. There is a lot of anger around and more interest in death than sleep. Death is seen as a kind of mystical deliverance. Many suicide attempts follow a row with the parents. Mistakenly it may seem the bad feelings can be patched up, sorted out, when in actual fact the row confirms the prolonged feelings of rejection.'

At the best of times, the death of a child is almost unbearable; to lose a child by suicide scarcely bears thinking about. Not surprisingly, for on the whole young people do not die, the most common cause of death among the young after accidents and cancer is suicide. Following a television programme *The Shadow of Suicide* shown on BBC 2 on 20 January 1986, in which three families who had each lost a child by suicide talked of their experience, 258 people who had also been bereaved through suicide rang in, of whom fifty-nine had lost a child. The parents of boys and girls who kill themselves must rate as the most distressing victims of all. Many others, like the drivers of locomotives and underground trains, are totally innocent victims, whose experience of being used in a suicide is one that often leaves a scar for life.[6] We also tend to employ people to pick up the pieces on our behalf, sometimes quite literally. The young police officer called to the scene when someone has jumped from a window, possibly impaling themselves on a row of spikes, has the gruesome task of inspecting the body, calling an ambulance and perhaps even breaking the news to relatives. Then he is usually expected to go straight back on the beat and be cheerful to everyone. Someone who deals with suicide every day, far more frequently in fact than any Samaritan, is a coroner's officer. One such, who volunteered for the job after eighteen years in the police force, and has been attached to his present coroner's court for the past seven years, explains his motives and his work:

'The reason I volunteered was because it gives me a social life I hadn't had for eighteen years. Now I work basically from nine to five. I think most of us get fed up with shift work. Apart from that, it's interesting. It's terrible to say that death is interesting, but it is. Over the years you are asked to do what we call death messages, to inform next of kin, and I suppose over the years you acquire an ability to talk to people. If a policeman can't talk to people he can't do the job. I mean, if you're in an alley with a big lout, if you can't talk your way out of trouble then you've had it. Last year I dealt with 356 deaths, of which fifty-eight

[6] Some train drivers claim to have been involved in as many as a dozen suicides, but in 1983 the Criminal Injuries Compensation Board ceased to consider compensation claims from train drivers arising from suicide incidents. The matter is currently under review.

resulted in inquests. That means almost all of those were suicides. I get very few road traffic accidents. I would guess that the youngest was about twenty-two. When I go to talk to the family I get the impression they know it was suicide. There's not many times it comes as a shock. The lifestyle has given them an indication. But they'd rather there wasn't a suicide verdict. Certainly in the Jewish community there's a stigma attached to suicide.

'My wife has said that I'm bloody miserable since I've done this job, that I've changed. I always think that the average copper, the ordinary bloke on the beat, hasn't got a great deal of brain, and if I thought very carefully about these cases then I think I'd probably commit suicide myself. So really I think we become very cynical, don't we? We laugh at death, policemen do. There's the old police joke about going round with the death message. You know, you've got to go round and do this death message, and you knock at the door and say, "Are you the widow Brown?" I mean, that's a policeman's joke. You're going to break the news to a wife that her husband's dead and you knock at the door and say, "Are you the widow Brown?" Now, this is funny to a policeman, but it certainly wouldn't be funny to an outsider.

'Nothing really bothers me. I don't think it does. I'm not bothered going into a post mortem room and seeing a chap being carved about. I'm not bothered when a woman comes in here and says her three-month-old baby's died. It doesn't bother me. I don't lose any sleep. But I think the one thing that upsets me is when I get an old girl or an old boy come in here, and they've sold up and they're going to move to Suffolk for their retirement. Now that does get to me.

'Don't get me wrong, we do give the public sympathy. We've got letters here saying thanks, and a couple of women have sent me a pen with my name on. I think we can appreciate how they feel, and I like to think that we do our best to console them. We are concerned. But if you ask, do I take it home with me, No. Once they've walked out of the door, then that's it.

'There's one case I did get upset over. One of our undertakers that we deal with, he phoned me up one morning and he was obviously distressed on the phone, and I thought he was having a bit of a joke at first, and then I realized he was crying, and he apologized for the state he was in. Then he said, "My son's committed suicide." It was the son I was concerned about. He was such a smashing fellow. It was out of the blue, but he had been a bit of a depressed lad at times, although he held down a job. He had a girl. The girl threw him up, so the son went out, hired a garage, got all the equipment needed, a professional job. Now that really upset me.

'I always think we're actors here. You always say to people, "I appreciate how you feel, dear", but we don't have a clue. And when Brian phoned and he was in tears we hadn't a clue what he must have been feeling. On many occasions we tell people what they've got to do, and you think, I'm wasting my time telling you because it isn't going to register, is it?'

If one excludes unofficial cases of euthanasia practised by some doctors, amounting in most cases to no more than a controlled withdrawal of life-supporting drugs in cases of terminal illness where a peaceful death, perhaps from pneumonia or some other natural cause, would normally ensue in the absence of 'scientific progress', few people in our day have ever actively assisted in a planned and deliberate suicide, and fewer still have been prepared to record their experience. But Betty Rollin was actually recruited to help her own mother to die. At the age of seventy-six Ida Rollin had developed inoperable ovarian cancer. She endured two horrific courses of chemotherapy, as a result of which her hair fell out, she lost control of her bowels and she started vomiting so much she could not even retain medication. She gained one year's remission. When the tumour and the pain recurred, Mrs Rollin decided that she wished to die while she still had the strength to swallow. She asked her daughter to investigate how best to end her life and to acquire the necessary drugs.

'The kind of suicide I experienced is very unusual', Betty Rollin explains. 'I was there. I can imagine how people must feel when someone they care about kills themselves and was alone at that moment. So that for me it was so different. We shared it. There was no shock. Well, there was, because I never really imagined this could happen. It was amazing. My mother acted in death as she had done in life. That's what makes my memory of it so good, she died in exactly the same spirit as she had done everything. She was organized. She knew that she had to be calm. She was extremely rational. It wasn't that she was a brilliant woman or an extremely intellectual woman, but she was very rational, and that was her guiding strength. One reason I think she felt so calm was because she knew she was going to be able to escape. When she knew she was going to be able to do this thing she almost physically changed. It was such a tremendous relief to her to know she wasn't trapped any longer. Just knowing that the pills were there, that this was going to happen, gave her such a sense of relief. And she felt confident because my husband and I were with her.

'She didn't want us to be there at first, but we insisted, and she was awfully careful about saying we mustn't touch this and we mustn't touch that. No one ever thought there would be a book[7] describing all this, and we all felt, well, who will ever know? And she had a lot of confidence in us. She knew we weren't stupid.

'Suicide is a word that has come to mean something really ghastly. When you say the word suicide you think of depressed people who do violence to themselves. It has every connotation of something really awful. So in a sense there should be another word for what my mother did. But I do think of it as suicide because there's no other word. There is a fancy word that somebody thought up which I think is rather pretentious, "self-deliverance", and I don't like that either, so I'm stuck with the word suicide. But then, I have to say quickly that I do think my mother's suicide was a good suicide. I think there is such a thing. And I think this death of hers illustrates that about as well as anything could possibly illustrate it. She had a good

[7] *Last Wish* by Betty Rollin (Viking, 1986).

life, she appreciated her life, she felt that it was over and she escaped at a moment, looking back on it, which seemed just the right moment, before once again she would be unable to ingest anything. She escaped as herself, and moreover, because of my own – dare I say it – good research, the medication she took afforded her this release painlessly, swiftly.

'I get hundreds and hundreds of letters – I almost dread the mail – about these ghastly deaths. Oh, do I hear about these deaths people go through! You can't imagine what people go through. The tone is always, "I wouldn't have believed it could be like this. My mother was such a strong person, such a vital person . . ." And when I think of *my* mother, I feel so good about it. People often say to me – well, like this woman on the breakfast show yesterday – "You *must* feel guilty." On the contrary, I would feel guilty if I had not stood by her.

'What I did was legally just over the line, that is to say, my mother was in fact able to take the pills herself, and mostly what I did was just stand by her. I didn't actually assist her. The assistance I gave her was really research, emotional support and that sort of thing. And of course I did have to purchase the pills. My mother was bedridden. The other reason I didn't get prosecuted when my book was first published in the States was that the district attorney in New York obviously didn't want to prosecute me. It was the sort of thing where an individual running for office might have tried to pursue this if pressure were brought to bear, but that didn't happen. The prosecutors don't like these cases. I mean, they don't like to come after people like me. There are a lot of bad people in New York, where I live, there are dope peddlars and criminals of all sorts and they don't want a case like that.

'I do have a certain sympathy with the law, you may be surprised to hear, because I don't think we can have a society in which people kill other people. That's not a good way to do it. You will have sons and daughters pretending to be kind when they really want the inheritance. I think the law has a real problem here. And yet something has to be done. In Holland a patient like my mother could have asked a physician for a shot.[8] This idea that painkillers do it all is just baloney. It's not true. If the pain can be arrested, fine, but if not, I think suicide should be an option. But I don't think most people would do it. I think the tendency in life is to live. But my mother had the option. To be in a room with a door – and this was my mother's own metaphor – that's locked from the outside, that's imprisonment. And that's a terrible feeling. Can you imagine what it would be like to be locked in and not to know where the key is? It must be just hell. If you know where the key is you don't necessarily use it, but think what it does for your state of mind to know that you *can* use it.

'I know about depressed people, and there's all the difference in the world between their sort of suicide and what my mother did. My mother wasn't depressed at all. And I did not need to write a book as some kind of therapy. I never had a bad moment about it. I needed to write it because I was so proud of her. I felt that what she had done was so remarkable. I couldn't get it out of my head. I just thought, my God, I'm so glad I'm a writer, because I can write the story, and what a thing she did, my little mother. But as it turned out it was horrible to write, because I had to live through the whole business of her sickness again, which was not enjoyable.

'It was a sad thing, and I wish she hadn't suffered as much as she did, but her death was a great death. Her suffering was over. It worked. She just went to sleep. So she had the kind of death that cancer patients of that kind don't usually have. And when I think what might have been! Once I was convinced this really was what she wanted, to me that was what mattered – that the person gets what the person wants. Would I want to be master of my own fate? Of course I would. There was no doubt in my mind that she wanted it. So it was a question of going along with her wish, her last wish. And that really had nothing to do with

[8] Euthanasia has not in fact yet been legalized in Holland, although it is known to be carried out and a blind eye is generally turned. It was to a doctor in Holland that Betty Rollin was obliged to telephone from the States for advice about appropriate lethal drugs for her mother.

what my opinion was. But it made perfect sense to me. And you see, she never wavered. It wasn't as if it was a bad day. There could be no doubt. And another thing; our relationship was so good. If our relationship hadn't been so good I think I might have doubted myself.'

After nineteen years as a volunteer, a Samaritan who lives in Kent experienced the ultimate horror, the death by suicide of her own son. 'My whole life,' she says, 'had gone by without knowing of anyone killing themselves apart from suicides in the Samaritan movement, and one then has a different picture altogether. Christopher would have been twenty-three the day after he died. He was a very clever boy – adopted. Caroline, his adopted sister, was then twenty. As a boy he read books on chess when he went to bed instead of story books. Much to my husband's annoyance, he could beat him at chess when he was seven. He had a mathematical brain, and did extremely well. He took the 11+, and went to grammar school. He was the sort of boy who only had to be told something once, and he knew it. If anyone repeated it, he didn't want to listen. So at about the age of fifteen he started to opt out altogether. Being so clever, he must have been very frustrated, and I think it was partly our fault for not realizing what was going on.

'Eventually he met a girl and all I can say is they loved each other very dearly but they couldn't live with one another. They would have the most terrific fights, and you'd think that must be the end, but the next day one of them would be ringing the other. It was a little bit wearing at home! One night Christopher and the girl had a terrific row, and then they were back together. But then they talked together very seriously, and agreed that although they loved each other they would have to part because quite frankly they were tearing each other into little pieces. And so they parted in love rather than hate. And that final parting was something I don't think he could stand. It was a rejection that he couldn't take.

'If I can go back to when he was adopted, at nine weeks, although most children want to know where they came from, Christopher could never bear to be told that he was adopted.

NOT LIKE AN ORDINARY DEATH

We did tell him, of course, but he didn't want to know anything about it. And I can only think, that night, he felt that was the end because he'd been completely rejected. He did say to one or two of his friends that he wanted to die, and what was the quickest way, but quite frankly they took no notice.

'We'd gone to bed. Christopher came home, and I heard him come up to his room and shut the door. Normally I never need to get up in the night, but for some unknown reason, I needed to that particular night. This was only a few minutes after Christopher had gone into his room, and passing the door I heard a sound that I thought was sobbing. I knocked, and there was no reply. I went in, and he was already unconscious, which didn't seem right as he'd only just that moment shut the door. He was fully clothed on the bed but he had removed his shoes. It's silly how you think of these things afterwards. No shoes.

'I called my husband, Peter, and we got an ambulance and they took him to the hospital, with Peter. Because of my Samaritan experience I thought, well, in a moment they're going to ring up and say he'll be home in so many hours, he'd have been pumped out and all the rest of it. But they phoned to say it was more serious than perhaps I realized, his heart had stopped. They put him on a life machine and a few minutes later Peter phoned to say could I come. They tried all sorts of things. They worked terribly hard for about five hours, and then told us that he'd died. It was cyanide poisoning.

'Although people say you bite on cyanide and you're dead at once, you're not. That was something else I learned. This really caused my husband great heartbreak, because he's a very keen amateur photographer, and in his cupboard was a bottle of cyanide. We handed it straight over, of course, but the police said it was very old and hadn't been used for years. They didn't think the bottle had been opened, so we didn't know where he had got it from.

'You are devastated at the time. You have to leave the hospital and go home. And then I got terribly angry! I was furious! Peter wasn't, and still isn't, but I am. Christopher knew that I would be the one to find him, if it was not that night then the next morning, but of course one also realizes that when a person is at that pitch of wanting to die they can't think of anyone else but themselves. I've heard Samaritans say to a caller, "Have you got a family? What would they feel like if you died?" But it's useless to say that, absolutely useless. But I didn't know that before. I thought, give them any little thing to hold them back. But that's one thing I would never say to anyone now. If they want to live they have to live for themselves.

'The next thing I heard was that the girlfriend was saying, "Oh, isn't it dreadful, he died for me." My daughter was absolutely wonderful. She supported the girlfriend, because I couldn't. I did at the hospital, at the time. I rang her, because I thought she should be there, but I couldn't support her after that. Caroline still sees her, but I'm not nice enough to take her under my wing. I suppose I've got to have someone to blame, and my son's not here, so I can blame her.

'Whether I shall ever be able to forgive my son I don't know. I can't see it at the moment, because I look at the hurt that's been done to other people, to Peter, and to Caroline, who was away at the time, which was even worse. And that's when the Samaritans were so superb, because they got in touch with her for me, so that she wouldn't suddenly get a policeman knocking on the door. She was in London, in digs, without a telephone. I phoned central London and this dear man who I'd never spoken to before went on and on and on. "Now, are you sure you're all right. Now, is everything going to be all right?" And afterwards I said to Peter, "He bloody well befriended me!" Which was awful because he did everything he should have done, but I was dying to get off the phone. That's another bitter lesson I've learned. If people really do want to go, let them get off the phone.

'Then of course there was the awful wait for the inquest. You just sit and wait. The first thing I remember was the number of bouquets of flowers that kept coming, and I said, "It's like a perishing funeral parlour in here," and it was, but people were so kind. We had over 200 letters and these had to be answered.

My own branch was superb, even down to ordinary things like someone bringing a bag of scones with jam and cream, so that I didn't have to bake. One character made the most gorgeous soup. Things like that helped. Endless telephone calls, endless letters. Then I think the hardest thing was to go back on duty, which I did after about six weeks. I went back on duty first of all with a very special friend, so that was good, but at first it was hard meeting people. Then I thought, what if there's a youngster on the line saying, "I want to die", that sort of thing? It didn't happen straight away but it has since. Being able to talk to my fellow Samaritans was an absolute bonus, because people will cross the street rather than talk to you. And they do. I couldn't believe it. People I had known for years were actually crossing the road rather than speak to me.

'Before this happened I thought I had learned it all off pat, from a book. Oh golly! I've changed my mind about suicide, in a way. I always thought, oh God, how dreadful, those poor people, but I think I feel a little now how selfish they are, but that's just me. I know in my mind they can't think about others, but I still feel it's a cowardly act. In preparation classes years ago we used to talk about Captain Oates walking off into the snow and how brave, the others were suffering and they needed the food and all the rest of it, but that's not true, he went because he bloody well couldn't face it any more. It wasn't an act of bravery. It was quicker to go that way. But my ideas have changed on so many things. I took a Samaritan call only this morning, about a seventeen-year-old boy who *will* stay in bed all day and doesn't do this and won't do that, and I couldn't help thinking – in fact, I did actually say – "Of course, he may be staying in bed because he can't face the outside, it may not just be laziness, and so he does need help," and before, I may have thought, it's time he got out of bed.

'I think it's made me a little more tolerant, although I did say I would never grumble at Caroline again, and within a week I was shouting my head off. You wonder, could you have helped? Then there's the guilt. If only one of his friends had phoned and said Christopher is in a bit of a state tonight. And then I think, one can only say it was his choice. This is very much a Samaritan thing. If he had waited until the next day it might have been better. But it may not have been. So he may not have had a choice. But if it was something he decided to do, who am I to say he shouldn't have? And we say that about our callers. It's their choice. But it's not something I would wish on anyone else. It's not the same as any other bereavement. One person came up to me not very long ago and asked, "Are you beginning to live it down?" The stigma is still there. It's not like an ordinary death. If Christopher had died from a disease people's attitudes would have been quite different.'

It seems appropriate that the last word should rest with someone who attempted to commit suicide and failed. Pat is thirty-one, married, with a six-year-old son. She lives in a rural town in Surrey and works, as anonymously as she can, in London. She finds it hard to articulate her thoughts, and harder still to come to terms with her inherent dislike of sex, the reason for the failure of her first, unconsummated, marriage and the cause of inevitable tensions in her second. Born in Canada, she was brought up in Ireland, being readmitted to the Catholic Church at her mother's request when she was sixteen, after her parents' divorce.

'When I was sixteen and living in Belfast I was going out with a paratrooper, so the IRA rang my place of work and said if I didn't leave I'd be shot. So the next day I got transferred to England. I didn't know anybody. I was living in a hostel, and I was really very, very lonely. So I went to see the Samaritans, although at first I hardly said anything. I found it really difficult to talk about things. Eventually I began to see the same person once a week, and she's now my son's godmother. Then I got married, when I was eighteen. My husband was twenty-four and very devoted to his mother. We were married for about three years but we never went to bed together. I know now I got married purely because I was lonely.

'Then I took up psychiatric nursing. I left my husband and moved into a nurses' home, but he came back and beat me up and everything. Four or five months after I'd walked out, well, I didn't ring the Samaritans, I just did it. I broke a milk bottle. I didn't even think about it. Now I've got this massive scar. I actually cut tendons and everything. It was lunch-time, in the nurses' home. I felt that nobody wanted me. I was terribly, terribly lonely. I mean, it was all right going to work and putting on an act, but I'd been thinking about it for a long time. I'd done various things like taking tablets but I never really took enough, but that day I didn't even think about it, I just slashed my wrist. Somebody found me and got me to hospital. When I came round I couldn't believe what I'd actually done to myself. It was a massive cut, and I'd fallen on top of the milk bottle afterwards and managed to do my knee as well! I was in hospital for four weeks, in a psychiatric unit.

'Anyway, I got married a second time. It's quite a happy marriage, but Christmas before last I really, really got depressed. I couldn't figure out why. But I always have this problem with sex, you see. I was getting depressed because we kept rowing, over sex, and I'd taken an overdose and I just slept and slept and slept. It wasn't a serious suicide attempt. If I'd wanted to I'd have done what I did before. That's when I went back to the Samaritans. I just don't like sex, but I've since discovered why. It's because of my father. He abused me when I was eight, and again when I was fifteen. I couldn't figure out why it was that every time he came to see me, which he did every three years or so, I absolutely dreaded it. I just couldn't stand being anywhere near him. It was my mother who said, "Well, it's because of what he did to you." She knew. He's been married five times. I've got one real sister and I've got a *lot* of step-brothers and step-sisters! My real sister was actually raped by my father's brother, when she was fourteen. Another uncle, when I was fourteen and he was fifteen, did the same thing to me. I remember all of it. My sister was in the other room. I don't think my father sees anything wrong with what he did. He's got no moral attitude towards anything. His wife rang me the other day and told me he's sleeping with two other women now. He just couldn't care less about women. When I was about eight we lived in one room, in a slum, frankly, and my father would take me shopping at Harrods. He's very well-off. He's a heart surgeon.

'With my father, I can remember what happened before, and after. I can't remember what actually happened at the time.

'When I first saw my present Samaritan befriender I couldn't talk about anything. It takes a long time to trust somebody anyway. The things that have happened to me, I wouldn't tell to anyone. I can understand it, but I don't think I've really come to terms with it. I keep thinking, maybe he didn't do it. But I know he did. There's no point in trying to make excuses. My husband finds it very hard to believe. I've been accepted by his family but they don't know anything about me. Nobody knows anything about me. I don't like people to know. I just wish I could take away the first twenty-four years of my life. In the summer I have to wear long sleeves, because people can see my scar, and people have said to me, "What's that?" and of course I'm not going to tell anybody what it is. It will never go.

'I always think, if people knew about me they wouldn't want to know me. There's a stigma attached, particularly to suicide. When I left nursing I went to the Department of Health and Social Security and the man actually said I should be registered disabled. I'll never forget that. I walked out, and I thought, never again will I go back. I'll find a job some other way. But incest isn't such a stigma because people don't believe it anyway. But there'd be no point in me making it up. If you met my father you'd understand.

'I couldn't have gone through it all without the Samaritans. They were the only people. There wasn't anybody else.'

SAMARITAN PRINCIPLES
AND PRACTICES

Principles

1 The primary aim of the Samaritans is to be available at any hour of the day or night to befriend those passing through personal crisis and in imminent danger of taking their own lives.

2 The Samaritans also seek to alleviate human misery, loneliness, despair and depression by listening to and befriending those who feel that they have no one else to turn to who would understand and accept them.

3 A caller does not lose the freedom to make his own decisions, including the decision to take his own life, and is free to break contact at any time.

4 The fact that a person has asked the help of the Samaritans, together with everything he has said, is completely confidential within the organization unless permission is freely given by the caller for all or a part of such information to be communicated to someone outside the organization. A Samaritan volunteer is not permitted to accept confidences if a condition is made that not even the director should be informed of them.

5 Samaritan volunteers, in befriending callers, will be guided and actively supported by experienced leaders who will have the advice, when required, of professional consultants.

6 In appropriate cases, the caller will also be invited to

consider seeking professional help in such fields as medical and social work, and material help from other agencies.

7 Samaritan volunteers are forbidden to impose their own convictions or to influence callers in regard to politics, philosophy or religion.

Practices

1 Samaritan volunteers are carefully selected and prepared by the local branch in which they are to serve.

2 The Samaritans are available at all hours to callers, and may be contacted (anonymously, if desired) by telephone or personal visit or by letter.

3 When a caller is believed to be in danger of suicidal action, the Samaritan is particularly encouraged to ask the caller's permission for contact to be maintained during the crisis.

4 Samaritans offer longer-term befriending of callers when appropriate, while recognizing that the branch may from time to time have to set limits.

5 Samaritans listen to those concerned about the welfare of another person and, if satisfied that the third person is despairing, depressed or suicidal, may discreetly offer befriending.

6 Samaritans are normally known to callers only by a fore-name, and contacts by callers made only through the branch centre.

7 Samaritan branches are banded together in a legally consti-tuted Association whose Council of Management represents all the branches, and reserves to itself the appointment of the person in charge of each branch.

INDEX

Aberdeen, 27, 29
Aberystwyth, 40
Abortion, 73–4
Addenbrookes Hospital, 163–6
Age Concern, 126
AIDS, 93, 128
Alcoholics Anonymous, 128
Alvarez, A., 203–4, 206
Armson, Simon, 42, 92–3, 118,
   132, 196–7
Ashford, 39
Ashington, 40
Assistant General Secretary, *see*
   Armson, Simon
Association of Suicidology, 28
Audience Selection, 188

Ballantine, Sheila, 117
Ballymena, 40
Banbury, 40
Bangor (Northern Ireland), 39
Bangor (North Wales), 40, 53
Bank of England, 193–4
Barnett, Lady, fn 126
Barnsley, 39
Barrow, 39
Basildon, 33
Basingstoke, 33
Bath, 32
Beaumont Society, fn 81, 128
Beaumont Trust, 81
Befrienders International, The
   Samaritans Worldwide, 39

Befrienders, The, 38
Belfast, 27, 29
Bexley, 33
Birmingham, 29, 42, 44, 140, 152
Blackburn, 33
Blackie, Professor James, 26
Blackpool, 40
Blind volunteers, 71–2, 154
Bognor Regis, 39, 48
Bolton, 32
Bombay, 27, 29, 38
Boston (Massachusetts), 184
Bournemouth, 27–9, 152
Bracknell, 39
Bradford, 27
Brazil, 38, fn 39
Brent, 33
Bridgend, 39
Brierley Hill, 39
Brighton (also Hove), 29, 33, 195
Bristol, 32
British Petroleum, 42
Bruce, Mary, 24
Burt, Jean, 22–3, 26, 32, 34, 75,
   92
Bury, 40
Bury St Edmunds, 39
Buxton, 40
Byron, 6th Lord, 204

Caithness, 40
Calcutta, 38
Cambridge, 29, 163, 176

Cancer Research, 188–9
Can I Help You?, 97
Canterbury, 33, fn 166, 198, 213
Cardiff, 32
Carlisle, 33, 53
Carrington, Dora, 203
Cato, 203
Central London, 18, 19, 22, 26, 29, 39, 45, 125, 135, 139, 140, 150–3, 173, 184, 185, 191, 213, 224
Chambers, Douglas, 211, 212
Chelmsford, 32
Cheltenham, 32
Chester, 33
Chesterfield, 39
Chiltons, The, 33
Citizens Advice Bureaux, 191
Cleopatra, Queen, 203
Colchester, 32
Coleraine, 39
Company of Samaritans, 21
Compassionate Friends, 79
Confidentiality, 12, 21, 24, 25, 44, 60, 107, 132, 175, 189
Cork, 41
Council of Management, 29, 30, 34, 43, 44, 49, 51–4, 90, 91, 230
Coventry, 32
Craigavon, 40
Crane, Hart, 203
Crewe, 32
Croydon, 29
CRUSE, 77

Daily Mirror, 17
Darlington, 33
Day, George, 88
Delhi, 39
de Mel, The Most Revd Jacob, 39
Derby, 29
Derry, 40
de Vigny, Alfred, 207
Dickens, Monica, 185
Dominica, Mother Frances, 59
Doncaster, 32
Dublin, 39
Dumfries, 40

Dundee, 29
Dunfermline, 33
Durham, 39
Durkheim, Emile, 206

Ealing, 35, 39
Eastbourne, 33
Edinburgh, 26, 29, 37
Eldrid, The Revd John, 19, 23–5, 125, 126, 135, 136, 152, 153, 172–4, 184, 215
Elgar, Sir Edward, Bt, 119
Elgin, 39
Eliot, T. S., 210
Elizabeth II, Queen, 15
Ellerby, Nick, 176–9
Ellis, Sir William, 204
Enfield, 40
Ennis, 40
Epicurus, 201
Esquirol, Jean, 204
European League for Medical Hygiene, 28
Evans, The Revd David, 11, 21, 34, 41, 42, 45–8, 50, 127, 212, 213
Executive Committee, 11, 27, 33, 37, 43, 46, 53, 54, 57, 132, 195
Exeter, 32
EXIT, *see* Voluntary Euthanasia Society

Falkirk, 37
Farnborough, 40
Feeney, Vera, 42
Festival branch, 39, 180–2, 184
Flying Squad, 75–6, 114
Folkestone, 32, fn 166
Forum, 36
Fox, Richard, 24
Fraser, Lady Antonia, 12
Freud, Sigmund, 215

Galway, 40
Gay Switchboard, 84, 128
General Office, *see* Slough
General Secretary, *see* Evans, David

Gertler, Mark, 203
Glasgow, 27, 29
Gloucester, 41
Grantham, 40
Great Yarmouth, 33
Grimsby, 32
Guardian, 194, 197
Guernsey, 29
Guildford, 32
Gulbenkian Foundation, 26
Gwynedd, 40

Halifax, 29
Halliwell, Kenneth, 117
Hamilton, 41
Hancock, Tony, 203
Hannibal, 203
Hanwell Asylum, 204
Harding, Annetta, 198–9
Harrods, 45
Harrow, 33
Harrowgate, 40
Hartlepool, 39
Hastings, 32
Haverfordwest, 40, 53
Havering, 32
Help the Aged, 191
Hemingway, Ernest, 203
Henrik, HRH Prince, 119
Hereford, 39
Higginson, The Revd Basil, 33–4,
    41–2, 116, 129, 170, 171
Hillingdon, 39
Himmler, Heinrich, 96
Homosexuality (and
    homosexuals), 60, 64, 73, 80–1,
    83–7, 101, 111, 124, 128, 135,
    137, 175, 176, 182
Hong Kong, 27, 29, 38
Horsham, 39
Hospital Chaplaincy Council, 26
Hough, Charlotte, 198–200
Huddersfield, 33
Hull, 27, 29

Incest, 59, 135, 138, 227, 228
Inverness, 39
Ipswich, 32

Isle of Man, 40

Jersey, 27, 29
Jones, Jim, fn 207
Judas (Iscariot), 203

Karachi, 27, 29, 38
Keats, John, 204
Keble College, 15
Kent, HRH the Duchess of, 39,
    159
Kilmarnock, 33
King's Lynn, 33, 159
Kingston-on-Thames, 33
Kirkcaldy, 39
Koestler, Arthur, 203

Lahr, John, 117
Lancaster, 39
Leatherhead, 33
Leeds, 33
Leek, 33
Leicester, 32, 172
Lewisham, 33
Limerick, 40
Lincoln, 33, 146
Lincoln Theological College, 16
Liverpool, 27, 29, 172
Lowestoft, 33
Lowry, Malcolm, 203
Luton, 33
Lynch, Barbara, 189–94

Macclesfield, 32
Madge, Charles, 16
Maidstone, 33
Malaysia, 38
Manchester, 29, 33, 152
Mansfield, 39
Martyn, Roger, 19, 20
Masalyk, Jan, 203
Mass Observation, 16
Masturbation, 49, 73, 111, 112,
    136–8, 140–6, 183, 204
Matlock, 40
Maudsley Hospital, 24
M-calls, *see* Sex calls
Medway, 33, 87

Meikle, Mary, 19
MENCAP, 189
Mental Health Act, 1958, 28
Milton Keynes, 39
More, Sir Thomas, 201
Moult, Ted, 209
Munrow, David, 203

National Appeal, 189, 191–3
National Opinion Polls, 42, 188,
    194, 199
National Trust, 188
National Wildlife Fund, 188
Neilson, Donald, 44–5
Newbury, 40
Newcastle, 33
Newport, 33
Newport (Isle of Wight), 40
Newry, 39
News of the World, 33
Northallerton, 33
Northampton, 33
North Devon, 33
North Hertfordshire, 39
Northwich, 32
Norwich, 32, 38, 93–4, 172
Nottingham, 29

Oates, Lawrence, 202, 225
Odlum, Doris, 28–9, 37, 83
Okada, Yukiko, 207
Old Bailey, 199
Omagh, 40
Onan, 204
Orpington, 33
Orton, Joe, 117
Owen, Wilfred, 202–3
Oxfam, 188–9
Oxford, 32, 42

Pendle, 39
Persistent callers, 35, 114, 117,
    129, 130–3, 186
Perth, 39
Peterborough, 39
Picture Post, 16, 20
Pilgrim Trust, 41
Plath, Sylvia, 203

Plymouth, 39
Portsmouth, 27, 29
Preston, 39
Profumo Scandal, 16
Prosser, Vivian, 18
Putney, 33, 89

Rachels, James, 201
Ramsey, The Rt Revd & Rt Hon
    Lord, 16
Reading, 29, 38, 49, 83
Redbridge, 33
Reid, The Revd Canon Eric, 24–6
Reigate, 32
Retford, 39
Rhyl, 40
Robertson, Fyfe, 16
Rochdale, 33
Rollin, Betty, 218–22
Rollin, Ida, 218–22
Rotherham, 40
Royal National Institute for the
    Deaf, 188

Saatchi & Saatchi, 194–5
Salisbury, 29
Salisbury (Rhodesia), 27, 29
Salvation Army, The, 189
Samaritans in the 70s, The, 37
Samaritans, The, 29, 30
Samaritan, The, 16, 35, 38, 48, 71,
    80, 83, 87, 93, 116, 140, 147,
    159, 169, 194, 196–7, 213
Samaritan Week, 169
Save the Children Fund, The,
    188–9
Scarborough, 39
Schwarz, Oswald, fn 144
Scottish Borders, The, 40
Scottish Correspondence branch,
    39
Scunthorpe, 32
Seneca, 203
Sex calls, 35, 47–8, 82, 111–13,
    123, 136–46, 155, 183–7
Sheffield, 33
Shetland, 40, 151
Shrewsbury, 32, 42

Silent calls, 56, 134, 155
Singapore, 38
Sligo, 40
Slough, 12, 33, 41, 191
Society of Authors, 12
Socrates, 203
Solihull, 40
Southampton, 32
Southend, 33
South Korea, 38
Southport, 40
Sri Lanka, 39
Stafford, 32, 44
Standard, 198
Stockport, 40
Stoke-on-Trent, 29
St Stephen Walbrook, 17–23,
    25–6, 36, 39, 153
Suicide Act, 1961, 28
Suicide rates, 18, 29–32, 153–4,
    206–8, 210, 214
Suicide statistics, 203, 205–6, 210,
    211, 214
Sunday Chronicle, 18
Sunday Times, 199
Sunderland, 39, 150
Swansea, 33, 42
Swindon, 33

Tamworth, 40
Taunton, 39
Teesside, 33, 36
*Telephone Masturbators and How to
    Befriend Them*, 37, 140
Telford, 40, 42
Terrence Higgins Trust, 128
Third-party calls, 146–7
Thomas, Dylan, 201
Times, The, 163, 166, 208–9
TM-calls, *see* Sex calls
Torbay, 32
Transvestism, 81–3, 93, 111, 128
Truro, 39, 53
Tunbridge Wells, 33
Turing, Alan, 203
Tushingham, Rita, 133

Urban Programme, 150

Van Gogh, Vincent, 203
Varah, The Revd Prebendary
    Chad, birth, background and
    education, 15, 16; journalism,
    16–20; offered St Stephen
    Walbrook, 17; founds
    Samaritans, 17, 19–22, 24; sex
    talks, 25, 26–8, 36–7; made
    OBE, 36, 38; becomes president
    Befrienders International, 39;
    resigns, 39; receives Albert
    Schweitzer Medal, 39; 116, 140
Voluntary Euthanasia Society,
    189, 199

Wakefield, 39
Walpole, Horace, 203
Walsall, 33
Ware, 33
War on Want, 191
Warrington, 33
Waterford, 40
Watford, 33
Waugh, Evelyn, 125
West Midlands, 42
Weston-super-Mare, 39
Weybridge, 32, 149, 150
Weymouth, 39
Whitehaven, 33
Whiting, Norman, 90–4
Wigan, 39, 172
Winchester, 40, 195
Wolverhampton, 33
Woolf, Virginia, 203
Woolwich, 29
Worcester, 32
Worksop College, 15
Worshipful Company of Grocers,
    17, 23
Worthing, 33
Wren, Sir Christopher, 17

Yeovil, 39
York, 33
Young Callers and the Samaritans,
    172

Zambia, 38

Oil Strike North Sea

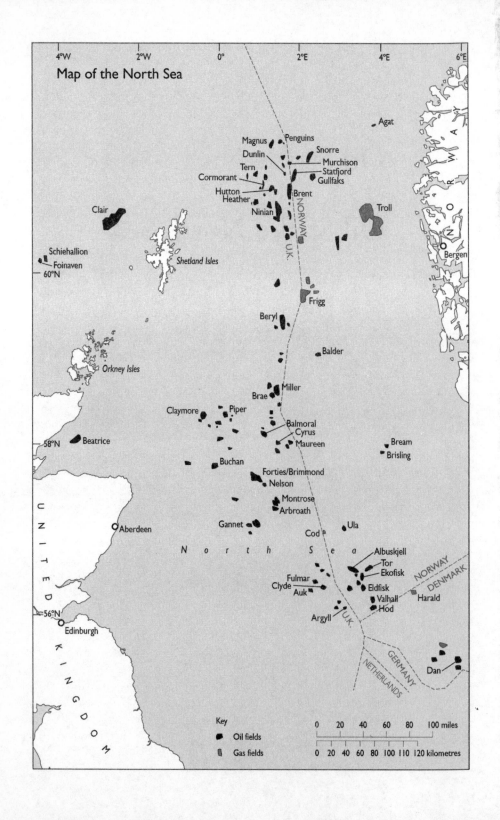

Map of the North Sea

4°W 2°W 0° 2°E 4°E 6°E

Agat

Magnus
Penguins
Dunlin   Snorre
Tern   Murchison
Cormorant   Statfjord
Hutton   Gullfaks
Heather   Brent
Ninian   Troll

Clair

Schiehallion
Foinaven
60°N

Shetland Isles

NORWAY
U.K.

NORWAY
Bergen

Frigg

Beryl

Balder

Orkney Isles

Miller
Brae
Claymore   Piper
Balmoral
Cyrus
Maureen   Bream
58°N Beatrice   Brisling

Buchan

Forties/Brimmond
Nelson

Montrose
Arbroath

Gannet
Cod   Ula

UNITED

Aberdeen

N   o   r   t   h   S   e   a

Albuskjell
Tor
Ekofisk

Fulmar   Eldfisk
Clyde   NORWAY
Auk   Valhall   DENMARK
Hod   Harald

56°N
Edinburgh   Argyll
U.K.

KINGDOM

GERMANY

NETHERLANDS

Dan

Key

Oil fields

Gas fields

0   20   40   60   80   100 miles

0 20 40 60 80 100 110 120 kilometres

Oil Strike North Sea

A first-hand history of North Sea oil

MIKE SHEPHERD

Luath Press Limited

EDINBURGH

www.luath.co.uk

First published 2015

ISBN: 978-1-910745-21-2

The author's right to be identified as author of this book
under the Copyright, Designs and Patents Act 1988 has been asserted.

The paper used in this book is recyclable. It is made from low-chlorine pulps produced in a
low-energy, low-emissions manner from renewable forests.

Printed and bound by ScandBook AB, Sweden

Typeset in 11 point Sabon by Main Point Books, Edinburgh

Map by Jim Lewis
Front endpaper image: oil rig platform
Back endpaper image: Aerial View of offshore jack-up drilling rig

To those who made it happen

Contents

Map of the North Sea 3

Acknowledgements 9

Preface by Diane Morgan 11

Introduction 13

Timeline 15

CHAPTER 1 Finding a North Sea Oil Field 17

CHAPTER 2 The First Oil Fields are Found 28

CHAPTER 3 Appraisal and Production 42

CHAPTER 4 Aberdeen 53

CHAPTER 5 Local Heroes 64

CHAPTER 6 New Challenges 72

CHAPTER 7 Offshore 81

CHAPTER 8 The Forties Field 89

CHAPTER 9 Big Money 100

CHAPTER 10 BP and Britoil 109

CHAPTER 11 Occidental and ELF 116

CHAPTER 12 Oil Reserves 124

CHAPTER 13 Out West 132

CHAPTER 14 The End of Oil 139

CHAPTER 15 The Geological Story 147

Endnotes 175

Acknowledgements

Many thanks to all those who helped me write this book. A special mention goes to Diane Morgan for inspiring me to write this book; Andy Gordon who helped me with the technical issues; Barney Crockett who gave me a deeper understanding of the political and social background to the arrival of the oil industry in Aberdeen; and to Ian Weiss, instrument technician on Forties Echo who sent me the fantastic photo used for the front cover. Sveta read the text and suggested several improvements – much appreciated! A final mention goes to Jennie Renton for her able and wise editing of the text, thanks Jennie!

Preface

GIVEN THE FINANCIAL importance of the exploitation of North Sea oil during much of the past half century, the essentially innovative nature of its technology and the larger–than-life reputation of its workforce, its literature, barring technical and economic papers, is surprisingly scant and heterogeneous.

But now Mike Shepherd has written his own history, *Oil Strike North Sea*. It is a neatly rounded, much needed history, providing us with the complete story of North Sea oil, and rather more. Given the depth of its subject matter, it is an amazingly readable book, replete in detail. An account of how techniques have changed over the past 40-odd years is one of its merits.

Each chapter is a complete entity, yet all flow smoothly, one after the other. The discoveries began with the giant Ekofisk oil field in the Norwegian sector in October 1969, followed that December by the oil company Amoco, making the first commercial oil find in the UK North Sea sector, 220 kilometres east of Aberdeen. The company was looking for gas rather than oil and lacked the necessary steel containers to ship the oil onshore for analysis. But oilmen are never at a loss, and an empty pickle jar, purloined from the galley, was used to transport the precious find from the rig back to the oil company office. Little touches like that are one of the delights of the book.

'Oil companies,' Shepherd writes, 'will search for oil relentlessly.' When oil is found, 'a patch under the North Sea is transformed from commercial nothingness to an oil field worth many hundreds of millions of pounds'. This is a staggering thought. But there can be a reverse to the coin: 'There is much agonising over whether there might be some oil in a moderate-sized bump 3,000 metres under the North Sea; you finally convince yourself and everybody else that there could be oil and then the oil company spends £25 million on a well which doesn't find anything.' This is not an unusual happening.

On being given a book on careers in science for his ninth birthday in 1964, Mike Shepherd was inspired by the chapter on geology: 'From then on I wanted to be a geologist when I grew up, little knowing that before long the services of professional geologists would be in heavy demand in my home city.' There was a touch of serendipity there.

Shepherd carries his learning lightly in this vital and enlightening study. Its appearance will hopefully mean that the geologists' input – a blend of knowledge and intuition – will become more widely recognised. Certainly, *Oil Strike North Sea* will now take its place in the front row of books on the industry, along with Anthony Sampson's superb *The Seven Sisters*.

Diane Morgan,
Aberdeen 2015

Introduction

THE GIGANTIC EFFORT involved in recovering North Sea oil became apparent to me one day in 1988. I was offshore for a meeting on the Magnus oil platform, the furthest north in the UK North Sea, and flew on a direct route back to Aberdeen by helicopter. It was a clear, bright evening and the chopper was flying straight down the axis of the northern North Sea basin. This was one of the most impressive flights I'd ever taken. At a height somewhere above a thousand feet I looked out of the window and saw platform after platform dotted across the shimmering silver-grey North Sea, each emitting a candle-like flame as they burnt off excess gas from their flare stacks. In between was a host of drilling rigs, either exploring for new oil or appraising oil pools that had already been found. I was acutely aware at the time that I was witnessing a significant moment in our history. The extent of the engineering I saw below me and the rapidity with which it had happened brought to mind a parallel with the construction of the British railway network in the 19th century. The first railway between Stockton and Darlington had opened in 1825, and in the subsequent railway 'mania' that took place in the 1840s, most of the cities in the UK had been connected.

Everything was on a huge scale; take for instance the Ninian Central platform, one of the platforms that I had flown past during that helicopter trip in 1988. Ten years earlier I had spent a summer carrying out geological field work on the Isle of Skye. One of my field areas, near the village of Broadford, faced north-east towards the deep waters of Loch Kishorn where you could see the Ninian Central platform under construction. The platform was said to have been the largest structure ever built in the UK and it was clearly visible from Broadford at some 20 kilometres distance.[1] One morning, I emerged into the open to find the platform had gone. It had been towed out onto its location on the Ninian Field in the northern North Sea. I regretted at the time not having seen it go. The statistics quoted for the tow out in May 1978 were impressive. Including ballast, the concrete and steel structure weighed a combined 601,000 tons.[2] It was reckoned that up until then, it had been the largest man-made structure ever moved across the surface of the Earth.[3] The platform had been towed by a team of eight ocean-going tug boats up the west coast and then around the northern part of Scotland, a distance of 690 kilometres. The trip was due to take 12 days at an average speed of just over three kilometres per hour.

The North Sea proved to be a new frontier for the oil companies when they first arrived. They had been offshore before elsewhere in the world, but never in waters quite so stormy or deep. They would try their existing technologies at first, but these were put to severe test and often failed. New ways of doing things were needed if the oil was ever going to be recovered and given the specific problems they faced, the engineering required was colossal.

With an effort on this scale, the North Sea oil industry has proved to be a major and tremendously exciting episode of both UK and Scottish history, yet only a handful of non-technical books have been written about it in the last 30 years. These tend to focus on specific aspects; for instance, two excellent books by Bill Mackie on the oral history of the industry (*The Oilmen; Klondykers*) and Alex Kemp's majestic two-volume tome based on government papers and largely dealing with the economic aspects, *The Official History of North Sea Oil and Gas*.

My approach has been to provide an overview of the North Sea oil industry with a historical narrative thread running through it. It's not easy to write a straightforward history of North Sea oil although this had been my intention. The industry is so complex that such a book would necessarily have to provide a large amount of context to explain everything that happened. It thus becomes part history/part overview as is the case here. In addition, once oil was found, events spawned a multitude of projects all taking place in parallel. It makes for a more readable book to write about specific themes concerning the industry rather than to itemise each individual project one by one.

At times I found myself close to major events. In consequence, some of the chapters, although they track the narrative history of the North Sea oil industry, do so by following my own first-hand experience. In places, I set out my own views on the political and global context of the oil industry and must stress that the opinions and judgments in this book are mine alone. They are not the views of any of the oil companies I've worked for at various times, including BP and Shell. I sell my labour to oil companies, I don't answer for them.

And finally, no geologist can write about the North Sea without extending the story back through geological time and explaining how the reservoirs and the oil in them got to be there in the first place. This is a separate narrative from the development of the oil industry, so I've placed it at the end of the book.

North Sea oil is a story of big money, big engineering, a few spectacular failures and many great achievements. But above all, it's the story of the men and women that made it happen. This book is dedicated to them, the North Sea Tigers who toil for oil.

Mike Shepherd,
Aberdeen 2015

Timeline

1964   Drilling starts in UK waters, with the search for gas in the southern North Sea.

September 1965   North Sea gas discovered by BP in the West Sole field off the Yorkshire coast.

September 1966   Oil discovered offshore Denmark by the Dansk Undergrunds Consortium. Now in production as the Kraka field.

1967   Exploration drilling starts in the UK central North Sea.

February 1968   Cod field discovered offshore Norway by Phillips Petroleum.

October 1969   The giant Ekofisk oil field is discovered offshore Norway by Phillips Petroleum.

December 1969   Montrose oil field discovered by Amoco in UK waters offshore from Aberdeen.

October 1970   The giant Forties oil field discovered by BP in the central North Sea.

June 1971   Oil production starts from the Ekofisk field in the Norwegian sector.

July 1971   Discovery of the Brent field in the northern North Sea.

October 1973   Yom Kippur war in the Middle East, the oil price increases substantially.

June 1975   First North Sea oil produced on the UK side by Hamilton Brothers from the Argyll field.

September 1975   Forties field on production.

July 1977   BP finds oil West of the Shetlands with the Clair field discovery.

March 1980   Alexander L Kielland accommodation platform capsizes in the Norwegian sector killing 123 men.

May 1981   Sullom Voe oil terminal in the Shetland Isles opened by the Queen.

1986   The oil price slumps.

November 1986 Chinook helicopter crash off the coast of the Shetland Isles, 45 fatalities.

February 1988   BP takes over Britoil.

July 1988   Piper Alpha production platform blows up, 167 men killed.

May 2001   Buzzard oil field discovered by Encana.

November 2001 Marjun oil pool discovered by Amerada Hess in Faroe Islands acreage.

September 2014 Scottish independence referendum held.

2015   Oil price slump.

I

Finding a North Sea Oil Field

THE SEARCH FOR oil is a chancy business. Your boss gives you an area under the North Sea to look at; you sweat the data for months, agonising over whether there might be some oil in a moderate-sized bump 3,000 metres underneath the seabed; you finally convince yourself and everybody else that there could be oil there, and then the oil company spends £25 million on drilling a well which doesn't find anything. Not a sniff.

You won't get fired for wasting the company's money like this even though there's nothing to show for the £25 million spent. What the oil company is doing is playing a percentage game for very high stakes. Oil companies live in a world of uncertainty and employ strategies to manage their luck. There is never an absolute guarantee of finding oil in any one structure, but drill several structures in a row and you maximise your chances that one will come in. The idea is to point the drill bit at an area under the sea that looks promising but which isn't necessarily a sure thing – nothing is ever quite a sure thing in the oil business. Maybe only one in three exploration wells will be successful in a good oily patch – but that's alright – if only one well finds a commercial field, then the effort is most certainly worthwhile; big, big money will be made, indeed far more money than will be involved with the cost of drilling all the wells.

And when a well strikes oil it's a memorable occasion. I was once offshore when a well came in; it wasn't the biggest field ever discovered in the North Sea, nevertheless every new field helps to add value to the oil company's portfolio. The circumstances were rather unusual; it was discovered by accident during the drilling of a conventional oil production well in a known North Sea field. Here's how it happened.

Our helicopter had landed on the Sedco 707 drilling rig at midday. It was Monday 23 December 1985 and I had gone offshore with another geologist, John Caldwell. John was gaining experience in offshore work and I was there to help him out. The rig was drilling a new oil production well into the south-east corner of British Petroleum's Forties field. It had been on the go for three weeks and we had arrived at a critical point – the section just above the top of the oil-bearing reservoir, the Forties Sandstone. Our objectives were clear: we had to decide where the long length of steel casing string should go in to shore up the well bore prior to drilling out the reservoir section. We would then track the reservoir down to the base of the oil zone and tell the drillers when to stop. Given the present depth of the well and the rate at which they were drilling I reckoned we had gone out a day before we were actually needed, but because no helicopters had been scheduled to fly out to the rig on Christmas Eve, we had arrived early.

Once we'd unpacked, I suggested to John that he should start work straightaway. John's job as a geologist involved analysing the rock fragments as they came out of the borehole. The rock material at this point in the well had been cut by the rotating drill bit almost 2,000 metres below the rig and was being brought up to the surface by the circulating drilling mud. The section we were drilling through comprises a monotonous sequence of mudstone, rock that had once been mud deposited on the sea floor 45 million years ago. The porous sandstone which formed the oil reservoir of the Forties field lay another 200 or so metres deeper than where we were currently drilling. John could anticipate having a boring time of it for the next day or two as he logged this section; his logbook would be filled with successive entries such as 'mudstone, greenish-grey, as above'. Nevertheless, this would help him get into a work routine ready for the main operation to come.

John had gone out to start work and I was lying on the top bunk in my cabin reading a book, when 10 minutes later there was a knock on the door and John came back in again, 'Could you come and have a look at the samples, Mike? We are drilling through sandstone and there is oil all over the grains.'

I went 'huh?' because this wasn't expected. The Forties field had at that time over a hundred wells penetrating it, and this section in all of the previously drilled wells turned up mudstone with only a few very thin sandstone streaks, none of them containing oil.

Pulling on my overalls, hard hat and rig boots, I followed John out of the rig accommodation to the logging unit, which was located in a portable cabin near the drilling area. Here, a specialist crew called mudloggers kept an eye on all the drilling operations and sampled the rock fragments at the 'shakers' in the mud room, mechanical sieves which removed them from the drilling mud. John had been sitting in the geologist's chair with a microscope in front of him. The rock samples which had been caught during the last few hours of drilling were on glass dishes nearby.

'Is this the latest sample, John?' I asked, and on the nod, I placed it under the microscope.

The sample was entirely sand and looked like the sand grains you would find on any decent beach. The grains had been held together in the subsurface as porous sandstone but were now loose after having been disaggregated by the drilling bit. I then placed the dish holding the rock fragments under an ultraviolet light. Any oil present on the grains would show fluorescence under the ultraviolet rays and that's exactly what I saw, bright yellow, shining fluorescence on the sand grains, lots of it. I took a small sample of the sand grains put them on a clean glass dish and added some solvent with a pipette. I could clearly see the fluorescent oil separating out.

Now this was a big surprise. We were at too shallow a depth for the oil shows to be part of the Forties reservoir itself. I knew it was possible for oil fields to be found at separate levels, one above the other and I realised that this was probably the situation here. In most North Sea fields, oil is found in porous sandstone rock but not in the intervening mudstones. The mudstones act as barriers to oil movement and will seal the oil in the underlying sandstone. I reckoned that John had discovered a new field about 200 metres above the Forties field and the mudstone underneath it was probably acting as an impermeable barrier in between the two oil zones. This was potentially a new oil field which could be worth millions of pounds to the company. The next step was to find out how much thickness of oil-bearing sandstone we had drilled through so far, a thin sandstone streak would probably not have been commercial. I looked at the previous two or three samples that had been collected higher up the rock interval and these all contained sand grains with shows of oil. That was promising, very promising.

In the old days, we would have found a 'gusher'. The oil under pressure at depth would have pushed its way up the wellbore and gushed out in a fountain above the drilling derrick. This is what happened to the first well to find a big oil field in Texas back in 1901, the Spindletop oil field. If oil gushes out of a well today, it's because a major blunder has been made and it's technically a blowout with all the resulting pollution and danger to life that this can cause. The drilling mud in the hole is designed to prevent any oil or gas from escaping out of the rock formation at depth and will be weighted up with the heavy mineral barytes to help it do this. In today's oil patch you strike oil the modern way – the geologist examines the rock cuttings brought up in the drilling mud to see if there is any oil on them as John had done here.

The logging cabin had a phone in it and unusually for a drilling rig it had a direct connection to the office. Normally you would have to go through the radio operator to contact 'the beach', the colloquial term the riggers used for anywhere onshore. I called my boss and told him what we had found. The news was to cause a sensation in the oil company. After drilling over a hundred wells in an established field, it was indeed astonishing to accidentally find a new and separate oil field lying above it.

The find was later called the Brimmond field and is named after a hill that overlooks the city of Aberdeen. The name is appropriate, as the telephone call I made to the office to announce its discovery was relayed through the communications system on top of Brimmond Hill. It's not the biggest oil field in the UK North Sea; that honour goes to the Forties field which sits underneath it. Published records show that the Brimmond field produced 2.5 million barrels of oil between 1996 and 2004.[4] Now I realise that this sounds like a lot of oil and in a way it is. A barrel is the unit of measurement commonly used in oil fields and this comes from the early days of oil production in the United States. Nobody uses barrels to store oil these days, nevertheless the term has survived. A barrel is equivalent in volume to 159 litres. The refined oil products from the Brimmond field would thus fill up many a fuel tank, yet for a North Sea field, 2.5 million barrels is small and puts the Brimmond field at the low end of the range of commercial oil field size offshore.

Let's talk money here; how much was the 2.5 million barrels of oil produced by the Brimmond field worth? I reckon the value created by John and myself going offshore a day early was about £38 million before tax and costs, not bad for a day's work, I suppose. One of today's oil company economists would not be too impressed by this figure, however, and perhaps with good reason; £38 million is almost petty cash for an oil company. Put into perspective, this sum could easily be the cost of a deep exploration well in the North Sea. OK, the oil price was relatively low at the time when Brimmond was on stream and yes the field is small; it might not even have been developed had it not been located in an area already kitted out with production platforms and a pipeline.

Yet, £38 million is £38 million and all these little projects add up to make big money for an oil company. Finding the Brimmond field also brought an extra bonus. One benefit of making an unexpected oil discovery somewhere different in the geological succession is that it makes you look to see what other oil pools could be lurking in the same area. Indeed, two more small oil fields called Maule and Tonto have since been found above the Forties field by the American oil company Apache and put on production. The Maule field is still flowing as of 2015 and according to UK government figures it has produced just over 2 million barrels of oil to date; the Tonto field has produced 770,000 barrels of oil and is still on stream.[5] In the oil biz this is referred to as unlocking value; if you find one oil field in a new patch, then similar-looking structures nearby are likely to yield oil too.

If the Brimmond field has recovered 2.5 million barrels of oil, the much larger Forties field just underneath it has today produced over 2.5 billion barrels of oil, a thousand times as much.[6] British Petroleum (BP) were making so much money from the Forties field in the late 1970s, one manager claimed that at the then tax rate, BP would eventually be able to buy up most if not all of the whole of the UK's manufacturing industry if they had ever wanted to.[7]

Only a few oil fields are discovered by accident as was the case with the Brimmond field. Usually the discovery of an oil field is predicted in advance by a team working in an oil company's exploration department. Oil companies will search for oil relentlessly. Their reserves deplete with time and will eventually run out unless they get hold of new resources somehow. Thus oil companies will spend a lot of money and take big risks to find more oil. And when a new oil find is made the hurrahs will resound. For instance, the American oil company Occidental made a big fuss out of any team finding oil in its North Sea acreage. An early morning ceremony would be held in the Aberdeen office with the members of the team awarded with specially made badges labelled 'oil finder'. Afterwards a bus would take the team out to a hotel north of Aberdeen, where a champagne breakfast would be laid on for them.

I once worked for a small exploration team on a block where oil was found in the northern North Sea. Not by us, although we did assess the acreage to be promising. The asset was sold on and it was another company who worked up the prospectivity in detail, drilled the area and found the oil. Altogether four oil pools have now been discovered in a cluster now known as the Western Isles Development. Here is the published information on the project taken from the website of the operator, Dana Petroleum: two of the oil pools are to be developed and they will be known as the Harris and Barra fields. An estimated 45 million barrels of oil equivalent are recoverable from them through five production wells.[8] Once the fields start production in 2015, the initial rate will be about 40,000 barrels of oil per day and the estimated field life is 15 years. The overall cost of the project is an expected $1.6 billion and it is anticipated that it will create up to 200 new jobs.[9]

This is an example of how value is created by those working in oil companies. The exploration effort had conjured up prospective oil pools which were then found. Thus a patch under the North Sea had been transformed in commercial terms from conceptual nothingness to oil fields worth many hundreds of millions of pounds. A large addition to the capital value in the global economy is made by oil company personnel finding petroleum in this way. Those that create value in the company's exploration or subsurface groups are well rewarded. Experienced personnel at the sharp end of the industry will earn a six-figure salary and highly experienced independent contractors in the same line of business have been known to charge the oil companies at least £1,000 per day for their services during the boom times.

The first step in exploring for oil offshore is to obtain seismic data over the area of interest. A custom-built boat is sent out to the North Sea to shoot the seismic; it does this by popping an air or water gun in the seawater. The sonic pulse is powerful enough to be sent down through the sea and then penetrate through several kilometres of the underlying rock. Some rocks in the subsurface are harder than others and will cause part of the sonic energy to be reflected back up to the surface again. The boat trails behind it a long tail of detector instruments to pick up the returning energy. The time it takes for the pulses to come back is also recorded. The energy travels fast so this may take only two or three seconds for the round trip. The seismic data is displayed in long sections and at a glance they resemble cat-scans through the crust of the Earth; it's as if the rock column in the North Sea has been cut away to shows its structure.

The seismic interpreter is given the job of making sense of the data and will be looking for any suitable feature that could potentially trap the oil. The simplest is a dome-shaped structure like the Forties field that catches the oil as it migrates upwards through the rock column. In the early days, seismic data would be printed out on long paper sections, often a metre or more in length. The interpreter would sit at their oversize desk picking out the geological markers with coloured pencils. Today, they track the seismic horizons with a computer mouse on the screen of a work station.

Every now and again, you get a hint from the seismic data that oil or gas may be present, not that often, but sometimes you do. It's commonly an indication of gas rather than oil, as a gas-filled reservoir shows a larger density contrast from the surrounding rock and can 'brighten up' on seismic lines. On other occasions you can see 'flat spots' on high-quality seismic data. The strata may be tilted at an angle or folded, yet cutting through the strata is a flat-lying seismic reflection that represents gas (usually) sitting on top of a flat contact with water or oil saturated rock. Back in the late 1970s, a friend of mine noticed a flat spot on seismic data which had been shot in the Norwegian sector of the North Sea. It looked like a direct indication of hydrocarbons, yet it covered a very large area. He knew only too well that these types of signal are often misleading. You sometimes get a feature equivalent to a mirage in the desert on seismic lines, a solid-looking reflection that cross cuts everything, but is in fact an artefact related to how the initial seismic pulse sent down from the surface has a tendency to bounce around between the rock strata. Yet could this flat spot possibly be a direct hydrocarbon indication showing that an enormous gas field extends over 700 square kilometres of four Norwegian licence blocks? Yes, became the answer once it was drilled. The Troll gas field, as it is now called, contains about 40 per cent of the total gas reserves in the Norwegian North Sea and is expected to produce for 70 more years to come.[10]

While the seismic is being interpreted, the geologist will be busy mapping out the subsurface geology. In addition to locating a suitable structure to trap the oil, a further requirement is that there has to be a reservoir rock present and a cap rock above the reservoir acting to seal the oil in. A typical North Sea oil field holds oil in a sandstone reservoir and the cap rock is mudstone. The sandstone was once sand, perhaps deposited on a beach, river, or in submarine channels. The mudstone was once mud, typically laid down in the open sea after the sea level rose quickly and drowned the underlying sands.

Sandstone provides the ideal material to form an oil reservoir as it is porous and the oil can be stored in the pores. It is surprising how many people outside the industry think that oil is found in some giant hole in the ground akin to an underground storage tank or cave. Forget that idea, oil is stored in pores within rock. The pores in sandstone are barely visible, generally a fraction of a millimetre in diameter, but there are a multitude of them. At shallow depths as much as 35 per cent of the sandstone rock is pore space, although with increasing depth the porosity tends to decrease perhaps down to 10 to 15 per cent or even less. The pores link up throughout the framework of the rock and this structure allows fluids such as oil to move in and out of the permeable sandstone.

Lying above the sandstone reservoir is the mudstone cap rock. The rock is fine grained and holds on very tightly to the water in its pore space. It acts like the most powerful sponge possible; even buoyant oil and gas under pressure cannot displace the water from the tiny pores of the mudstone and the oil is trapped in the sandstone reservoir underneath, unable to escape.

Having defined a reservoir interval and a cap rock to provide a seal, all we need to do now is to figure out if oil managed to find a way into the trap. Almost all of the oil in the UK North Sea is sourced from a 155 million year old organic-rich mudstone called the Kimmeridge Clay Formation. It's named after the village of Kimmeridge near the coast of Dorset where it outcrops onshore and is widespread in its distribution across much of the North Sea. A good source rock should contain a significant volume of organic material; organic material making up more than two per cent of the rock shows potential, 10 per cent would be a very good figure. In the case of the mudstones from the Kimmeridge Clay Formation, the organic material is largely the remains of marine algae and plant material which had accumulated in the sea bottom mud back in the Jurassic Period.

Oil takes millions of years to form as the source rock has to be buried to a sufficient depth before it will be generated. The floor of the North Sea is continuously subsiding and as it subsides, more and more sediments are deposited at the bottom of it. In the 155 million years since the organic mud of the Kimmeridge Clay Formation accumulated on the seabed, two to three kilometres of sediment has gradually been dumped on top of it by river, current and tide. And as the mudstone becomes buried deeper and deeper under this pile, the temperature increases. Eventually the depth of burial will be such that it is hot enough down there for oil to form as the organic material breaks down and liquefies. A temperature of 80–150° Celsius will suffice. However, if the organic mudstone ends up buried too deep, it gets too hot to generate oil and gas will form instead. Over large parts of the North Sea, the mudstones of the Kimmeridge Clay Formation are buried at just the right depth to generate oil – lots of it. Not only that, the oil is typically a light, sweet, low sulphur crude which commands a premium price compared to the lower quality crude oil commonly produced from elsewhere in the world.

If you can work out a spot in the North Sea where the various factors potentially combine together for an oil field to be present, then that's your exploration prospect. Yet it's not that straight forward. Often the only data you have available to help you comes from wells that have been drilled at some 10 or 20 kilometres distance from the exploration acreage you are investigating, sometimes more. If these wells are known to contain reservoir rock, you have to use your geological skills to try and predict whether the reservoir interval somehow manages to extend all the way over to your prospect. You can never be too sure about this, so you try and work out the probability of it happening. After also factoring in the probability that the trap seals and that oil has managed to get into the trap, you end up with an overall probability that the exploration target is likely to be successful. Because of the vast amount of money that will be required to test the prospect, ideally you want the overall probability to be as high as possible; a 20–30 per cent chance of success is getting there, although the threshold prompting a decision to drill will vary depending on the oil company involved.

The volume of oil in the prospect should also be big although just how big it could be is subject to much uncertainty. To quote a single exact estimate for the volume would be misleading in the extreme as it suggests that you are reasonably sure as to what might be there when you aren't. It is better to quote a range of volumes lying between a minimum and a maximum with a most likely volume somewhere in the mid range.

The large uncertainties involved in defining oil prospects have led to an element of teasing at the expense of the exploration team. Exploration geologists are referred to as 'arm wavers' on account of their vague, yet expansive gestures whenever they are asked to describe an exploration concept. Engineers, more used to micrometer-exact measurements, will quickly become exasperated when talking to geologists.

An engineer once told me his theory that geologists couldn't function at all if their hands were cut off.

'How so?' I asked.

'Because every time I ask them a question they answer on the one hand it could be this, on the other hand it could be that.'

The small low-risk exploration targets are frequently located close to existing fields, where oil migration and the presence of reservoirs are almost assured. The large high-risk prospects, colloquially known as 'elephants', are often in frontier areas, perhaps hundreds of kilometres from the nearest oil field. Exploration managers are partial to elephants. If the drill bit finds oil in one of them, their glory day will have come. The small but promising-looking bumps around existing oil fields were once typically left unloved and ignored at the bottom of the exploration portfolio ranking list, but as the elephants have mostly been picked off in the North Sea, they are attracting more attention these days.

Having defined your oil prospect, you then need to persuade management and the oil company partners with a share of the exploration block that it is worthwhile spending millions to hire an oil rig to drill it. There is a greater element of salesmanship here. You give presentations at technical meetings and try and persuade all involved to part with the money to fund the well. It's not too difficult if the prospect looks feasible.

On one occasion I helped to work up a North Sea oil prospect, yet ended up not rating the concept too highly as I reckoned there were too many ways by which oil could have leaked out of the structure. However, my French manager liked it on the basis that it could end up being a large oil field if everything worked in its favour. I presented the prospect to the technical staff from our partners in the exploration block and tried to sound confident. Our partners were sceptical and proved reluctant to commit funds to drilling the well. What happened next astonished me and I've never forgotten the experience. My French manager took over from me and refused to let the meeting finish until a positive decision to drill had been reached. He then spent the next three hours going over the arguments again and again. Air flights to London were missed, dinner engagements had to be cancelled, wives and husbands were leaving telephone messages, yet still he talked on. He eventually managed to grind everybody down into agreeing to fund the well.

I talked to him afterwards, congratulating him on what had been a remarkable performance. He didn't think anything of it. 'That's what you do,' he said and then he asked me if I knew what the French word *volonté* meant. The dictionaries translate the word into English as willpower, but as my manager explained to me, to him *volonté* meant much more – you define precisely what you want and you never, ever give up until you get it, 'Never, ever,' he emphasised. For the record, the well was drilled years later and it didn't find anything.

Not every oil find is commercial. The discovery may be too small or in much too complex a reservoir for there to be any chance of money being made. I once came up with an exploration prospect in the central North Sea that was drilled. The critical moment arrived when the geologist on the rig phoned through to our afternoon conference call in the office and announced that he had just seen oil shows in the sandstone returns from the drill bit. We cheered and cheered and cheered; our well had just come in. Unfortunately, it turned out to be a thin sliver of oil-bearing sandstone much too thin to be of any interest and that was all there was in the entire well. The remaining interval was solid mudstone for hundreds of metres below where the oil had been seen. We had carried on drilling in the hope that there might be a deeper reservoir interval but there wasn't any to be found. The well is even listed as a discovery on some of the published maps of North Sea oil fields along with the name I gave the prospect. The drilling operation was what exploration managers like to call a 'technical success' – the well had found oil – even though in reality it proved to be a commercial failure.

Sometimes a sizeable oil or gas field is drilled by an exploration well only for the exploration team not to realise it. A surprising number of oil and gas fields in UK waters were overlooked for various reasons when they were first drilled. One geologist even coined a term for these: 'undiscovery wells'. There are many explanations for this phenomenon, although bad luck and misjudgement are high on the list. Shell discovered one of the Gannet fields in 1969 but the well only penetrated the edge of the field finding a three metre oil column and not enough to get excited about.[11] The poor quality of seismic lines shot in the 1960s almost certainly explains this one. Even earlier, in 1967, Gulf Oil had drilled an exploration well into the centre of the Nelson field and found what is now known to be the worst quality patch of reservoir in the field. Gulf had also failed to notice that they had discovered the Morecambe gas field when they misinterpreted the well data. The discovery had been brought to their attention by the British Gas Council who had noticed the gas shows in the well whereas Gulf hadn't. Gulf had by this time announced that were giving the block licence back to the government and when the Gas Council told them they had overlooked a major gas field, the American oil company immediately contacted the government and informed them that they had changed their mind. The UK government were not impressed and refused to allow Gulf to hold onto the licence. They later awarded it to a subsidiary of the British Gas Council.[12]

Sometimes a reasonable-sized oil pool is found far from any existing infrastructure and then ignored for years. Because of the distance involved, the development costs of building new infrastructure can be so expensive it would swallow up any subsequent profits resulting from putting the field on production. Size can be relative. A small oil pool offshore may be too expensive to produce from, whereas the same-sized pool onshore will make money. Drilling costs are at least 10 to 20 times less expensive onshore compared to those in offshore wells. For example, the cost to hire a semisubmersible rig for an offshore well is currently about $300,000 to $430,000 per day and as a rule of thumb you can double that figure to include the operating costs of using the rig.[13] By contrast, you can hire a land rig in the US for $14,000 per day.[14]

It's a good idea to be the first to find oil in a new area, as you often find one of the biggest fields present there. The biggest fields get discovered first as they tend to be in obvious structures usually worth drilling. The field discoveries tend to get smaller and smaller after that. New fields are still being discovered in the North Sea; three fields came on the scene in 2010, the Catcher, Cladhan and Blakeney fields, although they are nothing like the size of the fields found in the early days. The last big field to be discovered in the North Sea was the Buzzard field in 2001, which is expected to produce over 700 million barrels of oil.

Once an oil field has been discovered, it gets a name. The bigger oil companies will usually follow a given theme in naming the fields they find. For example, BP named most of their North Sea fields after Scottish saints and the American oil company Conoco used the surnames of famous Scottish geologists; Murchison, for instance. The Nelson field was named in a flash of inspiration. The managing director of Enterprise Oil, Graham Hearne, was in his London office when he was asked what the company's new field should be called. Glancing out of the window he spotted Nelson's Column. 'Look no further,' he said.[15]

Shell name their fields after sea birds and by doing so created the biggest and longest enduring myth on the North Sea oil patch, endlessly recounted over pints of beer onshore and cups of coffee offshore. It was even mentioned once in the *Financial Times*.[16] Auk was the first oil field discovered by Shell in the North Sea and a fairly small one by comparison to what came later. The story goes that Shell were not that impressed by the find and nondescriptly named the field A-UK, the A field in the UK. The second field to be discovered by Shell was found several hundred miles further north, a clear indication that plenty more oil fields were going to be found all over the North Sea. Alas, they couldn't continue with their naming strategy. If and when they eventually got around to adding a sixth field to their North Sea portfolio, the name F-UK just wouldn't do. Fortunately, Auk just happened to be a sea-bird, thus establishing Shell's naming policy for the North Sea fields. The F field, when it came about, was called Fulmar.

I've investigated the story and can confirm it's not true; some mischievous riggers probably made it up. Shell did indeed set out to name their fields after sea birds. The suggestion came from Myles Bowen, Shell's UK exploration manager, who had been instrumental in the discovery of the company's first North Sea oil fields.

2

The First Oil Fields are Found

THE FIRST GEOLOGIST to get a hint that there was oil in the rocks under the North Sea was Hugh Miller (the Miller oil field is named after him). Born in 1802 in the village of Cromarty, north of Inverness, he worked as a stonemason and taught himself geology after being fascinated by the fossil fish he had found while working in the quarries. He later wrote several books on the geology of the north of Scotland.

In his autobiographical *My Schools and Schoolmasters*, published in 1854, he describes his childhood in Cromarty and how he had become fascinated by a mysterious rock formation that lay under the North Sea offshore from the village. He would drag samples into a cave on the shore:

Every heavier storm from the sea tells of its existence, by tossing ashore fragments of its dark bituminous shale. I soon ascertained that the shale is so largely charged with inflammable matter as to burn with a strong flame, as if steeped in tar or oil, and that I could repeat with it the common experiment of producing gas by means of a tobacco-pipe luted with clay. ... I used to collect it in large quantities and convert it into smoky and troubled fires, that ever filled our cavern with a horrible stench, and scented all the shore. Though unaware of the fact at the time, it owed its inflammability, not to vegetable, but to animal substance; the tar which used to boil in it to the heat... was as strange a mixture as ever yet bubbled in witches' cauldron – blood of pterodactyl and grease of ichthyosaur – eye of belemnite and hood of nautilus; and we learned to delight in its very smell, all oppressive as that was, as something wild, strange, and inexplicable.

This is a description of oil shale from the Kimmeridge Clay Formation and the source rock for almost all the oil found under the North Sea. It outcrops on the shore near Cromarty and extends offshore from there.

The scene had thus been set for North Sea oil, but as yet there was no script and no players. It was the search for oil and gas in the Netherlands in the 1930s that would eventually lead through a long chain of events to the discovery of oil fields in the North Sea.

Active exploration had started in 1934, spurred by the discovery of oil in neighbouring Germany and earlier indications of oil in the south of the Netherlands.[17] Yet, it was a serendipitous event in 1938 that grabbed the attention of the Dutch oilmen. An exhibition with the theme 'Living in the Dutch East Indies' had been organised in The Hague, the third largest city in the Netherlands and the location of the country's parliament. It was held in De Mient, an area of open green space close to the North Sea coast. The idea was to give the public an idea of what it was like to live and work on the Indonesian islands.[18]

On display was a drilling rig which was due to be sent out to the colony for oil exploration and production. Someone had decided that the rig should be used to demonstrate how a drilling operation works and the plan was to drill a token 500 metres below the grass lawns of the park before calling a halt. At 464 metres below the surface they were to get an enormous surprise – they discovered oil. The oil shows in the rock samples were tar-like in constituency with no economic value, but that wasn't what mattered, the well had given a clear indication that hydrocarbons had formed in the rocks underneath the west of the Netherlands. It was thus a critical piece in the petroleum geology jigsaw puzzle – oil shows had been found in Germany to the east, oil shows in the Netherlands to the south and with this bizarre find, in the west of the Netherlands too. The whole country thus looked to be a prospective petroleum province. With further exploration, the Schoonebeck oil field was found in 1943 and later, the Groningen gas field in 1959, one of the biggest gas fields in the world. It was a major discovery.

The Groningen gas field was found in a rock interval that is widespread throughout much of Northern Europe, 280 million year old desert sandstone from the Permian Period. The desert had formed on an enormous continent, extending westwards from Poland, through northern Europe and across the North Sea to the British Isles. The gas in the reservoir had migrated in from the underlying Coal Measures and these also cover a large part of Europe.

The presence of an enormous gas field in the Netherlands encouraged offshore drilling in the southern North Sea. The first gas discovery in the UK North Sea, the West Sole field, was made in Permian desert sandstone in 1965. Many more gas fields were found under the southern North Sea in the years that followed.

The drilling rigs ventured further north in the late 1960s. The American oil company Phillips Petroleum saw the potential for hydrocarbons in the North Sea when their Vice Chairman, Paul Endacott, went on holiday in Europe in 1962 and by pure chance he happened across an onshore drilling rig in the Netherlands. Professional curiosity took hold. The trade journals were reporting on the Groningen gas find after it had been mentioned during a European Parliament debate on energy policy in 1960. He also read that drilling was starting to take place off the Dutch coast and that seismic was being shot on the UK side of the southern North Sea. Something was afoot![19]

When Paul returned to work in Bartlesville, Oklahoma, he prompted an investigation within Phillips into the potential for finding commercial quantities of oil and gas in Europe. The results of the study showed that Western Europe had not previously been considered of any great interest for exploration. Although oil and gas had been discovered in several countries throughout the area, the finds were small by international standards. However, the Groningen find looked to have substantially changed that perspective. The staff from Phillips Petroleum knew through their investigations that the Groningen reservoir had been identified as Permian desert sandstone and this rock interval almost certainly continued offshore from the Netherlands into the North Sea. This was an area that had not yet been drilled by oil companies and which could potentially open up for exploration. Not only that, the world's second largest energy market was in Western Europe and growing fast. If commercial hydrocarbons were to be found off the coast there, then big money could be made.

A team from Phillips were sent around Europe later in 1962 to try and gain more geological data and make contacts in the various countries of interest. In Germany, they were told that the Federal Institute for Land Research had shot a seismic line over the southern North Sea and this had shown that a sedimentary basin was present there down to five kilometres depth. That was promising. Phillips were now convinced that the North Sea was prospective for hydrocarbons; the question now was whether they would get government concessions to drill there. They held talks with the German Ministry of Finance only to be told that they had not been the first oil company on the scene, others had been there before them and were already negotiating for deals. Further discussions led them to believe that the structures in offshore Germany were unlikely to be that prospective. Their mission then took them to the Netherlands, Belgium, Denmark and the UK. Again they were to find that other companies had also been there before them. The UK offshore waters looked very promising and they were to find out In London that the UK government were intending to award concessions, with all interested oil companies having an equal chance of being awarded acreage.

Norway had been ignored by the competition and Phillips was now convinced that a sedimentary basin could be found offshore from Norway; given the long length of the Norwegian coastline, it could be sizeable. On 29 October 1962 they met with a Norwegian government official to discuss the possibility of offshore drilling concessions. It became clear during the talks that the Norwegian government had up until then assumed that no oil and gas could be present around their coastline. Four years earlier, in 1958, the Norwegian Geological Survey had written a letter to the Ministry of Foreign Affairs stating, 'The chances of finding coal, oil or sulphur on the continental shelf off the Norwegian coast can be discounted'.[20]

How did the Norwegian Geological Survey get this wrong back then? They were not alone, as geologists elsewhere were saying much the same about the North Sea hydrocarbon prospectivity at the time. It is a curious fact that the discovery of North Sea oil overlapped with a major scientific revolution in the 1960s. This was when the theory of plate tectonics was established. According to this theory, the surface of the Earth down to below crustal levels is broken up into numerous plates which move relative to each other. They don't move very fast, a few tens of centimetres a year at the most, but move they do and they keep moving over a time span of millions of years. Tremendous forces are involved. The plates drift apart from each other, collide with each other or scrape past each other. Where they move apart, new oceans and sea areas form in between. When they move towards each other and continental crust is involved, the collision creates mountains such as the Alps and the Himalayas. Where the plates scrape past each other are found zones where major earthquakes occur, such as the San Andreas Fault located on the west coast of North America.

The significance of the plate tectonics theory for the North Sea is as a conceptual framework for predicting whether the geology is suitable for oil and gas fields to be present. Using the old ideas before plate tectonics, a geologist would have taken note of the ancient crustal rocks of mainland Scotland and the ancient crustal rocks of Scandinavia and from there predict that the North Sea was also underlain by ancient crustal rock. Not much chance of finding oil there then. Using the new theory, you could predict that the rocks under the North Sea were plausibly more recent in origin than the crustal material bordering the shores. A sedimentary basin could thus be present and these are where most of the world's oil fields are to be found.

The Norwegian government gave Phillips Petroleum permission to shoot seismic offshore from Norway in June 1963 and the survey was shot just afterwards. When the data turned up in Phillips' head office in Oklahoma, the long paper sections, almost a hundred metres long, were taken down to a local gymnasium and laid out on the floor. There was no mistaking what they were looking at on the seismic sections; a thick sedimentary basin was present under the North Sea offshore from Norway. The seismic also revealed many interesting structures that looked as if they could potentially provide traps for oil and gas. It was looking good.[21]

An outstanding issue had to be resolved before oil and gas exploration could start in earnest: the North Sea needed to be divided up between its neighbouring countries. This was an issue that was to provoke controversy later. On the face of it, nothing looks out of place: the North Sea has been divided along the median line between the UK and mainland Europe, with Britain receiving the western half and the rest split up between the European countries bordering the eastern margin of the North Sea. The UK thus controls approximately 46 per cent of the area of the North Sea.

Yet, this division hasn't rigorously honoured the intent of the convention that met in Geneva in 1958 to discuss maritime boundaries. Prior to the convention, nations had defined territorial waters as an offshore limit of anywhere between five and 20 kilometres from their coasts. With the increasing recognition that natural resources could exist under the continental shelves beyond these limits, agreement was now required to allow nation states control over the these resources.

The outcome of the 1958 convention was the publication of definitions of what a maritime boundary should be. A country's continental shelf was defined in article one as referring to the seabed adjacent to the coast down to a depth of 200 metres and submarine areas around islands. The articles also state that where two or more countries shared a continental shelf, the maritime boundary should be the median line between the countries involved.[22]

Although there are some ambiguities in the interpretation of the articles, the North Sea would appear to be mostly continental shelf by the above definition but with one notable exception, the Norwegian Trench which is over 200 metres deep and lies close to the Norwegian coastline. This leaves only a narrow continental shelf bordering the coastline of Norway. By contrast, the UK side of the continental shelf is continuous up to the western edge of the Norwegian Trench, way beyond the current median line. Through an accident of geography and by strictly holding to the statutes of the convention, this would have given the UK potential control of resources under most of the North Sea between Britain and Norway.

The 1958 convention agreed to adopt the statute for maritime borders. Understandably, the Norwegians were unhappy about being left with control over only a scrap of North Sea by this and they declined to vote. They sought out the British delegation at the convention and managed to persuade them that the maritime boundary should be the median line between the two countries, not the Norwegian Trench. This was later ratified in negotiations held between the two countries in 1965. The Norwegian government eventually signed the Geneva agreement in 1971 but only after they knew for sure that enormous oil reserves existed on their side of the North Sea.[23]

The British, through an act of goodwill to the Norwegians, had appeared to give away control over the resources of an area with a value now known to be worth many billions of pounds. Had the British been more robust in preserving their national interest at the time, it's possible that they could now control most of the oil in the North Sea.

Yet, it may not have been that simple. The 1958 convention provided the definition of what constituted maritime borders, but left it open for individual countries to negotiate specific treaties between themselves. This clearly would have been a very difficult treaty for the Norwegians and the British to agree upon once oil and gas had been discovered; the ensuing arguments could have delayed the development of large parts of the North Sea for years. The maritime boundary in the North Sea between Germany and its neighbours was hotly disputed, for example, and the issue was only resolved after it was submitted to the International Court of Justice. The British wanted to move fast and take the initiative because they were desperate for the cash from oil revenues to shore up the regular balance of payments crises that the economy was suffering at the time. This was the view expressed later by John Liverman, who had been Deputy Secretary at the Department of Energy with responsibility for North Sea oil and gas policy. At a 1999 seminar on the development of North Sea oil and gas held by the Institute of Contemporary British History, he described how he was put very firmly on the spot over the issue in 1979:

> When Margaret Thatcher first became Prime Minister – and breezed into government departments to see the officials she was going to be saddled with – she came in her electric blue suit, fixed me with a baleful gaze and asked, why did I allow the Norwegians to get away with it? I wasn't in the post at the time, but that wasn't accepted as a good answer. It may account for my lack of advancement from that point onwards. I thought of some good answers afterwards, as one does. I am not actually aware of how carefully it was considered at the time because of the desire for speed, but I can offer some observations...
>
> I think the chances of success in arbitration would have been slim, but that is speculation. What is certain is that, once you go to arbitration, you can say goodbye to any oil drilling in the disputed area for something between five and ten years.[24]

After the North Sea maritime boundaries had been ratified, the area under the North Sea was divided by the various governments into quadrants and blocks. A quadrant is an area of the North Sea within a grid drawn up at a spacing of one degree longitude and latitude. On the UK side, a full quadrant contains 30 blocks. The UK blocks vary in area from 210 to 240 square kilometres, the Norwegian blocks are larger. This influences the designation of the well names. For instance, the discovery well for the Forties field was named 21/10-1; the first well in block 10 of quadrant 21.

Thus oil companies could apply to the governments for the rights to drill in a block and if awarded to them, could produce any oil and gas found there. The companies don't actually own the blocks, they operate them under licence from the state. The blocks are put up for bid by the government in the various licensing rounds where a selected tranche of blocks are made available. Altogether, 28 rounds have been announced in the UK since the first licence round in 1964, the latest in November 2014.

The first significant North Sea oil find was made in Danish waters in 1966 by the Dansk Undergrunds Consortium.[25] A dome-like structure seen on seismic sections looked promising and became the target for an exploration well. The A1-X well was drilled and encountered oil and gas shows in a chalk reservoir which was then called the Anne prospect and is now the Kraka field.[26] After drilling 25 metres into the chalk, the drillers started to encounter severe well control problems, probably because they were losing drilling mud into fractures in the rock. Not only that, the weather blew up into a raging storm and the drill ship couldn't cope with the conditions. The well was plugged and abandoned before any further data could be gathered.

The consortium decided to have another go and drilled a new well a short distance away from the discovery well, and this time it was successful. The well was tested by installing temporary tubing in the well to allow the hydrocarbons to be produced to the surface and sampled for lab analysis. It would also give the company an idea of the likely flow rates to be expected from the new discovery, which in this case was up to 2,900 barrels of oil per day. Further data analysis showed that there was more water than oil present in the pore space of the chalk. There was thus a risk that any field development would result in major water production. The find was considered uneconomic as a result and was then ignored for almost 20 years. The Kraka field is now in production after larger chalk fields were discovered nearby which helped to understand how to best produce oil from complex chalk reservoirs.

Philips found the first significant Norwegian hydrocarbon accumulation in block 7/11 in 1968 and it tested as gas condensate; a peculiar hydrocarbon type which exists as a gas in the subsurface reservoir, but with the heavier molecules in the gas condensing to form a light petroleum liquid as it flows up to the surface. This is now named the Cod field. At the time the find was judged as too small to be commercial although it was not until two appraisal wells were drilled on the structure that this became known. The Cod hydrocarbon accumulation was developed later once other fields had been found in the area thus establishing the expensive infrastructure that a small field could tap into.[27]

The gas discoveries on the UK side of the southern North Sea had already prompted interest in what might lie further north. The rigs had become active on the UK side of the central North Sea and over 20 exploration wells had been drilled before commercial oil was discovered.[28] The lack of success up until then had been discouraging. After nine dry holes, one Shell manager grumpily noted that the company had done naught but drill a golf course off the east coast of Scotland.[29]

The first commercial find was made by Amoco in December 1969 when they discovered the Montrose field 220 kilometres east of Aberdeen.[30] The Amoco geologists had been following a hunch. The desert sandstone that forms the reservoir for the gas fields further south is also found onshore in Scotland. The objective of the well was to drill for gas in the central North Sea and prove that the area of southern North Sea gas fields extended further north. It was an excellent idea but with one major flaw, they had found oil instead.

It may seem strange today, familiar as we are with the idea of North Sea oil, but Amoco were utterly astonished to find oil in the well. Brendan McKeown, the petroleum engineer offshore, didn't even have any steel containers onboard to ship the crude oil samples back to the office for analysis. Desperate needs call for desperate remedies. It may not have been the most dignified way to store and dispatch the first commercial oil recovered from the UK North Sea, but it was effective. He raided the rig's galley and grabbed an empty pickle jar for the purpose.[31] He then caught a helicopter and brought the sample onshore. When he arrived at the company office in Great Yarmouth, he marched into his boss's office and placed the jar on the desk. His boss poured a small amount of its contents into a glass ashtray and had a sniff. It was good quality oil; it was also the start for the UK offshore oil industry.[32]

The status of the Montrose field as the first commercial oil discovery offshore from the UK is established as a fact in books about North Sea oil. Yet, the story is a bit messier than that, not the least because Amoco later split the Montrose field into two separate structures; one called Montrose the other called Arbroath. This looks to have been done for tax purposes rather than to confuse future historians. So the 1969 well discovered the area now called the Arbroath field but which was then called the Montrose field.

The Montrose field wasn't even the first North Sea oil discovery on the UK side. A small oil discovery had been made by Burmah Oil offshore from the Norfolk coast in the Southern North Sea in October 1966. The oil was found in some minor fractures in the rock and the volume proved to be too miniscule for anyone to get excited about it, both then and now.[33] The Nelson field was discovered in 1967 and the Gannet F field was discovered in March 1969, both before the Montrose field find and both currently in production, albeit the oil finds were considered uncommercial at the time they were drilled.

The discovery of the Arbroath/ Montrose field was hardly the defining moment for the UK North Sea either, as it was only declared commercial in 1973 and the Arbroath field didn't start production until April 1990. The 'Big Bang' for North Sea oil was when the news of the giant Ekofisk discovery in the Norwegian sector leaked out at the start of 1970. The field had been discovered by Phillips Petroleum on 25 October 1969, when the rock fragments coming up in the drilling mud were found to contain oil shows.

The rig geologist, Max Melli, was to describe the discovery afterwards in the book *Giant Discovery: A History of Ekofisk through the First 20 Years*:

> To our great surprise we started getting samples of chalk saturated with oil. The oil gave off a light golden sheen – almost transparent, like gold. To me it looked as if we had discovered a huge treasure of gold.[34]

The importance of the giant Ekofisk discovery can't be understated. It was huge and it was oil; the field is now estimated to hold almost 3.5 billion barrels of ultimate recoverable reserves. If any major oil companies had thought up until then that North Sea exploration was about gas, Ekofisk was to change all that. Oil is more valuable than gas as gas is bulky and difficult to transport. The easiest way to handle gas is to agree a local contract with the nearest sizeable country and then build a pipeline to transport it there. Oil is different. It can be poured into a tanker and then shipped anywhere in the world. It thus commands a price on competitive international markets and is a valuable commodity in consequence. The comparison of the oil in the Ekofisk reservoir to a huge treasure of gold is an apt metaphor; the discovery of the oil-field giant set off an intense phase of oil exploration akin to that of a gold rush.

Phillips were reluctant to drill the Ekofisk well when they did. The company had been expecting a bad year financially and their US-based management were less than keen to drill another expensive offshore well when the results of the exploration programme to date had been unimpressive. They decided to postpone the well and then look around to see if any other oil company would take the oil rig they had hired. The lease on it had yet to expire and if they could subcontract the rig to another oil company they would avoid having to pay the expensive daily rig rates. Nobody was interested, so they decided to drill the well anyway rather leave the rig idle.[35]

It's unlikely that the chalk reservoir was the original objective for the Ekofisk discovery well. Certainly chalk had not been known to be a significant reservoir rock prior to Ekofisk, the problem being that because the rock is so fine-grained and the pores so small, normal productive flow rates are low. The saving grace for the chalk reservoir in the Ekofisk field is that it is heavily fractured and the open fractures provide the means for the reservoir to sustain flow at commercial rates. Thus a poor quality reservoir rock with an enormous amount of oil stored in it had been transformed into a major producing interval by the presence of these fractures. As an American geologist once taught me about finding oil, 'It's better to be lucky than smart.'

The Ekofisk find beat the discovery of big oil on the UK side by just over a year, when in October 1970 the giant Forties field was discovered. BP had applied for the block containing the Forties field in 1965 even before North Sea gas had been discovered in the south. As Peter Walmsley notes in the book *Tales from Early UK Oil Exploration 1960–1979*:

> Applications and drilling commitments made at this time were very much an act of faith or a shot in the dark... There were no rigs capable of drilling in those water depths at the time, whilst if finds were made it was not known how they might be produced or how pipelines might be laid in such water depths.

Prior to the Forties discovery, there had been much anxious discussion amongst the BP managers as to whether they should drill the Forties prospect or not. The structure was mostly in UK offshore block 21/10, which BP licensed in its entirety from the government and it was not shared with any other oil company partner as is normal practice offshore. Most North Sea blocks are licensed to more than one oil company and in this way the companies share the expense and risk of drilling exploration wells. This meant that if BP actually discovered something they would make a hundred per cent of the profits, but would also have to pay a hundred per cent of the costs of the drilling rig. The BP board did not like this one bit as it left the company somewhat exposed to the cost of the well should it prove dry.

Logic was on their side. The oil price was low, the Middle East crises and the resulting oil shock of the 1970s were yet to come and it wasn't too clear that offshore production would make any money at the time. Additionally, there was a certain sceptism about the prospectivity of the North Sea that went right to the top. According to the BP website, the Chairman of the company, Sir Eric Drake, had told the Reuters news agency in April 1970 that there wouldn't be oil there. Six months later the Forties field had been discovered.[36]

The cost of oil had been stable at about two to three dollars a barrel ($20–25 at today's value) between the end of the Second World War and 1973. It was difficult for oil companies to make profits except on land and in shallow-water areas where drilling costs were cheap. The oil price had been so low for so long it had been difficult to envisage any future change to this.

In a telling submission to a 1999 seminar held by the Institute of Contemporary British History, Basil Butler of BP was to suggest that any move by oil companies to the North Sea in the 1960s and early 1970s had been on the basis of desperation rather than economics:

> All the companies were extremely concerned about the risks that were being taken in the North Sea. And it was breaking completely new ground. The technology of developing a field in deep water in the North

Sea did not exist at all; all we had to go on was the rather primitive technology based mainly in the Gulf of Mexico. Which is a very different situation indeed. So there was a great concern about the technological problems of actually producing oil even if you found it. Perhaps I could take up, while I'm up on my feet why companies went to the North Sea with all these difficulties. I was actually, at the time, general manager of the Kuwait Oil Company that was half owned by BP and half by Gulf at the time. And there was very great concern that we and all the other companies in the Middle East were going to be nationalised eventually, which indeed is what happened. I remember very vividly a Director of BP coming out to Kuwait and his passing words to me were: 'For God's sake, keep this thing going until the North Sea and Alaska come on.' And it was very much an attempt to diversify away from the Middle East that brought the companies into the North Sea, despite all the risks.

The BP board suggested making a deal with Shell. The details aren't known, but it may have involved giving a share of the Forties block to Shell and in return they would pay for drilling the well.[37] According to Richard Hardman, the renowned exploration geologist, a technical team within Shell had reviewed the data with a view to pursuing the possibility further. The team's initial calculations had shown the potential to be enormous: over a billion (a thousand million) barrels of oil reserves were potentially recoverable. They were due to give a presentation to their management where a decision would be taken as to whether to accept the BP offer or not. Let's remind ourselves what was at stake here. This was the block that would eventually turn out to contain the bulk of the oil in the biggest field in the UK North Sea. As the time for the meeting came closer, the team blinked at the enormity of their prediction; maybe the estimate of over a billion barrels of oil would come across to the management as ridiculous. They revised the reserves estimates downwards to 'over 200 million barrels'. This was still large enough to impress but much smaller than the original estimate. The Shell management took the presentation at face value and decided the volumes were too low to justify drilling an expensive offshore exploration well on the prospect.[38]

BP were still left with 100 per cent of the Forties block. They were to receive some unexpected information that helped to reduce the risk on the possibility of finding oil there. As mentioned, Amoco had discovered the Montrose oil field in 1969. Although they had been looking for gas in older rock, they had discovered oil in a location close to the Forties structure and in the same prospective reservoir interval. Amoco had hired the Sea Quest drilling rig from BP to drill the well and when they gave it back to BP again, there was an unexpected bonus for the British company. A copy of the well log showing the presence of oil in the Montrose structure had been inadvertently left behind on the rig by the geologist. BP were still reluctant to drill, however, the decision was forced upon them. The license for the Forties block was due to expire if they didn't drill on it soon and not only that, they had an expensive drilling rig on their hands which had been scheduled to drill elsewhere, but that plan had fallen through. In an uncanny repeat of the Ekofisk story, BP decided that rather than leave the rig idle they would drill the Forties prospect.[39]

A driller I knew had been on the Sea Quest drilling rig when the Forties field was discovered in October 1970. The company had wanted the drilling results to be kept ultra secret. The seismic had shown a very large structure at the drilling site and if oil-bearing, it would likely end up as a very large oil find. The information gained could give the company a lead to drill any similar looking structures in nearby blocks as yet unlicensed by the government and this could be worth billions of pounds. If the information leaked out, then there would be heavy competition for the nearby acreage and the commercial advantage would be lost.

When the exploration well was drilled and nearing the target zone, all non-essential personnel were kept inside the accommodation quarters on the rig and a temporary wall was erected around the drill floor.[40] Every message sent from the rig was scrambled or in code. On receiving the news of the find in the Great Yarmouth operations office, the senior geologist made a phone call with a vastly understated message to the home of his colleague, Peter Walmsley. It was about 4am in the morning when the phone rang. 'Peter, it looks good,' he was told. 'That's fine. Thanks for calling,' was the reply.[41]

This was positively revealing by comparison to the call made from the rig to the Stavanger office when the Ekofisk field was discovered. It was a pre-agreed secret message: 'We are still in it'. The acknowledgement came back as: 'That's too bad!'[42] The telex that announced the discovery of the Montrose field was as cryptic. Decrypted, it revealed a message that was in Arabic, a language that both the sender and the recipient would have understood, 'It's black and there's no water.'[43]

Secrecy was paramount in the early days of the oil industry because of the multi-million pound value of a single scrap of information. Since the start of oil drilling in the United States, oil companies had employed scouts paid to keep their eyes and ears open for any useful information. This would involve spying on competitors drilling rigs and hanging around nearby bars, hoping to overhear any unguarded talk from the roughnecks relaxing after a hard day's work on the drill floor. Scouts were active in Aberdeen in the early days and they are still employed today. The job is much less furtive than it used to be and usually involves keeping an eye on published trade journals to see who is drilling what where and to trade information with other oil companies.

A former geologist with Conoco, Dick Selley, has told of how in the early days of UK North Sea exploration the American oil company had drilled a well and the results had then been traded with other oil companies. By doing this, they had gained privileged access to several of the key exploration wells that had been drilled so far. Shortly after the well data turned up, the fire alarm sounded in the Conoco office, a false alarm, and when they returned, all the data had disappeared. A recently hired secretary had also vanished, never to be seen again.[44]

Despite all the secrecy surrounding the Forties discovery well, the details were leaking out. The *Financial Times* reported on 8 October 1970 that BP was believed to have come across encouraging shows of oil in the well.[45] The BP share price had been rising sharply for several days even before the news story appeared.[46]

BP had finished drilling the well and the crew were now about to test the new oil find. What happened next proved to be high drama and the details have only recently emerged in, of all places, the autumn 2010 *BP Pensioner Newsletter*.[47] Peter King, one of the petroleum engineers who supervised the well test, described his experiences:

I still clearly remember the white plume of gas from the top of the rig as the live oil rushed into a 600 barrel holding tank and the gas was separated off. The well flowed at 4,700 barrels per day on a restricted choke. I was told we would not light the gas as the length of the flame might tell surrounding watching boats of the discovery!

Immediately after the test there was a ferocious storm which raged for three days. The riser that connected the seabed well head to the Sea Quest snapped. Luckily we set a plug in the well before the storm and there was no leakage.

On the third day a nearby fishing vessel got into serious trouble and a helicopter was sent out from Norway to pick up the crew. While doing this the pilot encountered a serious problem with loss of hydraulic oil. He reckoned he had 10 minutes' flying time left and asked to try and land on our helideck. He was given the go ahead on the understanding that if he crashed the cranes would immediately push him off into the sea.

With live oil from the test in the deck tanks, we couldn't take the risk of fire. All hands were issued with a fire extinguisher and I remember crouching along with many others beneath the helideck, prepared for the unthinkable. Luckily, the pilot made a good landing even though the decks were rising and falling a good 30 feet or so. He was immediately lashed down. Another Norwegian helicopter came out with replacement hydraulic hose and oil and rescued the crew of the stricken fishing vessel.

Finally, the storm broke and we got ashore via helicopters. It was a perfect way of having a 'news blackout' as no one came ashore during the storm, and BP were able to announce the discovery at their leisure.

BP didn't relax too long before announcing the well results.[48] These appeared in the UK newspapers on 20 October 1970. The *Financial Times* reported the next day that the field was expected to produce about two billion barrels of reserves before the end of field life (Forties has to date produced more than this, over 2.5 billion barrels of oil in 2015). This was obviously a major find and comparisons were already being made to the Ekofisk field discovery. The UK was now on the verge of becoming a major oil-producing nation.

3

Appraisal and Production

ONCE A FIELD is discovered, the oil company will want to get more information to establish whether it is big enough to justify the expense of installing a platform and drilling the development wells. The discovery well gives you information that an oil field is there but it never quite gives you enough data to be certain as to how much oil the field contains. Given that a development could cost hundreds of millions of pounds even before the first oil is produced, the company will want to be reasonably sure that money is likely to be made from the investment. Thus an oil company will drill one or more appraisal wells to get an increased certainty that the development will make money and thus reduce the risk on the considerable outlay involved. The new information will help in making a decision as to whether the field should be sanctioned for development or otherwise.

Four appraisal wells were drilled by BP on the Forties field before the field was approved for development. At the other extreme, the Clair field was not developed by BP until they had drilled 23 appraisal wells and sidetracks in the structure.[49] It is unusual for such a large number of appraisal wells to be drilled as the costs of several tens of millions of pounds apiece will ultimately have to be subtracted from the profits once production starts. The money spent on drilling appraisal wells can erode significant value from the field and most oil company managers are reluctant to drill too many appraisal wells for this reason.

In one Norwegian field, the operator decided not to drill any appraisal wells at all. This was not a good idea. They had assumed that it was possible to map out the extent of the oil reservoir from seismic data and that this would save them the expense of drilling the wells. The managers declared the field commercial on the basis of the discovery well alone and a platform was installed to develop the structure. The production wells were then drilled from the platform; the first two, drilled on the flanks of the structure, failed to find any producible oil. Once all the wells had been drilled in the field, the reserves had decreased by a half compared to the initial prediction.[50]

There are times when a field is appraised and the subsurface team still have little idea as to what is happening in the reservoir because the geology is so complex. When it is difficult to model the geology of a field like this, it means that predicting the commercial potential of the field is prone to a much larger uncertainty than normal. An example of this is Shell's Puffin field where eight appraisal wells were drilled, each different from one another. The Puffin gas condensate pool was discovered in 1981, yet despite the size of the structure it has not been developed to date.[51]

Sometimes the estimated reserves in a newly found oil pool will diminish in size once the appraisal wells have been drilled. When the oil pool was discovered, the first well will have provided the only tangible data point to constrain the understanding of the field's three-dimensional make-up. The appropriate response to this information-poor situation is to quote a range of possible reserves, taking into account the large uncertainty involved. The proud oil company, having found the field and basking in glory, will often send out a press release stating that the new find could potentially contain up to umpteen million barrels of oil, where umpteen can be a very large number. The trick in reading these reports is to notice the qualifier 'up to'. In practice, the reserves will lie within a very large range of values. Once the appraisal wells are drilled, the subsurface team will gain a more realistic idea of what's there and should be able to narrow down the reserves range.

The information gained during appraisal is usually good enough to get an idea as to whether a new field development is commercial or not. Nevertheless, much uncertainty will remain and every now and again a sanctioned project can go on to massively underperform once it's on production. Laurie Dake wrote about this situation in his otherwise serious textbook *The Practice of Reservoir Engineering*. His advice to the ambitious reservoir engineer, having completed the appraisal stage of a new find, was to get a job with another oil company, preferably far, far away.

Not every new field will be sanctioned, but those likely to prove commercial will go ahead for development. The big fields have been produced from fixed platforms, costing hundreds of millions of pounds to build. These have a superstructure comprising the production plant, accommodation and galley areas for the men. Most will also have drilling facilities. In the 1970s and '80s it was a common sight to see the platform jackets (ie the platform substructure) being built at dedicated yards onshore around the coast, Methil in Fife, Ardersier and Nigg near Inverness amongst others.

Fixed platforms are suitable for water depths up to just over 180 metres; the Magnus platform stands in water that is 186 metres deep.[52] Anything deeper than this gets very expensive and structural stability becomes an issue. Platforms are not normally built for the smaller fields in the North Sea. An alternative method is to produce the oil to a ship known as an FPSO vessel. FPSO is an acronym for a Floating Production, Storage and Offloading facility. The oil is produced to the ship via a handling buoy and is stored in tanks until they are full. Once this happens, the boat unlatches from the buoy and sails off to dispatch the oil to a refinery. An advantage of using an FPSO vessel is that once the field it is producing from dries up, the ship can then be moved on to a new field development elsewhere.

Another method is to produce the oil via the wells to a subsea wellhead template on the sea floor. From there, the oil is transported by flowline (pipeline) to a nearby platform. A tremendous amount of expertise has been built up in the North Sea in subsea technology and Aberdeen-based companies lead the way globally in supplying it.

One of the reasons for the appraisal stage in field management is to get an idea how to develop the field. It is pointless spending over a billion pounds for infrastructure for a field that produces only a trickle of oil. On the other hand, if the production plant ends up being too small relative to the size of the field, then the revenue stream to the oil company will be much less than it should have been. The latter situation happened to the Ula field development in Norway. The field had been appraised and the platforms installed. Everything looked OK once production started, there was nothing untoward or so it seemed. Then in 1988 the operator decided to drill a water injection well on the eastern flank of the field just beyond the edge of the oil zone. The idea was to inject water into the reservoir interval in order to keep the pressure up and to push more oil towards the producers. When they drilled into the top of the reservoir interval, the geologist was surprised to find oil shows there. The drill bit dug deeper and deeper and they were still in an oil column – even more surprising. It would eventually take another 300 metres of drilling before the base of the oil column was found, much deeper than where it had been encountered in all the other wells in the field. It is possible that a fault in the reservoir interval had divided the field in two, with the oil column significantly thicker on one side of the fault than the other. The field thus proved to be substantially bigger than had hitherto been suspected; in fact two and half times the volume of what they thought had been there before the new well was drilled.[53]

Although this outcome may come across as somewhat careless, it has to be realised that incompetence is not the reason for these unexpected situations. A typical North Sea oil field can cover an area equivalent to a town or even a small city, yet the number of wells penetrating the structure can amount to 10, 20, 30 or so. The wells provide most of your data together with some rather fuzzy seismic lines giving an approximate outline of the field structure but not that much detail, if any, concerning the reservoir interval itself. The ratio between the volume of borehole providing information and the remaining volume of the reservoir can be at least one to one million. This means that you will have no data from a fraction that is equivalent to 999,999ths / 1 millionth of the oil field. The result is that when you produce a scientific model of the reservoir it comprises 0.1 per cent information and 99.9 per cent prediction. Your skill as a geologist is to fill in the gaps for the model using experience, knowledge, statistics and guesswork. This is not ideal, particularly when your boss is pressing you to come up with a location for a new multi-million pound well based on this model. However, the cost of drilling wells to get more information is too expensive and oil companies will accept the risk that sometimes things don't always turn out as predicted.

The North Sea oil, industry when it kicked off at the start of the 1970s, was built very quickly and with a colossal sum of money spent on the infrastructure. Much of it was in place by the end of the decade. Enormous platforms required to be built, hundreds of kilometres of pipeline installed, and a massive support network provided for.

The first indication of what was ahead for the population of the north of Scotland came in a meeting in London attended by Maitland Mackie of Aberdeenshire County Council. The British Petroleum officials told those present exactly how big the recently discovered Forties field actually was. There was stunned silence lasting for a long time. There was further astonishment when it was revealed that £370 million of investment would probably be required to develop it (it would eventually cost much more, the bill had risen to £850 million by 1977 and would rise further).[54] The Forties field is the largest field in the UK North Sea; nevertheless it was just one of many that were about to be developed.

Not everything went according to plan when the platforms were put in place in the North Sea. The French oil company ELF had a calamity with installing what was supposed to be the first Frigg field platform jacket in October 1974.[55] They had towed the 6,700 tonne jacket on a barge out to the field in the Norwegian sector. The plan was to upright the jacket in deep water and from there manoeuvre the structure to its exact location over the field. Unfortunately, when the jacket entered the water, one of the buoyancy tanks collapsed and it started to sink. Then the other buoyancy tank also burst open and the structure sank to the seabed, bending two of its massive legs in the process. The steel plating on the walls of the buoyancy tanks had been made too thin.

Several attempts were made to rescue the jacket. Two days after it had sunk, a crane ship arrived on the scene and managed to lift the jacket two metres off the seabed but then the weather worsened and the operation was abandoned. A second attempt was made the following spring when 30 giant plastic spheres were attached to the jacket in an attempt to help lift the structure. That didn't work. A third attempt was made to lift the jacket in July 1975 and it was moved a bit closer to the intended site, but it had become increasingly clear that it had become damaged beyond repair. ELF now had to commission another jacket to replace it. The costs of the Frigg field development escalated substantially after that, rising from an initial project cost of £750 million to £2 billion, an enormous sum of money at the time.[56]

Deciding where the platforms should be located was no easy task in the early days of the North Sea. One seismic interpreter I worked with told me the story of how he had started work with the American oil company Mobil, as a youngster with only a few years' experience. Mobil discovered the giant Beryl oil field in the northern North Sea in 1972 and had decided to develop it with an oil production platform. His boss came into his office one day and told my colleague to pick a spot to locate the platform. This was a major decision, the location of an oil platform which would cost many millions of dollars to build and all he had to help him was some shockingly bad seismic data. Today, seismic data is much clearer and sharper than it was back in the 1970s, as the result of improved technology, massive computing power and the better navigation techniques used for its acquisition. But back then, the seismic data to hand didn't even image the top of the reservoir properly, only a surface called the 'Base Cretaceous Unconformity', which was a bit higher up. What would happen if he put the platform in the wrong place and the decision turned out to be the world's most expensive blunder?

The map used to locate the platform showed the top of the reservoir for the Beryl field. It wasn't an accurate map by any standards. It was constrained by only a few well depths, appraisal wells drilled to establish how big the Beryl field was, and its shape mirrored the shape of the seismic reflection higher up, not necessarily a surface congruent with the top of the reservoir; but it was a map. This was not ideal material for justifying a multi-million pound investment, but what else could you do?

A plan came to mind: the platform should logically be placed at the exact centre of the field. He pasted the map onto a piece of card and cut out a shape corresponding to the outline showing the extent of the oil zone. He attached a paperweight to a piece of string, and drew lines using this plumb-line as a guide to find the centre of gravity of the field shape. He then read off the latitude and longitude of the point where the lines criss-crossed and that's where the Beryl Alpha platform is today. It's been said much later that the platform is in the wrong place,[57] but this is hindsight with the benefit of better seismic data, many more wells and new geological knowledge from the rest of the North Sea. The choice of location was the best that could be made at the time with the data available to hand.

The platforms provide a focal point for the gathering of oil offshore, not just for the big fields that lie underneath them but also from the smaller oil fields that feed into the platform from the surrounding area. From there, the oil is transported by pipeline to shore. In the Shetland Isles, land adjacent to a long inlet called Sullom Voe was taken over to provide a terminal for the pipelines coming onshore from the fields in the northern North Sea. It was to become one of the largest oil and gas terminals in Europe.[58] Oil tankers pick up the crude and deliver the cargo to refineries worldwide. A similar terminal at Flotta in the Orkney Islands services oil delivered by pipeline from the fields in the Moray Firth. The site includes six oil storage tanks capable of storing up to 3.5 million barrels of oil.[59]

Some of the pipelines continue on land. The Forties pipeline reaches landfall at Cruden Bay on the Aberdeenshire coast and continues to the Forth Estuary, where the hydrocarbons are processed either for export at a tanker terminal near the Forth railway bridge or passed onto the Grangemouth oil refinery. The gas gathering pipelines from the central and northern North Sea fields arrive on land at the St Fergus terminal near Peterhead and from there the gas is fed into the national transmission system of pipelines which extend throughout the UK.

My father worked as a pipeline inspector for the onshore pipelines in Aberdeenshire, including the BP Forties oil pipeline. His job was to liaise with the farmers whose land the pipeline passed through and to ensure that the contract companies reinstated the land properly after the pipeline had been buried in the trench. He was ideally suited for this, given his local farming background. He got me my first job, working on the onshore Frigg field gas pipelines in the summer of 1975, while I was a student at Aberdeen University. This was my first contribution to the North Sea oil and gas industry.

Local farmers had been paid money in compensation for the pipelines passing through their land and the disruption this caused. The task in hand was to restore the farmland to its original state and I was in a gang removing any large rocks that had come up to the surface once the pipeline had been trenched as these had the potential to damage the farmer's plough.

Health and Safety wasn't as paramount then as it is now, and it proved to be dangerous work. On one occasion I walked past a dumper truck without spotting that a JCB digger was lifting up a car-sized boulder on the other side of the truck and was about to drop it in. The boulder bounced out of the truck and fell out the other side, missing me by less than a metre. Another time, a group of us were being transported in the back of a flat-bed truck along the side of the trench. We were approaching a boulder several metres long, when it suddenly exploded in a shower of rock. When the dust had cleared, we could now see the red warning flag that had previously been obscured from our sight by the boulder. It was a warning that explosives were just about to be used. Fortunately nobody was hurt.

Later, I was assigned as assistant to a young lad whose job it was to test the welds on the sections of the pipeline, a mile or more long, before they were buried underground in the trench. This involved painting the weld with white paint and then sprinkling iron filings over the paint. He would then draw a large magnet around the weld, looking for any patterns in the iron filings that might suggest a crack or a bubble. His job was to test the welds both on the outside and inside of the pipeline. For the latter, he had a steerable motorised trolley that took him through the pipe. He would lie flat on his stomach on the trolley with a light to the fore and it could travel at a good speed. I had a go and it was great fun whizzing through inside the pipe.

I then worked with the welders themselves, handing over rods of solder to them as required. These guys were under a lot of pressure to work quickly and I would be screamed at for being a fraction of a second too slow in handing over a soldering rod to them. One Portuguese welder would shout at me in his own language, 'Burro! Burro!' ('Ass! Ass!').

I was told an anecdote at the time which sounds like a tall tale, but what the heck, here it is anyway.

A contractor working on the pipeline approached a local farmer and engaged him in friendly conversation. After some brief banter, he got to the point:

'You know you've got this massive gas pipeline passing underneath your fields and it comes pretty close to your farmhouse. As a special favour, because I like you, I reckon I could fix you up with a standpipe connected to the pipeline and you will get free gas for the rest of your days. There will be so much gas coming through the pipeline no-one will ever notice the small amount you would be drawing off. Just pay me £500 and I'll get the job done for you this week, but you must keep quiet about this as we don't want the law chasing us.'

The farmer was rightly suspicious and asked for proof that this could be done. So the contractor says to him, 'I'll do the work for you first and once you see you are getting free gas then you can pay me the £500.'

This the farmer agreed to, the standpipe was set up and the gas started to flow. The money exchanged hands and the farmer was happy with his side of the bargain until the gas supply from the standpipe ceased a week later. Suspecting a blockage, he dug down around the standpipe to see what could be done to fix the problem. There he found the standpipe connected to a buried portable gas bottle, now empty...

One bright sunny morning I had been helping out a French crew welding the gas pipeline as we moved through the Aberdeenshire countryside when all of a sudden they stopped working. Seemingly out of nowhere, they produced some gas stoves and frying pans, cooked up some steaks and opened bottles of champagne to wash them down. 'What's this?' I asked in astonishment.

One of the Frenchmen replied 'Can you not see it's the end of the job? We've finished the pipeline.'

It's true that we were very close to the site of the St Fergus gas terminal, I could see it across a field, but we weren't quite there yet. 'Ah,' I was told 'No, the farmer of that field is holding out for more money in compensation for the pipeline crossing his land. He's not going to get it, but that bit of the line is someone else's concern, we are finished here.' It was indeed the end of the job.

All things being well, the production platforms having been installed and hooked up to pipelines and power, the first oil will flow. Following the early discoveries, there was a rush to be the first to produce the first oil in the North Sea. This was achieved by Phillips Petroleum in the Norwegian sector when the Ekofisk field came on stream in June 1971. Oil was initially produced via loading buoys linked to a jack-up rig and loaded directly onto tankers from there. The production platforms were installed later. By comparison, the first oil from the Forties field did not arrive onshore until 1975. British Petroleum was beaten to the status of producing Britain's first drop of oil by the American company Hamilton Brothers. They had developed the Argyll field with an offshore loading facility and the first tanker turned up at the Isle of Grain refinery in the Thames estuary on 18 June 1975, three months ahead of the first oil from the Forties field. The date was auspicious: it was the 160th anniversary of the battle of Waterloo. The Energy Minister, Tony Benn, gave a speech at the ceremony to mark the occasion and found a more recent event to compare to the landing of Britain's first North Sea oil. His speech was reported in the *Daily Express*:

> This is a far more significant and historic for Britain than a moon shot. This is a day of national celebration. We will in time be one of the top 10 oil producers in the world.[60]

Some very big fields were discovered early on in the North Sea and six of them provided over 60 per cent of the UK's oil production in the first 10 years after 1975 – the Forties, Brent, Ninian, Piper, Magnus and the Beryl fields. All of these fields are still producing in 2015 and between them have produced almost a third of the UK's oil to date. They are the work-horses of the North Sea oil industry.

Once a new field is on production, the intent is to produce as much oil as practicable in order to pay back the large investment in the platforms and infrastructure. This shouldn't be difficult. The field at start-up is pristine and undepleted, reservoir pressures are at their highest and production wells will have penetrated through full oil columns. The production wells may have been drilled prior to installing the platform, or more commonly the platform will have a derrick and a drilling area and the wells are drilled after it has been put in place. The intent is to flow oil at a steady high level for several years – this is plateau production. Once the pressure drops and various production problems kick in, the production rates will fall off with time.

Some big surprises were experienced with the early platform drilling operations. The first production well drilled from both the Dunlin and Tartan field platforms failed to find any oil, although fortunately the later wells proved to be more successful.[61,62] Another Tartan field production well drilled early on encountered a reservoir zone containing oil saturated with hydrogen sulphide gas (H_2S). H_2S gas is a big problem for oil companies. Accidentally released at the wellhead, it's a killer. Slightly heavier than air, it will linger around the working and living areas of the rig. In small quantities you can smell the typical rotten eggs odour; at large quantities the gas overpowers the nose and you can't smell it at all. This is when the gas is at poisonous concentrations in the air and will kill you. In the worst incident of its kind, an incident on a Chinese gas well in 2003 resulted in the spread of a large volume of H_2S over the surrounding countryside, killing at least 243 people in the affected area while they lay sleeping at night in their houses.[63] The problems with H_2S are more widespread in oil provinces overseas, the Middle East for instance. In the North Sea H_2S only naturally occurs in any significant amount in the deeper reservoirs of the outer Moray Firth.

One of the big success stories of North Sea oil has been the provision of water injection support to oil field production. It hadn't been a universal practice in the oil patch before the North Sea started up. Most North Sea oil fields require water to be injected into the margins of the reservoir in order to keep the reservoir pressure up after the oil has been removed by production. The water also provides a cushion to push more oil towards the producers and can significantly improve recovery. Dedicated injector wells are drilled to deliver the water, conveniently extracted from the sea around the platform but with sediment, oxygen and microbes removed beforehand just in case they damage both the metalwork and the reservoir. I once saw an interesting sight on board the Magnus platform. One of the bays containing the wellheads shows an oil production wellhead and a water injection wellhead side by side. They are free-standing and not directly attached to the platform. The Magnus reservoir is moderately deep at around 3,000 metres below the seabed, and it's hot down there. The hot oil coming up the production well had caused the metalwork to expand such that the wellhead was standing proud above the well bay. By contrast, the injection wellhead lay almost two metres lower than the adjacent oil production wellhead, chilled by the cold seawater being poured into it.

A big advantage of keeping the pressure up in the reservoir is that it stops the dissolved gas escaping from the oil. Dissolved gas contains a large amount of potential energy for oil production. As the pressure drops in the reservoir the gas expands enormously helping to drive the oil towards the producers. If you lose the gas, the field ends up as lifeless as flat lemonade and the production rate will crater. For instance, in the early days of the Texas oil boom, many oil fields were damaged by rapid pressure depletion until the federal and state governments stepped in to regulate production.

One downside of water injection in North Sea fields is that the injected sea water reacts with the salty water produced from the subsurface.[64] A hard crust of scale forms in the wellbore and the surface production plant which is very difficult to remove. The scale is also slightly radioactive although this is generally not a hazard offshore as the emissions are fairly low-level. When it builds up in large quantities the scale can block wells and production tubing. Oil companies are reluctant to drill out the scale where it blocks oil wells as the radioactive scale could be potentially harmful if it is breathed in as dust. If there is any risk to a production well, oil companies will inject special chemicals into the well to inhibit scale formation before it accumulates to any significant volume.

As an oil field comes off plateau, the pressure drops and water starts to be produced from the wells. Production rates will inevitably drop in consequence. The water coming into the well is heavier than the oil and will increase the total weight of fluids in the wellbore. Pumps are used on some fields but it is more usual to depend on the natural reservoir pressure to push the oil and any water up to the surface tanks on the platform. Once water breaks through to an oil production well, it tends to increase in volume over time whereas the oil rate will drop off. Eventually, too much water comes into the wellbore to sustain oil flow at commercial rates. Oil companies are forever intervening in production wells to set plugs or cement up water producing intervals in order to keep the oil coming. Nevertheless, most oil fields in the North Sea today produce much more water than they do oil.

The fluid arriving from the wells is thus rarely pure oil; rather, it is a combination of oil, gas, water and sometimes sand brought up from the more friable reservoir sandstones. The mixture is then separated into its constituents; the water is dumped in the sea while the oil and gas are sent down separate pipelines onshore. Some of the gas can be converted into natural gas liquids and sent down the oil pipeline. The methane left over is used for electricity generation on the platforms, and the excess gas is flared off.

Produced water from a North Sea oil field became the subject of a joke that went embarrassingly out of control for one oil company. The operator of the field published a quarterly in-house magazine for its staff and for the April issue they liked to carry an April fool's joke, usually some mild, innocuous and very obvious spoof. The year it all went wrong was when they announced that one of their oil platforms would be switched to gold production on April 1st in order to recover gold from the produced subsurface water. The value of the gold production to the company was estimated to be worth over £200 million.

Curiously enough this was on the verge of being plausible. The water having been buried with the sediment in the distant geological past will with time become rich in dissolved metallic salts. However, no gold had ever been produced from the water in the field, indeed I very much doubt that any chemist ever had any reason to look for it as the quantity would be miniscule to non-existent.

The story was picked up and reported in the press as a serious story. The company managers were then astonished to receive two official letters from the UK government. The first letter pointed out that they didn't have a government licence to produce the gold and they should forthwith apply for one; the second insisted that if the company intended to produce gold as a commercial concern, they would be required to pay tax on this. There then ensued a cascade of letters to the company from various cranks, suggesting all sorts of joint ventures to produce gold by various means or other. The April fool jokes stopped after that.

4

Aberdeen

I SAW THE oil industry turn up in Aberdeen as a teenager and was well aware of what was happening. I took a keen interest in the arrival of North Sea oil and kept press cuttings of all the latest developments, particularly when new field discoveries had been made. All this stemmed from a childhood interest in geology. I had been given a book on careers in science for my ninth birthday in 1964, and had been inspired by the chapter on geology. From then on I wanted to be a geologist when I grew up, little knowing then that before long the services of professional geologists would be in heavy demand in my home city.

Aberdeen, which prides itself as the offshore oil capital of Europe, is a small city located on the north-east coast of Scotland with an estimated population of 227,000 in 2013. It's sometimes referred to as the Granite City as many of the buildings are built out of the locally quarried silver-grey granite, a stone that gives the city an austere look for some and presents a magnificent aspect for others, especially when the mica in the granite glistens in the sunlight. The dominant architectural style is 'Scottish baronial' with the city's houses and official buildings sprouting towers and turrets inspired by Scotland's medieval castles. The granite buildings make Aberdeen one of the most distinctive-looking cities in Europe.

The first oil boom in Aberdeen could be said to have happened in the early 19th century when the whaling industry prospered. Whaling boats based at the harbour ventured out to the polar seas on long expeditions. Oil from sperm whales was sought after as the best quality lighting oil for homes. Over-hunting eventually caused the whale population to collapse, and the price for sperm oil rose fast as the whales disappeared from the oceans. Whalers had by now resorted to sailing out into the remote areas of the world in order to find the remaining stocks. Things were getting desperate for both the whales and the whaling industry.

The whales may have been saved from extinction by of all things, the birth of the modern oil industry; petroleum was to become a cheaper and more available alternative to sperm oil for lamps. Two major developments were critical. Colonel Edwin Drake had discovered oil when he drilled a well in

Pennsylvania in 1859. This led to major discoveries elsewhere in the United States, most notably in Texas. A few years earlier, in 1850, the Scot James 'Paraffin' Young had patented a method of producing petroleum derivatives from coal and oil shale. The first commercial oil production was carried out in 1851 from a factory in Bathgate, Scotland. During the First World War, production peaked at over two million barrels a year of crude oil. Up until the end of oil shale production in Scotland in 1962, an estimated total of 75 million barrels of oil had been recovered.[65] This volume is equivalent in output to one of the smaller North Sea oil fields.

Several wells had also discovered oil and gas pools onshore in Scotland, although only two of these have been large enough to put on production. The Midlothian oil field on the south-eastern outskirts of Edinburgh produced 30,000 barrels of oil until it was abandoned in 1965. The nearby Cousland gas discovery started production in 1957 and over a 10-year interval provided gas for the Musselburgh Gas Works.[66]

The 1960s saw the end of one oil boom and the start of another, this time the centre of activity moving to Aberdeen and the north of Scotland. Back in the '60s, Aberdeen was dominated by the fishing industry and to a lesser extent it was a popular tourist resort. Its several miles of beautiful sandy beach led to the local tourist board's description of Aberdeen as the 'Silver City by the Golden Sands'. Other industries included ship-building, the manufacture of paper and textiles, and comb-making. The city also provided services to the extensive farming community in the north-east corner of Scotland.

My father was from a farming background, having been born on a croft near the village of Tarves in Aberdeenshire. He had dabbled in farming and the hotel business, but spent most of his career as a publican in the city. His business career came to an unfortunate end after he converted an old theatre to a restaurant on the beach front. The restaurant, named The Gaiety, opened in 1962, only to fold as a consequence of a big typhoid epidemic in Aberdeen in 1964. The epidemic was sourced to contaminated Argentinean corned beef which had been sold in a shop in the city centre. Over 500 people were infected, fortunately with no deaths. Nevertheless, the tourist industry collapsed as nobody wanted to visit the city following the bad publicity. Today, Aberdeen is known nationally as the UK's oil city; in the 1960s it was notorious for its typhoid epidemic.

I remember Aberdeen as a bustling city even before the oil came. Everything was centralised on the main downtown thoroughfare of Union Street, the Granite Mile as local historian Diane Morgan has called it. It was difficult to get moving on Union Street, it was so busy with people. People from town and country would visit the city centre for the day to do their shopping. The paradox is that Aberdeen before oil came looked more prosperous than it did afterwards. The buildings were well maintained, the city was awash with flowers and there was a strong element of civic pride. With oil, the property developers and the pension scheme managers moved in and many of the buildings were neglected until an opportunity came along to redevelop them and make money.

I recall that there were many concerns expressed about the future of Aberdeen at the time. Unemployment in the 1960s was above the Scottish average, wages were low and the city's major industries were in decline. The population in the Aberdeen region was falling at the rate of 4,500 per year as locals went elsewhere to find work.[67] Comparisons were made to the somewhat more prosperous city of Dundee, 110 kilometres down the coast, which had been successful in attracting new light engineering industries, whereas Aberdeen had not. Aberdeen and Dundee were about the same size at the time, both having populations of about 180,000 people. The advantage of Dundee over Aberdeen was that it was closer to the densely populated Scottish Central Belt, whereas Aberdeen was on its own with no major hinterland of population. Dundee had also been given special development area status from the government allowing grants to be given to new industries setting up in the city, whereas Aberdeen hadn't qualified for this. Aberdeen was in terminal decline economically and the oil industry was to be a matter of exceptional good fortune for the city when it arrived.

Aberdeen's excellent harbour, located onshore from the newly found oil fields, made the city an obvious base for the oil industry, yet the Labour government of the time had other ideas. They supported the idea of a planned economy, and they saw the North of Scotland as unsuitable for a nascent oil industry, the area held less than 20 per cent of the Scottish population and the social costs were likely to be high. They were keen to try and waylay as much of the oil industry as possible to the Glasgow area and the Central Belt, where there was an under-employed labour pool with heavy engineering skills. They started to set up oil offices in the Glasgow area, including the Offshore Supplies Office, the headquarters of the new government-owned British National Oil Company and a centre of drilling technology was established in Livingston. The early initiative to set up an oil industry heartland in the Scottish Central Belt did not survive the newly elected Conservative government of Margaret Thatcher in 1979. In any case, the oil companies had chosen to build their offices in Aberdeen.

There were only a handful of locals who knew anything about the oil industry, my father-in-law to be, George Ritchie, was one of them. He had worked as a petroleum engineer for the Iraqi Petroleum Company in the Middle East, quitting his job and returning to Aberdeen in the 1960s to spend more time with his family; his two children had been at boarding school in the city while he worked abroad. He then landed a job training apprentices at a local engineering works, only to be astonished to find the oil industry following him back home a few years later. He was given a job with the British National Oil Company in their operations office in Aberdeen. His colleague Jimmy Hay also arrived back in Aberdeen from the Middle East; he would later run the Aberdeen offices of Britoil and then BP.

From the early days, it was the American oil companies that took a major role in developing the North Sea. They dominate the international oil industry and when a new oil province is found, they turn up in large numbers, build the infrastructure and make huge sums of money. They don't hang around; they get in there with a can-do spirit and make things happen. Their presence in the early days caused controversy at a political level in the UK. The oil tax take in the 1970s was only about 70 per cent, and the American oil companies were making large profits. There was a feeling at the time that the UK government were being far too generous to them. In retrospect, this was no bad thing, the North Sea needed to be opened up and the Americans had the know-how and the financial back-up to make things happen.

The Brits in the industry were mostly grateful to the Americans who came to the city and taught everybody what there was to know about finding and producing oil. On rare occasions some of the Americans could be seen walking down Union Street, complete with cowboy boots, buckskin jackets and Stetson hats. A cigar would always be in their mouths, although they would chew the tobacco rather than smoke it.[68]

There was some friction at first. The American drillers were used to working in distant places where labour was cheap, unions absent and the men could be aggressively bossed around, 'kick-ass' style. Their outlook was that the job had to get done efficiently and quickly; if this meant getting results by bullying behaviour and putting performance ahead of safety, then so be it. This was also their attitude to the local workforce and it led to headlines in the local press about Scottish workers being treated like 'tartan coolies' offshore.

Once the Scots learned how to drill, they started to take over from the Americans and some also imitated their mannerisms, even affecting an American accent. This was not always appreciated. On one occasion, a Scottish drilling manager on an oil platform ordered a worker to carry his kitbag to the helideck for him, ready to be loaded onto the helicopter prior to his departure home. The bag was duly carried to the helideck, but then hefted over the side, falling 50 metres into the sea and sinking to the bottom of the waves. The driller got on board the helicopter, unaware that his luggage was never going to arrive back with him.

The Trinidadians also came to Aberdeen; they had experience in the offshore oil industry, having installed platforms in the sea around Trinidad from the 1950s onwards. The know-how was needed. The developments in the North Sea would be on a bigger scale than any previous offshore operation; the water depths are greater and the weather harsher. The northern Scottish climate could be difficult for the Caribbean islanders yet they endured it and consoled each other by keeping a strong sense of community in the city.

The British were to return the favour: the global oil industry today has been bolstered by professionals with up to 35 years of experience in the North Sea. They are much sought after. A few years ago, I overheard an advert on a local radio station which started out 'Have you ever wanted to work in a country where the sun shines all the time?' An Australian oil company was aiming to recruit staff from the Aberdeen area.

It was a Middle Eastern war that changed the North Sea forever. The Yom Kippur War started in October 1973 when a coalition of Arab states led by Egypt and Syria attacked Israel. In response to the US giving arms to Israel, the Organisation of Petroleum Exporting Countries (OPEC) announced a partial oil embargo to the West and the oil price quadrupled from $3 to $12 per barrel. This transformed the North Sea from a marginally economic petroleum province into one that had become highly attractive, especially as the oil was located in a politically stable area. Up until then, nobody was too sure as to whether the discovery of oil in the North Sea was merely the hydrocarbon equivalent to a flash of gold in the pan; something of interest that wouldn't last too long.

I've heard the opinion expressed that without the oil price hike in 1973 none of the oil companies already involved in developing North Sea fields at the time would have lasted too long either. The costs of development, already massive, were ramping up enormously. Nobody had tried anything like this before in such deep water with poor weather conditions; the oil companies were learning while building and the designs kept changing as they went along. There were serious delays in putting the platforms in place, with many projects ending up one, and some two years behind schedule. The costs, after accounting for inflation, escalated by 80 per cent per year between 1973 and 1975.[69] The oil companies got lucky when the oil price quadrupled; instead of financial misery, it was boom time for all. A further price hike came after the Iranian revolution in 1979, when the oil price increased from $13 to more than $30 per barrel.

I was 14 years old when the first commercial oil was discovered in the North Sea and I was living in Aberdeen at the time. The big changes to the city started to happen in the early 1970s as industrial estates and housing complexes sprung up. Apart from the building work, one thing I noticed was that Aberdeen had become more cosmopolitan. Up until then, it seemed to me that many of the inhabitants shared a dozen or so surnames, such as Milne, Gordon, Pirie and Sinclair. Then the city saw an influx of foreign nationals, the most prominent of which were the Americans; over 3,000 had arrived by 1975. An American food store was opened in the city selling bourbon, tequila, tamales and barbecue sauces.

The food in the supermarkets was becoming more varied and exotic, probably a UK-wide phenomenon, but for me it was associated with the strange accents I heard around me in the Aberdeen city streets of the 1970s. I remember in particular marvelling at my first sight and taste of an avocado pear.

The incomer's first exposure to Aberdeen was a conversation with a taxi driver en route from the airport to their city-centre hotel. The common experience was to find the local accent almost incomprehensible. Aberdeen came to be known to the incomers as the 'furry boots' city, not on account of an appropriate sartorial response to the northern Scottish winter weather, but because the first question a taxi driver would ask their passenger was, 'furry-boots div ye come from?' – which translates into conventional English as, 'Where about do you come from?'

The attitude of the incomers towards living in Aberdeen was mixed. Some were keen to get out as soon as possible, seeing the city as cold, provincial and miles away from where it mattered (London, basically). Other reluctant incomers came to love their new lifestyle with a passion. It was possible to live on a smallholding in the countryside and combine this with a short commute to the office. For some, Aberdeen was just about big enough to have a cultural element and small enough to take a conveniently short trip downtown to meet people socially. A manager at Shell told me that there was a saying amongst the Aberdeen management concerning efforts to move staff to the city: 'You can't get the beggars up here, and once you do, you can't get them out again.'

About 500 companies arrived to set up offices between 1970 and 1977.[70] Almost out of nowhere, there was a tremendous pressure on the limited resources that the city had to offer. In the late 1970s between 5,000 and 6,000 people per year were arriving in the Aberdeen area.[71] Over 30,000 new houses were built, 55 per cent of these provided by the public sector. It still wasn't enough; house prices and rents increased massively, house prices by over a factor of four.[72] Schools and other services had to be built to accommodate the incoming oil men and women. Areas of the city were zoned for offices, industrial sites and warehouses; not only that, the transport infrastructure desperately needed to be upgraded.

The unsung heroes were the local councils who stepped up to the mark and somehow coped with the influx while still preserving the essential character of the city and region. The villains were and are the national governments, delighted to take billions in tax revenue from the oil bonanza but most reluctant to finance a region, suddenly under stress and requiring resources and assistance to cope with the arrival of a new industry on its doorstep. The result is that the local infrastructure required to accommodate the needs of the oil industry was paid almost entirely from out of local rates and council taxes with very little government assistance. It's been estimated that between 1975 and the early 1990s that local council expenditure on oil-related infrastructure was somewhere in excess of £100 million per year.[73] According to the Scottish government statistics for 2012–2013, the municipal debt for the City of Aberdeen is now £619 million and for Aberdeenshire it's £473 million.[74]

It's ironic that two regional areas elsewhere have been supported by North Sea oil revenues, but not the Aberdeen region. As a deal to secure maritime boundaries in 1966, 2.5 per cent of North Sea royalties are paid to Northern Ireland, while the Isle of Man (not even part of the UK) received 0.1 per cent. The Manx government took the royalties up until 1991, when they made a deal to increase the extent of their territorial waters from three to 12 nautical miles in exchange for giving up their North Sea dividend.[75]

Why has Aberdeen been short-changed? In the 1970s, the national government under Labour didn't want the oil industry in the North of Scotland; it wanted it located in the Central Belt. When the Conservatives took control in 1979, they substantially increased oil taxes. Nevertheless, they showed little interest in Aberdeen and the North of Scotland; the region was too far from London, politically insignificant to them and it wasn't their style to give generous financial grants to development areas even if it was the pertinent thing to do. The Scottish government when it arrived in 1999 would also largely ignore the needs of the Aberdeen area. The motorway network in Britain stops at Perth and the road connection to Aberdeen via Dundee is by dual carriageway. The road network north of the city has been largely neglected, while a recent decision to build a bypass around Aberdeen left both the city and shire local governments having to fund 19 per cent of the total cost between them. Even today, the railway connection south from Aberdeen is single-track in one place and badly in need of upgrading. Once the oil runs out, the north-east of Scotland could easily be just as remote as it always was, with little prospect of attracting alternative industries.

The oil boom saw the decline and cessation of much of the industry that existed before oil, most obvious being fishing; the big fish pongs that used to emanate from the harbour and linger around the city centre have long since gone. Two out of the three paper mills have shut to be replaced by housing schemes and the old Crombie woollen mill, which supplied the Confederate army with uniforms during the American civil war, has gone too. The result has been an increasing reliance on oil which is not healthy for the long-term economy of the city.

Aberdeen harbour expanded considerably from the 1970s onward to cope with the traffic in supply boats which serviced the oil rigs. The traffic reached about 4,000 shipments per year in the mid-1970s.[76] Several supply bases were built around the harbour parameter and they could be recognised by their tall, brightly coloured tanks containing cement and mud to be transported and used for the drilling and well operations offshore. The fishing village of Old

Torry was bulldozed in 1975 to make way for one of the supply bases; 140 flats and houses were demolished and about 350 people moved elsewhere.[77]

Despite all the construction work, there was still not enough room at the harbour. The platforms and rigs needed to be supplied with drilling equipment, mud, food and water on a regular basis and large oil supply boats were required to transport this. The boats had to compete with a port holding Britain's third-largest fishing fleet.[78] There are few trawlers left today, the effects of over-fishing, catch quotas and the closure of the Icelandic cod grounds in 1976, but back in the 1960s there were just over a hundred fishing boats in Aberdeen harbour. Aberdeen harbour wasn't merely a fishing port. It was and is an important ferry terminal for the Orkney and Shetland Isles; two ship-building yards were also active back then around the harbour perimeter. And another ancient economic activity was on the go too. In the 1970s, salmon was still being netted on the south bank of the River Dee within the harbour area, a source of lucrative income for the Harbour Board.

The oil companies were forced to grab what space they could in the other harbours along the east coast. Dundee harbour was an obvious alternative to Aberdeen but it never proved popular with the oilmen. BP initially set up their supply base there but not many other companies followed their lead. Reasons put forward to explain this, include union difficulties amongst the harbour workers and Dundee's limited airport facilities, but it's also known that the oilmen had problems back then in dealing with Dundee city council, variously described as disorganised and unwelcoming.[79]

The August 1977 edition of *Noroil* magazine recorded that Aberdeen airport was having to deal with the fastest air traffic growth rate in Europe and had finally upgraded the airport terminal building that year at a cost of £8 million. Previously, the much smaller airport building had been jokingly referred to as Fort Apache by the city's American community.[80]

Just how small was revealed in comments made by Shell employee Bernard Rollingson on arriving there in 1972, as recorded by Bill Mackie in *Klondykers*:

The airport was quite basic and the arrival/departure building was an old Nissen hut. It had one counter in it. One end was the bar, the other end was the ticket and seat sales. The same bloke did both jobs.[81]

A heliport was established at Aberdeen airport to service the rigs and later the first oil platforms. Up until then, helicopters were a rare sight over Aberdeen. I recall as a child jumping up and down with excitement at seeing a helicopter with the Duke of Edinburgh on board landing at a local hospital on an official visit. The first helicopter on North Sea oil business flew out of Aberdeen airport on 1 August 1967 on its way to a Shell exploration rig.[82] In 1997 at the peak of North Sea activity, 479,100 passengers were flown in and out of North Sea installations and rigs by helicopter.[83] In the late 1990s the flight path was so busy, you could lie on the beach north of Aberdeen and see helicopter after helicopter moving through the skies above.

The early 1980s was when the oil boom took off big-time in Aberdeen and life in the city became somewhat exotic. The good times lasted until 1986, when the oil price crashed to $10 per barrel. The oil price had been high for some time after the Iranian revolution of 1979, reaching $36 per barrel at the end of 1980.[84] However, production had then increased markedly from the non-OPEC countries, including both the UK and Mexico. The Saudis had taken up the slack by cutting production to try and keep the oil price high. Disillusioned by their efforts to support the oil price, they finally gave up on this and the oil price collapsed.

Ten thousand oil jobs were lost in the Aberdeen area and thousands of houses and flats went up for sale.[85] The Bridge of Don area of the city, where many oil workers lived, was badly affected with unemployment recorded as 81 per cent following the slump.[86] One street, Lee Crescent North, became notorious for the number of the houses in the street displaying For Sale signs. There were few buyers. Oil rigs were no longer drilling in the North Sea and many could be seen anchored in the sheltered areas around the Scottish east coast, having no projects to work on.

A car window sticker being seen more and more at the time said: 'Please God, let there be another oil boom, we'll promise not to piss it away this time'. This referred to the excesses of the early '80s, when the city was awash with money. Many of the locals had got jobs on the rigs, usually working two weeks offshore and then back home for two weeks. For some, the time onshore were spent drinking in the city bars. These were young men, unmarried, cash in their pockets and with lots of mates in the same situation. It was common for Aberdeen bars to be busy during the day. A familiar scene on trains to and from the city would be travelling riggers enjoying lively conversations, the table between them crowded with cans of beer.

A medical study titled *Alcohol Consumption in Offshore Oil Rig Workers*, published by the *British Journal of Addiction* in 1982,[87] reported that 59 men and nearly 30 per cent of the sample studied had drunk the equivalent of four pints of beer a day during the week before they went offshore. (This is above the safe limit as suggested by the Royal College of Psychiatrists.) Six men had drunk more than eight pints a day, another five had emptied at least a bottle of spirits every day and the heaviest drinker had drunk the equivalent of a bottle of spirits and four pints daily. The doctors seemed surprised to find that:

From the total offshore workforce of approximately 2,000 from which this sample was taken, there were only eight medical evacuations in a year which were certain, or likely to be due to alcohol abuse – two cases of alcoholic hallucinosis, one of delirium tremens, three grand mal fits, one case of pancreatitis, and one of hepatomegaly.

There was no drink to be had offshore, it was too dangerous an environment and you needed to be alert at all times. In the early days, an exception would be made for Christmas Day and New Year's Day, when you would get two cans of beer and a glass of wine. This practice stopped after a serious incident took place on a North Sea platform in the early morning of New Year's Day in 1989.[88] I hasten to add that today's offshore workers are a relatively sober bunch. It's an older workforce, the men are mostly married and they have a more balanced outlook on life.

For others, the big money from working in oil bought them fast cars, personalised number plates and they would pursue the local women. Weekend nights in downtown Aberdeen could be wild. What would surprise the overseas visitors was the sight of young Aberdonian lassies, out and about on freezing-cold winter nights, wearing short skirts and exposing more skin than the weather warranted.

Aberdeen was generally a safe place to work at the height of the oil boom. You would get the usual drunken fights between young guys on a Saturday night and every now and again a domestic murder or two, enough at any rate to keep Stuart MacBride's fictional Aberdeen-based Detective Sergeant Logan McRae hard at work. I attend the monthly meetings of the Aberdeen city centre community council and they start with a police report of the latest crime statistics for the previous month. They are dominated by petty theft, in particular the theft of unattended mobile phones from pubs. One petroleum engineer and a foreign national told me that what he liked about Aberdeen was that there was no danger of you or your family being kidnapped, unlike many other places in the oil patch.

One crime anomaly was the presence of the Italian mafia in Aberdeen for 24 years, specifically, the Camorra mafia from Naples, rather than their Sicilian cousins.[89] They were based out of an Italian restaurant in Union Terrace and used the city for money laundering. From there, the mafia took control of health and fitness centres, restaurants, import-export food firms, pubs and betting shops throughout Scotland. They kept a low profile and attracted little attention. Aberdeen probably suited their purposes well as with the oil industry present, large amounts of international money were being moved through the city's banks without drawing too much attention. They were eventually shut down in 2005, although rumours persist that they are still present in the city.[90]

It was difficult to impress anyone in Aberdeen by driving the latest expensive car, Porsches and the like were commonplace on the city's streets. One recent car theft caught my attention, however. In 2013, a local oil man had five luxury cars stolen from his house in Banchory-Devenick, a rural area on the outskirts of Aberdeen. These were his Aston Martin, a Ferrari, a Porsche 911, a Toyota Land Cruiser and an Audi A5.[91] I would like to think that when I worked for BP in the 1980s, it was my car that got the most attention. It was a red and yellow Hillman Imp with black and white chequered go-faster tape along both sides and powered by an 875cc aluminium engine at the rear of the car. The Imp was one of the last cars to be made in Scotland before the manufacturing plant in Linwood shut down for good in 1981. I had bought it from my older brother Sandy, who loved to tinker around with cars. He had fitted a large motorbike exhaust to the back of the Imp and I never replaced it because I had no idea how to. So when I turned up to the BP office every morning my colleagues would tell me they already knew I was on the way.

Riches and luxury could, however, impress some of the locals. I once overheard a conversation between two elegantly dressed local women in a city restaurant; their American husbands were also there but didn't say much.

One of the women, ensuring that all around could hear, shrieked out in a strong Aberdeen accent, 'Would you believe this, the bathroom in the master suite in our hotel in the Sacramento Holiday Inn was fitted with gold taps!'

I was fairly boring by comparison. One day at the oil company office, the mail boy brought me a letter in amongst the usual office memoranda that usually arrived with the mail round. I was astounded to find it was a bill for several hundred pounds for women's jewellery, a sizeable fraction of my annual salary. The bill was for someone with a similar name as me, a drilling engineer who obviously made far more money than I did and liked to hang around a lady with expensive tastes.

The seriously rich oilies could buy a house in Aberdeen's most expensive streets, Rubislaw Den South and the parallel street, Rubislaw Den North. Many of these resembled small castles and had been built by rich merchants in Victorian times. Between the two streets lay the 14 acre private park of Rubislaw Den, owned by the residents and available for their exclusive use only. They access the park through their back gardens, the entrance gates for the public having long been padlocked shut.

For most Aberdonians, the most memorable event of the early '80s was a football match. This took place on the evening of 11 May 1983, when Aberdeen beat Real Madrid 2-1 in the European Cup Winners cup final.[92] The final was held in the Swedish port of Gothenburg and the considerable travelling support had been transported there by a large ferry. For those who stayed at home like me, there were wild celebrations that night, cars drove up and down Union Street hooting non-stop and even the boats in the harbour joined in sounding their horns. I would have liked to have travelled with the Aberdeen fans to the match, but then again I was far too busy getting the nation's oil out of the ground.

5

Local Heroes

THE YEAR WAS 1971 and Shell were planning a wildcat well, the term given to an exploration well drilled miles from any known oil field and where there is no guarantee that you will find anything. The name comes from onshore America where wildcat wells are typically drilled where the wild cats live. The wells are high risk ventures, but also high reward if you strike a big oil field in an area where nobody else has found one before and you can use this information to furtively grab the nearby acreage knowing that it is prospective.

The wildcat well was located in block 211/29, 240 kilometres to the north of the nearest well drilled so far in the North Sea.[93] The previous oil field discoveries had been made in the North Sea offshore from the Scottish mainland between Aberdeenshire and Edinburgh; the 211/29-1 well was to be drilled approximately 160 kilometres to the north-east of the Shetland Isles.

The Shell exploration team had defined a very large prospect in a fault block located beneath the prominent seismic marker called the Base Cretaceous Unconformity, a feature which could be picked over large areas under the North Sea. There was a degree of uncertainty about the interpretation. A large structure was clearly there, but what if there wasn't any reservoir rock within it? When BP had found the Forties field the previous October they had carried on drilling to see what lay underneath the reservoir interval. When they drilled through the Base Cretaceous Unconformity they had gone into a pile of volcanic lavas, a rock type that has no porosity and does not usually contain oil. Perhaps BP had found the 'basement', the level in a petroleum province below which no oil is found.[94]

Shell took a chance and the well discovered the giant Brent field in July 1971, a field which would go on to produce two billion barrels of oil. The find was of great importance. It was almost certain that similar fields would be found in the area and the fact of the discovery was highly privileged information of immense commercial value to the company. (The Shell exploration manager at the time, Myles Bowen, took special care to see that the information was kept quiet. This apparently even extended to displaying fictitious maps in the Shell office, showing the well to have been dry.)[95] Shell never even tested the well, which is normal practice for a discovery.[96] The burning flare from safely burning off the hydrocarbons produced from the well test would have been visible to any passing ship.

The well had come in at the same time as the government had announced details for the next licensing round. The fourth licensing round was a big one as 436 exploration blocks had been put on offer and following the announcement of the Forties discovery nine months earlier, there was clearly going to be a tremendous amount of interest amongst all the oil companies. Many of the blocks on offer were in the immediate area of the new discovery including one where sealed cash bids were being asked for.

Shell took care not to announce the Brent find until August 1972 after the results of the licensing round were announced earlier in the year. Because they had kept quiet on this crucial piece of information, Shell had been able to secure acreage in an area where several large oil fields were later discovered. They had even offered £21 million in the fourth licensing round for the so-called golden block near the Brent field. Oil was found there too, and it would later be developed as the North Cormorant field. Shell secured several blocks in the area and found numerous oil accumulations including Dunlin, Eider and Tern fields. The other oil companies didn't hang around either. Much of the northern North Sea had opened up as highly prospective, with major discoveries made at what would become the Magnus, Ninian, Thistle and Alwyn fields, among others.

Shell and everyone else were now looking for a suitable onshore terminal as a landfall for the oil produced from their newly discovered fields. The only feasible choice was the Shetland Isles, nowhere else was close. The oil company onslaught that had piled into Aberdeen was now going to hit the Shetlands. Big Oil was about to negotiate with one of the world's smallest municipal authorities, the Zetland County Council, which was based in Lerwick town hall and looked after the interests of a Shetland Isles population then numbering 17,325. It was Godzilla versus Peter Rabbit, or so it seemed.

Many Shetlanders were less than enthusiastic about the oil business turning up on their shores. The 1973 Interim County Development Plan drawn up by the council summed up the prevailing attitude at the time:

This Council, recognising that it may be in the national interest that Shetland be used for oil installations, and having sought to devise policies and to provide machinery which recognise the national interest while protecting those of the Shetland community, will continue to have regard for the national interest but will give no encouragement to developments and will oppose proposals where these developments or proposals put Shetland at unnecessary risk or fail to provide available safeguards and will at no time put commercial or industrial interests before those of the Shetland community.

Given this somewhat lukewarm response, it looked as if the oil companies would have a lot of wooing to do. It's not as if the Shetland Isles needed the economic boost of North Sea oil, it was doing rather well on its own, despite the dire state of the rest of the British economy at the time. Its small population were working in long-established industries such as fishing, agriculture and knitwear; unemployment was minimal.

A pivotal role in handling the oil companies was taken by Ian Clark, the manager of the county council. A devoutly religious man and a lay preacher, his life has been motivated by deep moral principles. Born in industrial Motherwell, one of a family of six, he would leave school at the age of 15, Ian Clark then qualified as a chartered accountant by correspondence course and worked his way through local authorities, eventually becoming County Clerk and General Manager (chief executive) of the Zetland County Council in 1970.

His background growing up in the depressed Central Belt of Scotland would give him an insight into what the Shetlands was facing with the arrival of the oil companies. He had seen what could happen to a close-knit community when the coal industry it depended on went into decline. He was acutely aware that the arrival of the oil industry into a community with a currently thriving mixed economy could have a destabilising influence, perhaps shattering all that had been there before. Ian Clark and the council didn't wait for the oil companies to take the initiative. Big Oil was moving into the Shetland Isles whether the local population liked it or not, so it was clearly a situation that had to be managed somehow. The council moved fast.

What happened next was heroic. If you are up against a tank, you have to become a tank. The council mirrored the good business principles that come naturally to a large oil company. First you need to know the exact outcome you want out of any situation. Then you have to work out what you need to know to bring about that outcome and to identify the key tasks required to get there. And like any tank, you proceed directly to your objective, no matter what gets thrown at you.

In early 1972, the council brought in technical experts to identify the best sites to bring oil onshore and they reported their findings in July 1972. The entire consultation exercise, including this first study, would eventually cost them more than a year's total income from the rates, but it would bring dividends in the end. Yet there was something highly unusual about all of this – the study had been launched and completed before any oil discoveries had been announced off Shetland, there hadn't even been any credible rumours as such. Although oil had been found, little in the way of information had leaked out from Shell and the Brent discovery would not be announced until the beginning of August 1972.[97] Nevertheless, something was going on; the oil rigs had started appearing off the shoreline, the supply boats were leaving Lerwick harbour and the land speculators had already moved in. The council were not messing around. They would be ready and waiting, whatever happened.

What the council didn't want was for each individual oil company to build their own separate oil terminal dotted around the coastline and marring the landscape in an environmentally sensitive area. Whether the oil companies liked it or not, they would have to share the use of an enormous oil terminal built in one place only. Another advantage was that if an accident happened, it would be more manageable if the facilities to cope with it were all together. The most likely area identified by the Council for an oil terminal was Sullom Voe, 46 kilometres north of the island's capital Lerwick. It is a long, deep, sheltered inlet ideally suited for berthing large oil tankers with relatively flat-lying land on the eastern shore. Hardly anyone lived in the area and it had another advantage; there was an abandoned Second World War RAF air force base nearby at Scatsta which could be resurrected as small airport to service the new terminal. The inlet had been used during the Second World War as a base for flying boats from where they would take off looking for German U-Boats in the North Atlantic. The RAF base had been constructed for fighters to protect the flying boat base from attack.[98,99] It was needed; the first bombing raid on the British Isles during the Second World War had been at Sullom Voe.

The council drew up a plan ahead of any discussions with the oil companies. They decided to locate the new oil terminal at Sullom Voe as recommended by the consultants and perhaps lesser developments would be allowed in places where the work was needed. The council would own the land that the terminal was going to be built on and they would become joint owners of the Sullom Voe terminal along with all interested oil companies. Revenue would come to the council from the operation of the terminal and the adjacent port.

When the oil companies came in for talks they were taken aback at what was being proposed. They could not believe that the council wanted to have an active involvement in the oil terminal, and informed Ian Clark that they had produced oil all over the world and had never been asked to do anything like this. He would not give in.[100]

If the oil companies were to prove difficult to the Zetland county council, so would parts of the local population. Local councils in general are not universally trusted by the populace at large. Most do difficult and demanding work which isn't always appreciated by those they serve. Nevertheless, they are prone to common problems inherent in their political structure and often an administration gains power on the back of promises made, only to fail to deliver. They are considered to be partial to business interests at the expense of the general population and this has frequently proved to be a valid criticism. And some councillors want to put their name out there too: it's not enough to be seen to have efficiently managed the refuse collection, why not come up with some grandiose mega-expensive plan that is clearly seen to be your initiative? And what could be more grandiose than a tiny county council, serving a population of 17,325 people, entering into a mega-expensive joint venture with the biggest oil companies in the world?

In their defence, the Zetland council were pragmatic enough to see that it would be impossible to stop oil-related developments in the Shetlands, the appropriate response was therefore to keep control of developments and get some benefit from the situation. They recognised that they had some leverage over what would happen. As the planning authority, they had jurisdiction over any proposed developments for the islands. The UK government could overrule them, but that would bring practical problems before long. It was very likely that more plans would be submitted by the oil companies to the council for planning permission, and if the council made stipulations on these, the national government couldn't overrule them all every time; public opinion in Scotland would move strongly against the government if the perception was that the Shetlanders were being trampled on by vested interests.

Not all of the islanders saw the logic of the council's proposal and many expressed the opinion that the oil companies should be kept well away from their shores – the environment and the Shetland way of life needed to be preserved. What would happen to the existing businesses once all their staff had left to make big money for the oil companies?[101] Could this mean the end for Shetland's fish industry? The nay-sayers also viewed with suspicion the talks going on behind closed doors in the Lerwick council chambers. Where was the openness and transparency in all of this? Was the Shetland way of life about to be bulldozed as a result of concessions made by councillors under duress from Big Oil?

The council also received incoming fire from the UK Government. The oil price had ramped up following the 1973 Yom Kippur war and this provided the frenetic backdrop to the discussions that were taking place. The government was desperate both for the tax revenue to shore up its dire economic situation and to secure a source of oil independent of Arab control. They were worried that the Zetland council's stance could hold up the flow of North Sea oil. Additionally, the outcome of this would be a large sum of money going to the council which would reduce the government's tax take. The government exerted a tremendous amount of pressure on the council behind the scenes and the final agreement with the oil companies was considerably diluted as a result.[102]

If the powerful forces of Big Oil, the UK Government and the sceptical council's voters were not enough to deflect the council off their chosen objectives, another threat to their plans appeared out of nowhere. A consortium of Edinburgh-based financiers and other interested companies had sensed a business opportunity whereby they could operate an oil terminal as a service for the oil companies and charge them for its use.[103]

They made a visit to the islands in the summer of 1972 to investigate and soon discovered the council's plans for Sullom Voe. They had worked out that the council would have to compulsory purchase the land before building could start. They decided to nip in first and pre-empt this possibility, forming a subsidiary called Nordport, headed up by the managing director of a local knitwear factory. The name Nordport was mischievous as it was taken from the council's own name for the Sullom Voe project. In a very short period of time, Nordport was able to buy or secure options for 40,000 acres of land in the Shetlands, including land surrounding Sullom Voe.[104] They submitted their own plan to build an oil terminal but it was rejected by the council planning committee in February 1973.[105] The Nordport initiative spilled over into the political campaign for the county council elections in May 1973.[106] The issue of whether business or the council should be steering the construction of an oil terminal was prominent in the lead-up to the vote. A political party was formed calling themselves the Shetland Democratic Group. One of their prospective candidates was the managing director of Nordport. Their aim was to force the council to rethink their strategy on the oil terminal. Their opposition to the compulsory purchase of property by the council appealed to some Shetlanders who were anxious about this policy. The Group put up candidates for election, securing 10 councillors, the Nordport boss was one of those winning a seat – but not enough to give them a majority in the council administration. With Nordport out of the way and a democratic mandate, the council could now concentrate on building a consensus for their proposals.

What was seen as rampant land speculation by big finance incensed opinion around Scotland and the oil companies realised that public relations were going the council's way.

The council moved to enable what would become an Act of Parliament, the Zetland County Council Act of 1974. This gave them powers that included compulsory purchase over any land needed for oil installations, granted them port and harbour authority over Sullom Voe, and allowed them to take part in commercial enterprise on behalf of the community so as to create an oil fund. The next step was to establish a joint company with the oil companies. The Sullom Voe Association was set up with the council holding 50 'A' shares and the oil companies 50 'B' shares. It would be responsible for the design and construction of the facilities at Sullom Voe, and for leasing the land.

Although everything was in place, there was as yet no agreement on what the payments to the council would be. The detailed negotiations with the oil companies now started in earnest. Ian Clark gained a reputation as a hard-edged negotiator with the oil companies (documents released by the Scottish Office in 2004 show how an oil company executive considered him more difficult to deal with than Colonel Gaddafi of Libya).[107] Clark has something approaching mythical hero status amongst many in today's Shetland Isles.

Essentially he was one of a team of focused and dedicated council officials and councillors who were to achieve the breakthrough with the oil companies. This is not to belittle his achievements, but to emphasise that what happened was a team effort with a remarkable man in the lead.

With an agreement in place, construction work started on the Sullom Voe terminal in 1974, the first step involving the removal of 13 million tonnes of rock and peat from the site. This was dumped into the sea to create extra land for building the terminal. Construction took place over a seven-year period, the workforce reaching 7,200 labourers at one point. When it was opened by the Queen in May 1981, the Sullom Voe terminal had the capacity to receive and transport one and a half million barrels of oil a day. The partnership included 31 oil companies, with BP nominated as the operator of the terminal. It had cost £1.2 billion to build.

Chief Executive Ian Clark and the council team were responsible for extracting a good deal from the oil companies. The money, in regular payments, came mainly from two sources: the first, a disturbance agreement, based on a formula accounting for the number of pipelines accessing the terminal, the volume of oil passing through and a guarantee over the minimum payment ; the second, the revenue from the Sullom Voe port run by the council. The council also gains income as landowners and by investing in local commercial enterprises. The main revenue agreements lasted until the year 2000.[108]

So in oil-company speak – once the council had negotiated a favourable deal over Sullom Voe – what were the 'deliverables' for the people of the Shetlands? Today, an oil fund of over £400 million is held in two separate trusts for the 23,000 islanders.[109] Jonathan Wills in his book A Place in the Sun: Shetland and Oil has described the benefits that arose out of the oil fund. New schools were kitted out with modern equipment; leisure centres and community halls were built. The Shetlands now has eight sports halls complete with swimming pools. Three of these costing over £1 million each were built on the islands of Unst, Whalsay and Yell, each with a population of a thousand.

The oil fund also paid for a miniature welfare state for the Shetland islanders. An annual £200 Christmas bonus was provided to every household with a pensioner or a disabled person. The oil fund managers have since cut back on this provision now, but the intent was there in the early days. Pensioners living alone were given home helps and specialised care when it was needed. Their houses were improved, bathrooms, kitchens and toilets upgraded courtesy of the charitable trust. Disabled people are provided with day-care centres and given subsidised holidays. Carers could leave their disabled relatives in respite care homes and get away for a holiday every now and again.[110]

This story was also repeated in the Orkney Islands. Here, the efforts of the local council to establish revenue from the oil industry provided the inspiration for the popular film *Local Hero*, a whimsical comedy based on the efforts of the American oil tycoon Felix Happer (played by Burt Lancaster) to set up an oil terminal next to a Scottish village. The inspiration for the film had been the visit of Armand Hammer to the Orkneys to establish an oil terminal on the Island of Flotta.

Like the Shetlands, Orkney has a single oil terminal on the island of Flotta which handles oil produced from fields in the Moray Firth such as Piper and Claymore. The deal is a bit different from that of the Shetlands. The council are not direct partners in the oil terminal but nevertheless receive disturbance payments based on the volume of oil handled by the terminal.[111] The Orkney Isles Strategic Reserve Fund (the Oil Fund) was worth £198 million in 2013 for a population of 21,400 people.[112]

6

New Challenges

THE NORTH SEA provided a new challenge for the international oil industry. The oil companies had ventured offshore before, most notably in the Gulf of Mexico along the southern coast of the United States. Here the weather conditions, give or take the odd hurricane or two, were mostly benign and the water depths under investigation at the time were relatively shallow, generally less than 90 metres. The shallow water depths of the southern North Sea at less than 40 metres were thus accessible as a result of the technology transfer from the Gulf of Mexico.

The northern North Sea was deeper than this. In the area north of a line drawn east from Aberdeen, the water depths are typically between 75 and 180 metres. The weather conditions could also be much harsher than is normally experienced in the Gulf of Mexico. Oil rigs and oil platforms had to be built to handle these conditions.

First of all, the oil fields needed to be explored for and found. The quality of seismic data used to locate them improved considerably during the lifetime of the North Sea oil industry. As mentioned earlier, the early seismic lines gave only a crude image of the subsurface structure. They were good enough to give an indication of where the big bumps lay and where there was potential for oil and gas traps. Sometimes you would drill into the edge of the structure rather the crest because the resolution wasn't that great, but if there was oil you would know it once the drill bit got down there.

As we have seen, it could prove a major challenge when the seismic interpreter was asked to use the data to locate a multi-million pound platform for the field. And it didn't help when you were drilling new production wells on one of these fields that you weren't absolutely sure where the faults were. Faults are where two segments of rock have moved relative to each other as a result of earthquake activity in the geological past. They separate an oil field into different sectors at different levels. Another reason to pick out faults on seismic data is that you wouldn't want to drill through them if you could avoid it – if you do, you will find that a substantial portion of the reservoir will have been cut out by the fault and the well will produce less oil as a consequence. Trying to pick reservoir faults on the early seismic data was tricky, indeed almost impressionistic given the fuzzy nature of the data. It led to the phenomenon whereby, when a new seismic interpreter came into a reservoir team, the new reservoir fault pattern produced would often be substantially different from the one made by their predecessor. Fortunately, the seismic quality improved over the decades. Seismic processing techniques improved vastly, computing power increased incrementally every year and better navigation techniques meant that you knew more precisely where the seismic reflection had been sourced from.

The development of 3D seismic data was a major technological advance in subsurface seismic resolution. This type of seismic survey is shot to gain data from an array of points at close spacing within the subsurface. Not only did you get a much more detailed image of the substructure, the vast amount of data obtained helps to ensure that everything is imaged in more or less the right place in the subsurface, given that the seismic energy creating the signal could be bouncing all over the place after having struck the top of the reservoir rock. It was later discovered that if you repeated a 3D seismic survey on an oil field which had been producing for several years, the signal from the reservoir would change slightly as the oil had been produced and the reservoir pressure dropped. If you could map out the changes, then this would give you a direct indication of where the oil had been produced from and would also show you where there might be pockets of bypassed oil. This technique has been called 4D seismic in that it is a repeat 3D seismic survey which provides the extra dimension of time. It works on some of the North Sea fields, particularly the shallow ones, but not all of them. Where it does work, the value of being able to guarantee that you could target all the oil in the field and monitor its depletion was worth millions. BP has even found it cost effective to install permanent seabed seismic recorders on two of its fields (Clair and Valhall) so as to monitor oil depletion as it happens.

Once you have your exploration target then you need a rig to drill it. The shallower waters of the southern North Sea were suitable for the use of jack-up drilling rigs. These are used in water depths between six and 45 metres. The jack-up rig has three or more legs that sit on the sea floor. In deeper water such as in the northern North Sea, a semisubmersible rig will be used. This type of rig floats on pontoons and is normally kept in place by several anchors attached to the seabed.

The harsh conditions of the North Sea would put the various rig designs to test. Waves with heights up to 18 metres have been recorded and the oil companies would have to cope with this and more: the rigs and platforms operating in the North Sea are designed to handle wave heights up to 30 metres and wind speeds up to 114 knots, the so-called hundred year storm.[113]

Early on, the North Sea saw several disasters and incidents involving drilling rigs during bad weather.[114] The Sea Gem jack-up rig capsized as it was being prepared to be towed off location in December 1965; 13 men were killed. It had just discovered the West Sole gas field off the Yorkshire coast.[115]

In March 1968 the Ocean Prince semisubmersible rig was destroyed in a severe storm in the southern North Sea.[116] The rig had been drilling with its base resting on the shallow seabed in the Dogger Bank. A gale whipped up in the early hours of the morning; the wind was gusting up to 80 knots and 15 metre waves buffeted the rig. The waves were lifting the rig up and slamming it down repeatedly against the sea floor. The 45 men on board watched in horror as large cracks started to appear in the superstructure.

A radio call was sent out with a Mayday message and to the rescue came Captain Robert Balls, the rig's regular helicopter pilot. Wind speeds were in excess of the safe flying limit, but that didn't stop him. He was on his way in a Wessex helicopter 45 minutes after being woken up by the emergency call at 6am. He kept the fuel load to the minimum so that he could carry off as many men as could be safely carried. The helicopter could normally carry up to 16 men.

Just after 7am, the portside pontoon of the rig split in half and part of the deck collapsed into the sea, taking with it the drilling derrick, the drill floor and the radio room. Things were getting desperate for the crew. Nevertheless, the heroic Captain Balls managed to land his helicopter on the heaving rig and ferried off 19 men to another oil rig which had been drilling 30 kilometres away. He came back, took another 18 men and then returned a third time to pick up the remaining eight crew members. Less than an hour after the last men had been taken off, the entire rig disintegrated.[117] Captain Balls was later awarded an MBE for the immense bravery and skill he showed on that day.[118]

The worst disaster of this kind occurred on the Norwegian side of the North Sea, when the Alexander L Kielland rig, in use to provide accommodation for the men working on the Edda platform, capsized during a storm in March 1980. The wind speeds had been 60 to 75 kilometres an hour and the waves were up to eight metres high.[119] A support pillar gave way, causing the rig to suddenly lurch by about 30–35 degrees to one side, partially submerging the accommodation level at one corner. There then ensued a desperate rush by the men on board to launch the seven lifeboats, but the atrocious weather conditions combined with the tilt of the rig hampered the effort. Only two would eventually be launched and one of them fell upside down into the water. Three of the lifeboats with men in them were smashed against the rig's legs by the waves while being lowered.[120] After 20 minutes the rig capsized, drowning many on board. The disaster prompted a major rescue effort carried out in the strong gale conditions. It involved 71 civilian ships, nine naval vessels, 19 helicopters and seven planes. One British helicopter winchman, Mike Yarwood, rescued 36 men.[121] Some managed to swim to the nearby Edda platform where they were picked up, others were rescued by the early-arriving rescue vessels. Of the 212 men on board the rig, a total of 123 were killed. Rig designs were substantially improved after that.

Underwater engineering would also need to come up with new ways of doing things, particularly given the water depths in the North Sea off the Scottish coast. Offshore operations require divers to work on the underwater kit, more so in the early days than now. Today, underwater robots known as Remotely Operated Vehicles (ROVs) have replaced much of the underwater work that divers used to perform.

The diving method used depends on the water depth. Light tasks can be undertaken by scuba diving down to 30 metres depth. Air diving is used down to 50 metres depth with the diver wearing a diving suit attached by an air hose to the surface. Below 50 metres, the specialist technique of saturation diving is required. It is a sophisticated operation that requires the use of a diving bell and careful decompression. The diver is given a mixture of helium and oxygen to breathe instead of air. The helium replaces the nitrogen in 'normal' air and avoids the problem with nitrogen whereby it forms bubbles in the blood stream as the water pressure decreases as the diver comes up to the surface. The bubbles can block blood vessels and damage the surrounding cellular tissue, a very painful condition known as 'the bends' which in extreme circumstances can kill.

Diving proved to be a hazardous job when the North Sea started. Fatalities occurred at a frequency of about 50 times that of workers onshore.[122] Forty-two divers died in the period between 1971 and 1978.[123] *Noroil* magazine for March 1975 explained why the job was so hazardous. Many divers were inexperienced, would lie about their qualifications to get a job and the diving companies they worked for lacked the financial resources to train them properly thereafter. There was fierce competition amongst the diving companies for work and the smaller companies often found themselves being given contracts for operations that were beyond their capabilities. Much of the work available was at depths reaching the limit of the diving technology available then and the diving technology was primitive.

Per Rosengren writes in *Safety of Diving Operations* about a diving accident in Norwegian waters in 1971. Two divers had been sent down to inspect the drilling equipment on the seabed at a water depth of 68 metres. The operation had been completed without problem but they then got into difficulties on the way up, essentially because of the primitive equipment they were using. They were required to halt their ascent every so often to allow time for decompression so as to avoid suffering from 'the bends'. They didn't have heated diving suits and became chilled in the cold sea water, to the extent that one of the divers became partly unconscious. The support team on the surface lowered a harness to get the unconscious diver back up. When the harness was lowered into the sea again to pick up the second diver, he had gone. His body was never found. Today, that operation would have been considered to have broken every rule and regulation made for offshore diving. Heated suits are now worn and a diving bell is available for use during the dive.[124]

The UK and Norwegian governments, under pressure from the medical profession, eventually stepped in with new regulations to enforce a framework for health and safety in the diving support industry.[125] Today, diving is a far safer job due to these regulations.

Another technology under development at the time was the laying of underwater pipelines in water over 100 metres deep.[126] BP had worked out a method of doing this and spent the summer of 1972 making practice runs in a deep water area of the Mediterranean before laying the Forties pipeline in the colder and choppier waters of the North Sea. The pipeline was incrementally released off the end of a barge, flexing down into the sea. It was coated in high-strength concrete to give it enough weight such that it would lie on the seabed.

The depth at which pipelines could be laid was initially restricted by both pipeline-laying technology and the safe depths at which divers could operate should they be required. This was a particular issue for the Norwegians, where the deep Norwegian Trench intervened between the coastline and the oil fields. When it came to laying pipelines for the Ekofisk field, they would have preferred to land them onshore in Norway but this wasn't practical at the time. The oil pipeline was eventually laid to a landfall to an oil terminal in Teesside in the north of England. This route would take the pipeline to a maximum seabed depth of 92 metres whereas the maximum depth would have been 372 metres on the alternative route to Norway. The gas pipeline from the Ekofisk field also avoided the Norwegian Trench and was laid along the continental shelf to an onshore terminal on the coast of Germany. Norwegian policy was to try and land oil and gas on Norwegian shores if possible and there was a drive to push the limits at which divers could safely operate so this could happen.

In 1981, the Norwegians decided to lay the Statpipe pipeline over the Norwegian Trench, where it would reach a maximum depth of 300 metres. Shell also wanted to develop the Troll field which would require diver intervention on the seabed at water depths of 350 metres.[127] This was deep and would require intensive research into advanced diving equipment, procedures and methods of repair at these depths. The Statpipe was eventually put into operation in 1985.[128]

A dangerous job offshore in the early days was crane operator and there were fatalities before regulations were put in place and new crane designs came about. The cranes were mainly used for transferring supplies from a boat onto the platform or rig, and sometimes for maintenance tasks. They were risky to use in high winds and the crane itself could be vulnerable to shock loads (where a heavy load puts a tremendous stress on the crane following a sudden stop or start).

A crane operator friend who works offshore explained to me what could happen when transferring a load from an offshore supply boat. The boat pitches up and down with the waves and if you hoist the cargo as the boat drops into a wave or it snags on the boat, the shock load can increase the force on the crane by up to three times the weight of the cargo being lifted.[129] In the worst case, the crane could be ripped off its pedestal, toppling into the sea along with the operator.

This has happened several times. In one such incident on a North Sea oil rig in 1975, tragedy was to ensue. The crane had been lifting a 16 ton load from a supply boat alongside the rig. The boat did not have the typical design with a clear stern. When the boat moved with the waves, the load snagged on the tailgate of the vessel and the crane came crashing down into the water. The crane operator, David Murray, managed to escape from the cab and was seen swimming in the sea. Knotted ropes were lowered from the side of the rig and lifebelts thrown to him but he was unable to catch hold of them. When a lifeboat was finally launched, one of the knotted ropes fouled the propeller and rudder, leaving the craft unusable. The waves pushed David Murray away from the ropes; he then hit the side of the rig and drowned.[130]

Safety offshore has improved drastically down the decades. The oil companies instil a strong ethic of safety even with their onshore staff. If you work for an oil company you are obliged for safety reasons to hold the handrail when using the stairs and to reverse park your car in the company car park. This ensures a more orderly evacuation of the company's premises should the need arise.

If you work offshore, you are required to undergo safety instruction courses. I have been trained in offshore survival and fire-fighting techniques, the latter involving fighting real fires ranging from the kitchen hob variety up to a full-scale simulated oil platform fire. Amongst other pieces of knowledge, I now know how to get out of a ditched helicopter sinking upside down through the sea and to escape from a smoke-filled room (crawl along the floor with your nose against the ground as there is a thin layer of fresh air drawn into the room at this level).

Drilling technology also improved considerably over the decades since North Sea oil was discovered at the end of the 1960s. One technique that made a difference in many North Sea fields was the ability to drill horizontally through the reservoir interval. The well starts normally, drilling vertically down from the seabed, but then the wellbore trajectory is gradually turned round until it is orientated horizontally once the reservoir horizon is reached. This has many advantages. It is possible to drill through thin oil zones and produce them effectively. Where the reservoir rock has low permeability such as chalk, a long well in contact with the reservoir can produce at much higher rates than a vertical well. They are also used in the heavy-oil reservoirs that are increasingly becoming targets in the North Sea today.

Yet, horizontal wells are not easy to drill. The problem is that even with today's improved seismic resolution, you still don't quite know where everything is in the subsurface. And when you are drilling a horizontal well this is the major problem. In the early days of drilling horizontal wells, a Shell petroleum engineer carried out a straw poll of his colleagues throughout the industry to try and get an idea of just how effective these type of wells were proving to be. He discovered that about half of the attempts were successful, and the other half were either described as failures or 'too early to say yet'.[131] The most successful horizontal wells end up as the best producers in a field; the failures are calamitous.

Steering a horizontal well can be a sophisticated operation. Measuring devices just above the drilling bit record the physical properties of the rock in the borehole. The data is sent digitally as a series of pulses up through the drilling mud in the borehole and a detector on the rig converts the mud pulses into electronic signals. These are then passed over the internet from the rig to the oil company's office offshore, where the geologist reads the data and then works out what type of rock was being drilled through. If the geologist then decides that the information shows that the drill bit is straying out of the formation, they will ask the engineer to alter the angle of the drill bit so that it stays within the target zone. Signals are sent to the drilling assembly in the hole via mud pulses from the surface and the drilling bit will be oriented in the direction you think you need to go in.

I know from my own experience that even with all this hi-tech equipment, it is possible for things to go wrong with these operations. The information you have from the subsurface is often too imperfect for the level of confidence you need to keep the well on track within the oil zone.

A colleague told me about a horizontal well that had been planned for a northern North Sea field. The well found the reservoir target more or less in the right place but the interval was full of water as a result of the oil having been produced from a nearby well. That wasn't supposed to have happened and everyone was in despair. While the managers met to figure out what to do – the sensible decision was to abandon the well – the drill bit crossed an unmapped fault in the field and the reservoir sandstone on the other side of the fault was full of oil. And it kept drilling within oil-bearing sandstone. They took that well result thank you very much, even if they didn't have much idea why it had happened.

Horizontal wells are ideal for producing heavy oil. The younger sedimentary rocks of the North Sea commonly contain heavy oil pools. These are shallow reservoirs where the conditions are just cool enough for a particular type of microbe to survive in the subsurface. Unfortunately, they consume the same light fraction of the oil that is refined to make the petrol in your car and the more tarry and low-value part of the oil is what remains afterwards.

I was surprised when working on the oil fields of the Moray Firth in the 1980s to come across a large heavy oil pool in the shallow interval. It didn't appear on any maps and hadn't even been given a name. 'Curious,' I thought and made some rough calculations, coming up with an impressive oil in place estimate of over half a billion barrels for the unnamed field. The well that found it had tested the oil zone to get an idea of the flow rate and it had barely dribbled out of the reservoir. I showed the results to the reservoir engineer in the team and he was not impressed, saying, 'That oil sample has the consistency of a house brick.' We then concluded that this was an opportunity for the 21st century, not the 1980s.

We were right. With the cheap and easy oil becoming harder to find in the first few years of the 21st century, oil companies are targeting heavy oil pools, particularly in the northern North Sea. A notable development is Statoil's Mariner field.[132] This is expected to start producing in 2017, with anticipated reserves over a 30-year life span of at least 250 million barrels out of the 2 billion barrels of oil in place.[133] It is one of several similar heavy oil pools in this part of the North Sea.

Heavy oil is not easy to produce. Its syrup-like viscosity causes it to flow at sluggish rates. Onshore, heavy-oil fields are produced by injecting steam into them to make the oil flow that bit more easily. It's even been known for onshore operators to produce heavy oil by setting fire to one end of the oil zone. They inject air to keep the flames going – the heat and the gases driven off help to mobilise the oil so that it can be produced at the wells. These methods are impractical offshore.

The alternative is to drill long horizontal wells through the oil zone and with more oil in contact with a longer well, the higher the flow rates will be. Water is also injected into the field to keep the pressure up. Many wells are needed to get a reasonable field production rate. Statoil are anticipating drilling about 140 targets within the Mariner field reservoir for both production and injection purposes.

The heavy oil fields are not the only challenging reservoirs that the oil companies are now developing. One other category comprises the deep High Pressure High Temperature (HPHT) reservoirs, technically defined by the UK government as fields with pressures in excess of 10,000 pounds per square inch and/ or temperatures in excess of 300 degrees Fahrenheit.[134] The pressures are so high that the pressure in one of the fields was once described as the equivalent of two elephants standing on a postage stamp. The temperatures can reach a point where it is too hot for welded equipment to be used in the wells as the solder will melt. Electronic instruments can also fail due to the excessive heat.

The fields are deep, commonly 5,000 metres or more below the seabed.

Productive gas condensate fields found at these depths in the central North Sea include the Shearwater, Elgin and Franklin fields. The West Franklin field is the deepest in the North Sea with the crest of the reservoir structure at a depth of 6,000 metres under the seabed.[135] Astoundingly, due to an accident of circumstances, the sandstones are still porous at this depth despite the crushing weight of rock lying on top of them. Reservoir sandstones with properties that would be excellent for much shallower oil fields have survived at depths of up to six kilometres, depths where elsewhere geologists normally find cemented, low-porosity rock with very little hydrocarbon-bearing potential.

The first well drilled in this area in September 1988 became a disaster when the well blew out on encountering a high-pressure gas condensate reservoir.[136] The hydrocarbons escaped to the surface under the drilling rig and caught fire. The rig crew managed to get into the life boats and evacuate the rig in time, but unfortunately a decision was made to send the radio operator back onto the rig to call for help and a life was needlessly lost.[137] Timothy Williams was 25 years old and this was his first time on a North Sea rig. He had been on holiday from his usual job in Hong Kong and had taken the radio operator's post to raise money for a holiday flat back in the UK.[138] The blowout took place only three and a half months after the Piper Alpha disaster.

The burnt-out rig, the Ocean Odyssey, was moored at the Dundee waterfront for several years; I saw it several times from the window of a train crossing the Tay railway bridge. It was later bought, refurbished and adopted for a totally different role. Relocated to the South Pacific, it was used as a commercial launch pad for rockets delivering satellites into Earth orbit.

Only the major oil companies now get involved with these HPHT fields given the experience, know-how and investment required to operate these fields safely. This knowledge is transferrable elsewhere. Many of the world's recent hydrocarbon discoveries have been in HPHT areas offshore – Brazil for example, where some enormous discoveries have been made in the Santos basin.

7

Offshore

THE BIG EVENT of the 1970s was when the Queen pushed a button at BP's Aberdeen office in 1975 and inaugurated the Forties oil pipeline. For me, it was when I graduated with an honours degree in geology and mineralogy from Aberdeen University in 1977. Whereas many of my colleagues went straight into the oil industry, I was focused on an academic career, pursuing research instead.

It may seem strange to some that despite the oil industry turning up in my home town, I should spurn the possibility of starting a promising and well-paid career in oil in order to pursue academic research. Here's why. The science of geology grabs those initiated into its mysteries by creating a sense of awe and wonder. Most geologists become obsessed with the subject. It is nothing less than the study of the history of the Earth over billions of years and how life started and evolved. It's a profession where you can visit localities all over the world and uncover moments preserved in the rocks that are snapshots of the march of geological time.

For instance, the same year I eventually started work for North Sea oil and on my 25th birthday, I visited a clay pit near London's Gatwick airport to help a colleague collect samples for his research on fossil plankton. This is a research topic of enormous interest to the oil industry as fossil plankton is used as an indication of the age of the rock being drilled through. The clay was part of the Wealden Group of rocks laid down in the early part of the Cretaceous Period between 125 and 140 million years ago.

We asked one of the workmen for permission to enter the pit. Like many quarry and pit workers he was fascinated by geology and knowledgeable in the subject. He told us that the occasional dinosaur bone turned up in the pit, the last one only a few years previously. He had noticed that the clay around the bone had been discoloured a distinctive red colour. 'Now it just so happens,' he said, 'I noticed a red-coloured patch just like that yesterday.'

We wandered over to the spot and there in front of us was a dinosaur thigh bone almost a metre long sticking at an angle out of the ground. The bone was later identified as belonging to a species called *Iguanodon*, a relatively small dinosaur at three tonnes weight and 10 metres long. They were herbivores, browsing leaves off the trees in large quantities. The popular image of dinosaurs as terrifying carnivorous aggressors is misleading, as almost all of them were vegetarian. As in any predator-prey community, the predators such as *Tyrannosaurus rex* were very much in the minority.

Geology is like detective work. The closest comparison is perhaps to the methods of Sherlock Holmes, using detailed knowledge and hard work to build up a body of facts before presenting evidence-based analysis to explain the turn of events. Geologists looking at the Wealden Group rocks have deduced that the clay was laid down in a lagoonal area with the occasional river cutting through the lagoons on the way to the sea. Dinosaurs wandered along the shoreline and fed on the leafy woodlands to be found there. This is one example out of many such geological case histories. A vast body of knowledge has been built up in this way to give geologists an overall picture of the history of the Earth from its origins to the present day.

I was keen to do my bit and add to the intellectual stockpile of geological knowledge. When the opportunity came up to move to London and start work as a research and teaching assistant in the geology department at the City of London Polytechnic, I grabbed it. I was to spend three years before the start of my oil industry career studying the volcanic rocks on the Hebridean islands of Skye and Rum. I had been especially interested in examples of where the intense heat of the magma as it rose up through the volcano had caused the surrounding rock to melt. My favourite locality was in Kinloch Glen on Rum, where an erupting volcano had forced its way through an expanse of ancient sandstone rock. The margin of the volcano was surrounded by a zone where the sandstone had melted over a width of about 10 metres. On cooling, the molten material had recrystallised into a bleached-white rock with a beautiful honeycomb texture.

I returned to Aberdeen three years later. My venture into academia had proved a personal disaster, I had fallen out with my supervisors over the scope of the project and relations were very bad between us. The outcome was that without their cooperation I was unable to finish the PhD I had been aiming for despite my determination to do so. I had even been offered a research post in the United States but that depended on gaining my doctorate which was now impossible. My professional career was destined to take another path.

After being unemployed for three months I managed to land a job with an oil service company as a mudlogger, monitoring drilling operations. Mudloggers are usually graduate geologists, yet in spite of their professional status, mudlogging was actually the lowest paid job of any on the rigs. The mudlogging companies were in vicious competition with each other and salaries suffered as a result. Ambitious mudloggers didn't hang around in the job too long, they would use their offshore experience to get a better paid job on the rig or else return to university to get a Masters in petroleum geology or geophysics and hope to get a job with an oil company. The job was an important one, nevertheless. The mudlogger would often be the first to recognise where something has gone dangerously wrong with the drilling operation, alerting the drilling crew accordingly.

I was given my initial training in the office and then hung around onshore for another three months while they tried to find me a hands-on training spot on an oil rig. The highlight of my day involved rising out of bed and walking into the city centre for a lunchtime pint at the Prince of Wales pub.

The regulars in the pub would ask me if I was unemployed and I would reply that I was working for an offshore service company, 'Which rig?' they would ask.

'Dunno,' I would reply, 'I've been waiting over two months for them to set up my first trip offshore.'

They would marvel at the idea of been paying paid a salary for doing nothing. 'I wish I could get a job like that!' I was often told.

I was eventually sent offshore over the Christmas week of 1980 to an oil rig in the Norwegian sector. The semisubmersible rig was drilling an appraisal well for one of the early Norwegian oil discoveries. I had a new career path now and after my false start, I was determined to succeed in my new role. I was keen to learn everything there was to know about the oil business and this was my first opportunity to do so.

I took a scheduled flight to Stavanger and from there flew out to the rig by helicopter. The first thing you are told when you land on an oil rig or platform is how to escape from it in an emergency. You get taken to your muster station, the area where you go if the general alarm is sounded, you are shown where the life jackets are and then assigned to one of the lifeboats. The accommodation on the rig wasn't great; I was in a four-man cabin next to the rig generator and it was very noisy. As a trainee, I couldn't really complain. The food was good and sometimes exotic – it was rather strange to eat a reindeer steak in Christmas week.

The drilling technology I saw on the rig was impressive. Wells are often drilled to depths of two to three kilometres, sometimes more. The drill pipe is typically only five inches in diameter (drillers haven't discovered the metric system yet), and the whole length of pipe in the hole is referred to as the drill string, an appropriate metaphor. The entire string is rotated at the surface by a motor. Everything needs to be kept in tension to ensure that the rock bit turns at the bottom of the hole and the attached spaghetti-like drill pipe doesn't buckle or twist apart. This is achieved by placing heavyweight drill pipe just above the bit. The pipe is hollow and drilling mud flows down the inside exiting through nozzles in the drill bit at the bottom of the hole. The mud acts to cool down the bit and also lifts the drilled rock fragments up to the surface as it circulates back up between the outside of the drill pipe and the borehole wall.

I was to learn the hierarchy of the various jobs in the drilling operation. The roustabouts carry out the ancillary work on the drilling operation while the roughnecks operate the drilling equipment on the rig floor to aid in screwing in 30 foot lengths of drill pipe as the drilling proceeds; or alternatively unscrewing the entire drill pipe as the bit is pulled out of the hole. The driller is on the brake in the 'dog house', his cabin overlooking the drilling area. Here he keeps an eye on various dials so he can judge how much weight to put on the drilling bit at the bottom of the hole to ensure that it drills ahead efficiently. The boss of the operation is the toolpusher who coordinates the activities of the drilling crew.

These guys are mostly contractors working for the company hired to do the drilling. The oil company would have a drilling rep on board called 'the company man', who would keep an eye on things to make sure everything was being carried out according to the oil company's wishes. Often the only other oil company representative on the rig would be the geologist, everyone else worked for contracting firms. The geologist acts as the eyes of the operation. They keep an eye on the rock fragments coming up in the drilling mud as we have already seen and they are the first to know when oil has been struck.

Most exploration and appraisal wells are drilled vertically down into the subsurface. Deviated wells are required when you are drilling from a fixed oil platform or pre-drilling wells prior to installing a platform. The wells are initially drilled vertically but at a given depth they turn outwards from underneath the platform, commonly at angles up to 60 degrees from vertical. For reservoirs at normal depths in the subsurface it's possible to drill up to a three kilometre radius outwards from a platform in this way. This is the main reason why the larger fields have more than one platform, so as to ensure that the field is developed with a reasonable spread of wells.

Every now and again, there will be a requirement to core the reservoir interval. This is where the drill bit is replaced by a core barrel, a specialised assembly which will cut a cylindrical core of rock from the formation, typically four to five inches in diameter and 30 feet long, longer if two or three extra barrels are added in tandem. It's an expensive operation as every time the core barrel fills up, the drill crew then have to haul it up to the surface and then run in again to take more core. It could sometimes take a week of drilling time to take core from a thick reservoir interval. Nevertheless, it is important to get core from the reservoir; it gives you a great deal of information essential to understanding how the reservoir performs, how much oil is stored in the rock and what geological processes were responsible for forming the reservoir rock itself.

One of my jobs offshore as a geologist would be to retrieve the core as it came up to the surface. I would stand on the drill floor as the core was emptied vertically from the core barrel onto a mat, being careful not to get any of the core landing on my hand – the weight of the rock would have crushed it. Cylindrical columns of rich-brown oil-bearing sandstone were laid out before me, dark gobbets of oil bubbling up from the rock in places. I would carefully lay out the lengths of rock in marked trays making absolutely sure that each section was laid out in the same order as it had been in the reservoir.

Sometimes things go badly wrong with a drilling operation. The drill pipe can get stuck if the rock on the outside of the borehole collapses on top of it. In the shallower rock strata of the North Sea, the clay in the mud rock has been known to react with the water in the drilling mud by absorbing it and then swelling up. The American drillers in the early days used to call the swelling clays 'gumbo' because when the material came up in the drilling mud it would look to them like the viscous, thick, chunky soup of that name, a speciality of the state of Louisiana. Drilling through 'gumbo' was once a big problem in North Sea wells and the hole would often collapse in on itself when the rock lost cohesion. The use of oil-based rather water-based drilling muds means that this section of the hole is no longer a big concern for the drillers.

Another common problem happened on my first well operation. A section of drill pipe twisted off and fell to the bottom of the hole. The drillers had to spend a couple of days trying to retrieve the detached pipe. This is what they call a fishing operation. Specialist tools are used to try and fish out the drill pipe. Sometimes after a day or two of frustrated attempts to retrieve the pipe, they would just give up and pull what was left of the pipe out of the hole, put a new drill bit on and then branch off the hole to drill around the abandoned pipe.

Problems can also arise when the drilling mud starts to disappear into the formation, commonly through open fractures in the rock. This is a hazardous situation as one of the functions of the drilling mud is to contain any oil or gas from coming up the hole. It achieves this by sheer weight of the fluid in the hole pressing down on the reservoir and if the mud level drops off too much, then oil and gas can enter the borehole with potential to blow out at the surface. When this happens, the drillers will top up the well with mud from their reserve tanks while throwing anything in the hole that could clog up the feature that's drinking the mud in large amounts. This includes amongst other materials, sawdust, shredded newspaper and even walnut shells.

The world's most spectacular example of lost drilling mud happened in 1980, a month before I first went offshore.[139] Texaco had been drilling in a Louisiana lake just inland from the Gulf of Mexico. Unfortunately, they had overlooked one critical factor in their planning – there was a working salt mine directly under the rig site and they drilled into it. Not only did they lose control of the fluid levels in the well, the lake waters started to enter the borehole. Fortunately, the men in the salt mine managed to escape as the mine shafts started to flood. The force of the water entering the borehole soon widened it into a gaping sinkhole large enough to swallow the drilling rig itself, 12 boats and a large number of trees that had fallen into the lake when the banks were undermined by the fast flowing currents rushing towards the hole. Nobody was killed, but a tremendous amount of damage was done to the lake environs and the salt mine.

During my first trip offshore, I was to learn about the problems drillers encounter with shallow gas found in the Ice Age sediments. The methane gas is a by-product when microbes digest organic material buried in the subsurface. Some shallow-gas zones may also have been sourced by gas leaking from the deeper oil reservoirs. You can see evidence for gas leaking off some of the deeper oil fields on seismic data. The gas causes the seismic response to become fuzzy and diffuse where it leaks off from these fields, a feature referred to as a 'gas chimney' by seismic interpreters. Shallow gas has nothing to do with oil company activities, it's a natural phenomenon.

Once the gas builds up in the shallow sands, it leaks from there up to the seabed. When oil companies surveyed the floor of the North Sea in the early days of operations, the seabed was found to be covered in craters several tens of metres across, marking where the gas was escaping out of the subsurface. Underwater photographs show parts of the sea floor resembling the cratered surface of the moon. In the year 2000, a curious find was made as part of a study to investigate the craters on the seabed in an area of the North Sea known by fisherman as the Witch Ground, 150 kilometres north-east from Aberdeen. The largest crater, known as the Witch's Hole, is at least 100 metres in diameter. Sitting upright within the crater is a sunken early 20th century steam trawler, raising speculation that a giant burp of gas had escaped from the crater directly underneath the ship, causing it to lose buoyancy and sink, perhaps almost fall, through the gas-charged water.[140]

If a well encounters shallow gas while drilling it's a potentially dangerous situation. Most of the time there is no problem as the gas can be contained. Every now and again the situation can arise whereby the gas rushes up the borehole, escaping at the well head or into the sea. This is a major hazard as the gas can ignite in a fireball that can kill people.

In one incident on the Danish sector in October 1977, a gas blowout occurred on a jack-up rig. An eyewitness present on the rig saw the blowout incident as it developed.[141] He had been inside the rig when the general alarm was sounded. On coming up onto the deck of the rig he heard the roar of the gas which sounded like a jet engine as it came out of the wellhead under great pressure. From there, a column of gas, mud and water could be seen shooting over 50 metres into the air.

Debris was also escaping from the wellhead. I've seen samples of the material which landed on the rig floor after a similar shallow-gas blowout. A number of pebbles were in the sample bag and the first one picked out was a flint. A flint hitting the metalwork of the rig could easily cause a spark to ignite the escaping gas. Something like this must have happened on the Danish rig, as the gas then exploded in a massive roar, a ball of flame briefly covered the entire area of the rig and it then shot skywards in a burning column hundreds of metres high. The blast was powerful enough to knock over the derrick, the metal framework that supports the weight of the drilling apparatus. The intensity of the heat from the flames turned the men's faces red within seconds. Parts of the rig were now on fire and the whole structure was rumbling and vibrating. No instructions were given to abandon the rig but the men jumped off anyway to escape from the intense heat of the flames.

It's a desperate measure to jump from the relative safety of a drilling rig into the sea. The average temperature of the North Sea can vary from about 5° Celsius in winter to about 14° Celsius in summer. Hypothermia can result in less than half an hour in winter, sometimes much sooner. Yet it is not necessarily the cold that will kill you directly; you fall unconscious first, the wave slap fills your mouth with water and then you drown.

In a choppy sea, there is no guarantee that you will be spotted too soon.[142] Fortunately, the weather was calm and the men in the water were quickly picked up by the standby boat that is always kept on station around a floating rig in case of situations like these. Despite the massive explosion, there were no deaths or serious injuries. Two men, who were slightly injured, were airlifted by helicopter and treated for burns in hospital.

The fire burnt itself out after 12 hours leaving an erupting column of gas, water and sand emerging from the well.[143] About a thousand tonnes of sand built up on top of the rig over a period of several weeks and there were concerns that the rig might collapse under its weight. Two months later the well was eventually brought under control and the escaping gas was plugged off.

Another type of shallow-gas hazard comes about if the well is being drilled by a floating semisubmersible rig. The released gas escapes into the sea in such large quantities it turns the water into bubbly froth. The rig can't float in the froth and will sink to the seabed, drowning all on board. You can't even get into the lifeboats because they will sink too.

This is what had nearly happened to the oil rig that I was on in 1980. The manager of the rig told me that their previous well had experienced a shallow-gas blowout. Strangely enough, the drillers hadn't noticed that gas was escaping from the well into the sea and were drilling on regardless. The manager had been on shift at the time and was in his office drinking a cup of coffee and doing his paperwork. One of the kitchen stewards came in to tell him that big gas bubbles were popping out of the sea underneath the rig – 'and was this normal?'

He got an instant answer as the manager pushed him bodily aside and dashed out the door to check for himself. Immediate action was called for.

The anchors were removed in great haste and the rig was towed away from the blowout zone to prevent it from sinking through the gas-charged water.

Another shallow-gas blowout, also in Norwegian waters, threw up what is possibly the oddest story in North Sea oil and gas exploration. This took place in October 1985 on the semisubmersible rig the West Vanguard. Unfortunately, this blowout resulted in an explosion with one fatality. The rig had been damaged by the explosion and was listing to one side. The anchor chains holding the rig's eight anchors were cut to allow the rig to be towed away.

Sometime later, an attempt was made to locate the anchors with view to recovering them. A ship arrived on the scene and a remotely operated vehicle (ROV) was launched into the water. The vehicle was equipped with sonar detection equipment as well as a camera and these allowed the operator on board the ship to steer the ROV in the search for the anchors.

Seven out of the eight anchors had been found by the remotely operated vehicle when in the search for the eighth anchor the sonar detection picked up what appeared to be a very large object. To the operator's immense surprise this showed up on the vehicle's camera as a World War II German plane lying on the seabed.

The subsequent archaeological investigation, as related on a Norwegian military history website, revealed the circumstances as to how the German plane came to be there.[144] This was a Heinkel HE 115, a reconnaissance plane armed with bombs and torpedoes which had been sent out in 1940 to investigate the sighting of British warships in Norwegian waters. On encountering the fleet, it was intercepted by a Skua from the aircraft carrier Ark Royal and was badly damaged by the fighter plane's machine guns. While the Heinkel was returning to Trondheim, it ran out of fuel and was ditched in the sea by the pilot. Another Heinkel reconnaissance plane came out to rescue the men and before returning to base it machine gunned the ditched Heinkel and sunk it. The plane is still there on the seabed. There was some talk of recovering the wreckage for the Norwegian Defence Museum but the cost proved to be too high.

It's usually possible to detect shallow gas and thus avoid drilling into it. Every oil company these days will commission a shallow seabed survey to ensure that no nasty surprises await them when they start drilling at a new location. In some areas of the North Sea shallow gas occurs over such large areas, it may even be a commercial source of gas. Some of it is produced in the Dutch sector of the North Sea. A drawback is that as the gas is so shallow, there is a not a great deal of pressure to push it up a well to the production plant on a platform. Only a small amount of the gas will be produced as a result.

8

The Forties Field

THE RETURN FROM my first trip offshore was memorable to say the least. On 31 December I flew off the Norwegian oil rig to the heliport near Stavanger and then transferred to the airport, arriving at 7pm in the evening. I was a bit early for the scheduled flight to Aberdeen and found myself in the airport departure lounge all by myself. Things livened up when a large crowd of riggers walked in, mostly Glaswegian Scots and Clydesiders going by their guttural, growling accent, a sound which gives them the nickname of 'bears' offshore. They were all in a very buoyant mood at the thought of returning home for the Hogmanay celebrations.

One of the riggers started talking to me and instantly recognised the accent of a fellow Scot. He shouts out to his mates, 'Meet Mike, he's one of us, he's going back home too.' Then my newfound friend informs me that they had all been working on hooking up a Norwegian platform to a pipeline and that their company had hired a private jet to take them back to Aberdeen, 'and the boss has bought an enormous carry-out with all sorts of booze and we are going to have the most outrageous drunken party on the flight back to Aberdeen. Do you want to come with us?'

The idea of a boisterous evening of carousing on a private jet flying over the North Sea appealed very much, especially after a week on an oil rig. There was, however, the nagging thought in the back of my mind that this was not a sensible idea. I would probably have to wait an hour for my luggage to turn up at the other end on the scheduled flight, that is, if it ever turned up at all. I would also be in no great state on arriving at Aberdeen airport after a full-blown session of boozing. With great regret, I caught the regular flight back home.

When I got back to my flat in Aberdeen that night, a Hogmanay party was in full swing. Everybody was well on the way to an advanced state of merriment and the Clash's album *London Calling* was being played over again and again on the sound system. I was sober and couldn't somehow match the boozy frivolity of my friends partying around me. I noticed there were a few letters waiting for me and I opened them. One was from British

Petroleum (BP) offering me a job as a geologist in their Aberdeen office. That cheered me up again and put me in a much better mood to enjoy the New Year celebrations when they came.

I resigned from the service company and started with BP a week later. I had applied not thinking I was likely to succeed; as it turned out, my main qualification for the job was that I was an Aberdonian and perfectly happy to live in the city for the duration. The company had found that few of their staff were keen to stay long in Aberdeen when there was the chance to work in exotic places overseas. BP was therefore looking to employ staff on a local basis, to provide an element of long-term continuity of experience for their producing fields. I joined BP in January 1981 and spent my first three months under the guiding hand of one of the experienced geologists, Hugh MacDonald. Hugh worked on a group that held the miscellaneous oil fields in the companies UK portfolio; fields that were not big projects at the time. Nevertheless, they were an impressive collection which included the West Sole field, the first commercial gas discovery in the North Sea in 1965; the Clair field, not yet developed at that time but with several billion barrels of oil in place; the Wytch Farm field, located on the Dorset coast and Britain's largest onshore oil field and finally, the Beatrice field, which is so close to shore it can be seen from the coast of Caithness.

After this initial training period, my boss Rowland Speers called me into his office and told me that I was to be moved on to my first proper role – planning new wells on the Forties field and helping the engineers work out their development strategy. I was astounded. This was a great deal of responsibility to heap on someone with so little experience. The Forties field was the biggest in the UK North Sea and together with the giant Prudhoe Bay field in Alaska, it kept BP afloat following the nationalisation of their oil field interests in Libya, Iran and Kuwait in the 1970s. I rather unwisely asked my boss if he was sure that he wanted me to do the job given my lack of experience. Rowland told me to have a look around and to see if there was anybody else with the relevant experience that could do the work. He had a point. Back in the early 1980s, the company was almost entirely staffed by youngsters. The old-timers who had worked on its Middle Eastern fields had either retired or were in management. I found out later that none of the other geologists wanted the Forties job. It sounded much too much like hard work and was considered none too glamorous a role. The career-making positions were in the exploration groups where BP was making numerous new finds. If you could get your name associated with the discovery of a big oil field then you had it made forever. Some of these guys are now or have been managing directors of top British companies.

I can't complain, and indeed I am very grateful to BP for giving me the work; the Forties field provided an excellent grounding for my petroleum geology career. The field at the time was producing oil through four fixed platforms, Forties Alpha, Bravo, Charlie and Delta; three more were added later. Each of the platforms had drilling facilities and all four were seeing back-to-back drilling operations, the wells taking about six weeks to complete.

New wells were needed to ensure that that there is sufficient production for the field to make money. Individual wells on the Forties field at that time could produce 10,000 to 20,000 barrels a day, some even produced more than that. Collectively, they would provide a production rate for the whole field of over 400,000 barrels per day in the early 1980s. Many wells would be needed to cover the field; even the best could only access a limited volume of the reservoir. Although a large number had already been drilled in the Forties field so far, more were needed to keep up the overall production rate.

My job was to help plan these wells and to go offshore to bring in the critical reservoir interval. I was also the guy, who after checking that we had drilled a suitable distance through the oil zone, told the drillers when to stop drilling. It always gave me a thrill when I told the drilling manager to call a halt to what was multi-million pound operation. Although I would work a week or more offshore, I never got any time off unless I worked weekends, in which case I would get two days leave in lieu. I always had to go back into the office to plan more wells.

In the 1980s, the job of a reservoir geologist was not as sophisticated as it is now. Today I will build a three-dimensional graphical model of the reservoir geology using specialised computer software; back then I would depend on drawing a series of maps of each of the reservoir zones. The rock formations forming the reservoir and its cap rock are arched into an enormous dome some 90 square kilometres in area. A large pile of hard volcanic rock lies several hundred metres below the reservoir, and when the surrounding sediments compacted and shrunk in response to the immense weight of sediment piled on top of them, the sandstones of the Forties reservoir draped around the volcanic rock to form the dome. The easiest datum to establish was the base of the oil zone. It was almost perfectly flat, with the oil floating on top of water-filled porous rock at a depth of 2,217 metres below sea level.[145]

The first task in planning the well was to justify the operation in the first place. Given that the cost of each platform well would be in excess of a million pounds, we had to show that it would produce extra oil that none of the other wells would produce. Only in this way could the new well be said to make a profit. My maps of the field geology and rock property variation were used to build a reservoir simulation model by the reservoir engineer. This worked like an enormous three-dimensional spreadsheet, with each cell tagged with the rock properties derived from my maps. The reservoir engineer would add in the physical properties of the fluid in the reservoir, the formation pressures and all the production data for all the wells in the field. The idea was that the model would replicate how the field performed as oil and water moved from through the field towards the various production wells.

Once the model had been fine-tuned to match the historical production data from the existing wells on the field, it could then be used to make predictions as to how much oil would be produced in the future including any production from planned wells. These computer simulation models had so many complex calculations to perform; they would take several hours to run before they would give you an answer.

Once the new well location was approved by management, I would then work closely with the well engineers to plan the well path in detail. My maps of the geological structure of the Forties field allowed me to predict where the various formation tops could be found at any new well location. The key formation top was where the top of the Forties Sandstone reservoir was expected to come in. This spot would provide the target for the offshore drillers to aim at while drilling the well. I also provided the depth at which the well should stop, about 50–70 metres below the base of the oil column. The wells were designed to branch out from underneath the platforms to target different parts of the field. In cut-away view the wells under each platform would resemble roots spreading out from beneath a tree. While the well was being drilled, I would plot up the well track in the office to check whether it was on course for the target I had provided. If the well looked as if it might miss the target, I would call the drilling engineers to discuss with them how the well could be brought back on course. The drillers had little tricks they could use in altering the drill-pipe configuration so as to steer the well back to where it was supposed to go. I would also receive telexes from the mudloggers on the rig giving me a description of the rock fragments as they came up from the drill bit. As the expected depth for the reservoir section approached, I would book myself on a helicopter ready to make the 180 kilometre trip from Aberdeen out to one of the platforms on the Forties field.

My trips offshore started with me taking a taxi from the office to the helipad, booking in and waiting along with my fellow passengers to board the chopper. When it was time to do so, the heliclerk would tell us, 'OK guys, on the bus.'

Flying in the helicopter was none too comfortable. It was so noisy inside the cabin you had to use ear defenders. You also had to wear a survival suit over your clothes, which was bulky and would leave you somewhat sweaty after even a short trip offshore. It was designed to keep you that bit warmer and thus keep you alive longer should you somehow end up in the sea. There were no toilets on the helicopter, which was OK if it wasn't too long a journey offshore.

I remember on one flight offshore, reading a newspaper article which quoted the statistic that helicopters were more likely to be involved in a fatal accident than fixed wing aircraft. In a helicopter there were too many moving parts to go wrong and cause it to crash, whereas an airplane could still glide to earth after an engine failure.

There have been some bad helicopter accidents in the North Sea. These included the Brent Spar crash in 1990 (six killed), near Cormorant Alpha in 1992 (11 killed), the Super Puma crash on the way back from the Miller field in 2009 (16 killed) and the more recent crash in 2013 near Sumburgh (four killed). The worst was the Chinook crash of November 1986 with 45 fatalities. The Chinook was essentially a military helicopter with two rotor blades that could carry more passengers and a heavier pay load than the more typical single-bladed helicopter. They were unpopular with the offshore oil workers because they had two engines as opposed to one; that is, double the chance that one of the engines could come apart and cause the helicopter to crash.

The Chinook helicopter was carrying passengers from the Brent field and had been approaching Sumburgh airport in the Shetland Isles when the transmission failed and the two rotor blades collided with each other.[146] The helicopter reared up and then fell tail-first into the sea, breaking up on impact. Remarkably, there were two survivors. A Coastguard search and rescue helicopter had just taken off from the airport on a routine flight and by chance one of the crew spotted an oil slick in the sea. When they flew over to investigate they noticed the two men in the water, one holding onto a piece of wreckage, the other hanging onto the side of a life raft. The men were rescued and flown to Lerwick Hospital, suffering from hypothermia and minor injuries only.

One of the survivors, Eric Morrans, later gave a harrowing account of the disaster in an interview with Scottish Television.[147] He described how he had been half-asleep until the moment the pilot had announced that the helicopter was five minutes away from landing. Seconds later there was an enormous, indescribable bang; the helicopter cabin shook violently, the tail dropped towards the sea, the nose up in the air, and then it started free-falling almost vertically from a height of at least 50 metres. He looked up from where he was sitting – he had been facing the rear of the aircraft – and saw what he described as an audience of faces, all in total shock. There was no noise, no panic, just shock. He remembered to go through his safety drill, checking the exit, ensuring that his life belt was secured and his survival jacket zipped up. He was sitting next to one of the emergency exits and this probably saved him. It was also established later that the section he had been sitting in survived relatively intact after hitting the sea, whereas most of the rest of the helicopter fragmented on impact. Everything happened in a matter of seconds.

He remembers the helicopter twisting as it fell backwards through the air and then he passed out. The next thing he knew was that he had just emerged from the sea. He was totally bewildered and didn't know where he was or what was happening to him. Miraculously, a liferaft popped out of the water just 10 feet away, almost fully inflated. This brought him to and with a few kicks he reached it and managed to grab hold of it. He couldn't get onto it as his shoulder was dislocated and broken, as was one of his wrists, so he just held on tight and blacked out again. The sound of the rescue helicopter brought him around again and it was at this moment he realised that he might be saved. He then saw someone being pulled from the water and the rescue helicopter seemed to move away from him. He had never been so scared in his life before. He couldn't shout, he couldn't wave and he prayed to God that he would be rescued. The next thing he knew was that he was sitting on board the rescue helicopter after having been winched aboard. He attributed his survival to a twist of fate and the grace of God.

Chinooks were not used in the North Sea again. Nobody would have wanted to fly in them after that.

Landing on the platform by helicopter could be a memorable experience; the craft would fly to a point directly above the platform and descend vertically down to the helideck. If you were on the appropriate side of the helicopter you could see the flare stack, where they burned off the excess gas, and you could even feel the heat of the flare through the cabin window. I enjoyed the trips offshore, finding the atmosphere relaxed and friendly. You could sense a strong spirit of camaraderie amongst the workers offshore and they shared a distinctive, dark, sardonic humour, often involving taking the mickey out of one another. There was much practical joking. If you worked on the drilling side and were new to the job, you would be asked to go and ask the drilling manager for the key to the vee-door. The vee-door was a gap in the side of the derrick where pipe and equipment could be lifted into the drilling area and as such the key didn't exist. Of course, the appropriate response was to come back with the biggest key you could find on the rig and present it to the guy who had asked you to fetch it.

Another favourite joke would be played on the divers in the decompression chamber. They would be stuck there for days on end while their body systems slowly became used to normal pressures after coming up from the depths. They couldn't leave in a hurry as they would get the bends on decompressing and being exposed to normal pressures. Stuck in the chamber, there wasn't anywhere they could go. So the riggers would run past the windows of the decompression chamber in large numbers, screaming and waving their hands in the air as if they were escaping from the platform in blind panic.[148]

Not everything was jolly offshore. As onshore, conflict could arise between the workers and their bosses and this had led every now and again to rows on the oil platforms. For example, 35 men were flown onshore from a Brent field platform in January 1976 after a dispute over the hours they were expected to work in icy conditions.[149] In September 1977, 119 men were flown off the

Dunlin Alpha platform after their service company management refused to recognise a workers committee. When they arrived onshore, some of the men claimed that the managers had threatened to call in the Royal Navy, on the grounds that if they didn't leave the platform, they would be legally guilty of mutiny.[150] In October 1978, eight policemen wielding batons and gas pistols were sent off to the Statfjord A platform in Norway to keep order during a strike held by Spanish, Mexican and Portuguese workers protesting against their treatment by an American service company.[151]

The unions have historically failed to gain much influence in the UK North Sea, although there is now union recognition offshore. The offshore workforce have felt themselves vulnerable to instant dismissal if they stepped out of line, even if they raised safety issues. There has been continuing controversy over the allegation that the oil companies maintain a blacklist of workers deemed to be troublemakers, and that they were tagged on the list with the initials NRB: Not Required Back.[152] The UK Offshore Operators Association have said they are stamping out this practice, insisting that if any offshore worker is dismissed, that the reasons for doing so should be fair and transparent.[153]

We were well looked after on the Forties platforms. The galley would provide an excellent spread of food. If you wanted T-bone steak you could have T-bone steak, and it was tempting to try a bit of everything on offer and overeat. If you were worried about this, you could visit a gymnasium on the lower floor to work off any excesses. At seven o'clock every morning and evening a film would be shown in the small platform cinema. The films were usually of the guns, explosions and car chase variety. However, every now and again one of the more arty-type films would get shown. These were never too popular and sometimes I would be the only one left watching the film after all the men had walked out, the projectionist shouting out to ask me if I really wanted to watch this movie. I usually did, as I appreciated the change from the usual fare. Instead of watching the film, you could phone home instead. There was one public telephone on the platform and a long queue of men would be waiting there to phone home to their wives and girlfriends.

Some companies would organise day-trips for the wives to come out to see where their men folk worked. These would be jolly occasions that could sometimes be vulnerable to the quirky sense of humour of the riggers, for instance announcing that a trophy could be claimed by the first couple to 'consecrate' the platform. In reality, any personnel caught attempting to win the trophy would have been instantly dismissed.

Non-human visitors include migrating birds stopping off on the oil rigs and platforms to take a welcome breather on their long flight across the North Sea. Exhausted starlings would commonly land on the Forties platforms and I would feed them scraps of bread. Other creatures also found their way offshore; a hare, probably caught napping inside pipe, and a stray cat that probably wandered into a rig-bound container onshore.

There were occasions when life offshore could be distinctly surrealistic. I had been working on a drilling rig for two weeks and was zombie-tired having had very little sleep all trip. On my way outside to the logging unit, I heard the distinctive sound of the whirring rotors of a helicopter on the helideck, 'Funny,' thinks I, 'I didn't reckon there was a scheduled chopper flight today.'

Then down the stairs from the helideck walks a group of five young women, smiling and laughing at the thrill of being on an oil rig. They looked absolutely stunning to me, despite being dressed in bright orange survival suits. I just stared open-mouthed at them in total astonishment and was given some knowing looks in reply.

Their male chaperone greeted me at the foot of the stairs, despite my blatant rudeness (I was still staring), and said to me in a Canadian accent, 'We're from Dome Petroleum and we are visiting your rig for the day.'

I grunted back at him. I never did find out why the women were visiting the rig. I was much too busy with my work to have time to ask any questions. A few weeks later I was offshore on one of the Forties platforms and I had some idle moments to spare. I walked into the drilling office, located in a portable cabin, and picked up an old copy of the *Oil and Gas Journal* to read. There was an article in there about Dome Petroleum. The Canadian government had introduced a law whereby each job in Canada (with only a few exceptions) had to have a quota of women employees. Dome Petroleum were therefore required to have a certain quota of woman working on all oil-related jobs and had decided that for the drilling operation they would create an all-woman drilling crew. This they had done and the article went on to mention that for their first well, the entire rig crew was female, with the exception of the geologist. My eyes widened as I read this. The article immediately brought to mind my previous meeting with some of the women from Dome Petroleum and I must confess that I went to sleep later that night thinking about what it would be like to work as a geologist for the company. Unfortunately, the company fell into major financial problems shortly afterwards and was taken over by the American company Amoco in 1988. I was never to fulfil my secret ambition of working for them.

These days there are more women offshore than when I worked there although it's still only about four per cent of the regular workforce.[154] Nevertheless, something akin to the spirit of equal opportunity has finally made it out to the North Sea oil industry, although they could do much better.

I had a great deal of work to do offshore on the Forties platforms and would be mostly awake while they were drilling. Every now and again the drilling bit would lose its bite as it became worn down after a few days of use. When this happened, the drill crew would haul all the drill pipe out of the hole, change the bit and then run all the way back in again to start drilling

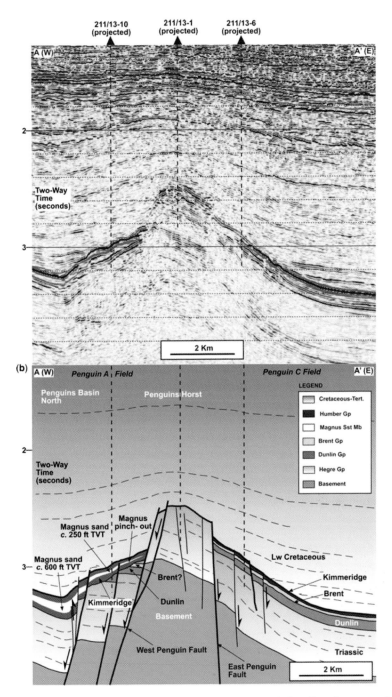

Seismic line through the Penguin Ridge in the northern North Sea (Domínguez, 1995).
A seismic line shows a slice through the subsurface rock and helps to locate oil and gas fields.
The interpretation of the geological structure based on the seismic is shown at the bottom.
(Reproduced courtesy of the Geological Society of London)

The Beryl Alpha oil platform. Deciding where to locate the platform was no easy task given the poor quality seismic data available in the 1970s.
(Courtesy of the Apache Corporation)

The Sea Quest drilling rig. The rig discovered both the first commercial oil field in the UK sector and the largest, the Forties field.
(Reproduced with permission of the BP Archive)

The Queen inspecting a model of a Forties platform, 1975.
(Reproduced with permission of the BP Archive)

Aberdeen heliport. In 1997 at the peak of North Sea activity, 479,100 passengers were flown in and out of North Sea installations and rigs by helicopter.
(Photo: Mike Shepherd)

The helideck on the Thistle oil platform.
(Courtesy of EnQuest)

BP headquarters, Aberdeen.
(Photo: Mike Shepherd)

Shell headquarters, Aberdeen
(Photo: Mike Shepherd)

Aberdeen Harbour from the south. The blue tanks on the right hold drilling mud for
transportation offshore by supply boats.
(Photo: Mike Shepherd)

Union Street, Aberdeen – dubbed 'The Granite Mile' by local historian Diane Morgan.
(Photo: Mike Shepherd)

Triton FPSO vessel.
(Courtesy of Dana Petroleum)

Above: Sullom Voe oil terminal, Shetland.
Revenue to Shetland Council from the
operation of the terminal has created an oil
fund worth over £400 million.
(Reproduced courtesy of the BP Archive)

Right: The Magnus oil platform. Fixed production platforms are suitable for water depths
up to just over 180 metres; the Magnus platform stands in water that is 186 metres deep.
(Reproduced courtesy of the BP Archive)

The BW *Athena* FPSO vessel. An FPSO is a floating production facility that stores the produced oil. It can then be directly offloaded onto a tanker for transport.
(Courtesy of Ithaca Energy UK)

Installing the subsea drilling manifold for the Stella field.
(Courtesy of Ithaca Energy UK)

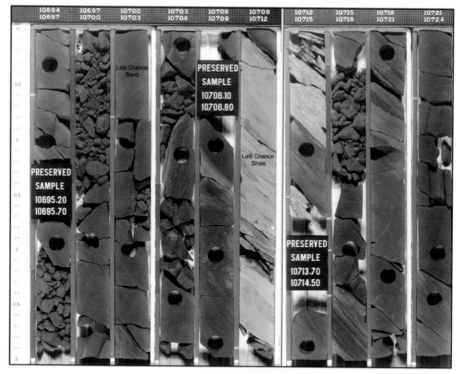

Slabbed core material from the reservoir of the Nelson field. The sandstone beds are stained brown by oil. The light grey rock is mostly siltstone. The round holes are where plug samples have been taken to measure the rock properties.

From Gill and Shepherd, 2010: 'Locating the remaining oil in the Nelson field'.

(Courtesy of the Geological Society of London)

A drill bit used offshore for a North Sea well.

The author retrieving oil-stained core from the reservoir of the Forties field: 'Cylindrical columns of rich brown, oil-bearing sandstone were laid out before me, dark gobbets of oil bubbling up from the rock in places. I would carefully lay out the lengths of rock in marked trays making absolutely sure that each section was laid out in the same order as it had been in the reservoir.'

The Forties Bravo oil platform. In the 1980s the author's job was to help plan new production wells for the Forties field. He would then fly out to monitor the wells as they were being drilled through the oil zone.
(Courtesy of the Apache Corporation)

Reservoir geologist working on a 3D computer model of an offshore field.
(Courtesy of EnQuest)

March 2015: the Mexican President, Enrique Peña Nieto, President of Mexico, in Aberdeen to sign a memorandum 'of understanding on collaboration in the energy sector between Mexico and the UK'. This could be a significant development should more governments with national oil companies follow this example.
(Photo: Mike Shepherd)

Helicopter returning onshore with workers undoubtedly looking forward to some time off.
(Photo: Mike Shepherd)

The Rowan Gorilla VI jack-up rig drilling an appraisal well for the Jackdaw discovery in 2008, central North Sea.
(Photograph courtesy of Stephanie Kape)

Model of the Murchison oil platform, Maritime Museum, Aberdeen. The model gives an idea of the massive scale of engineering that was needed to exploit the North Sea oil fields.
(Photo: Mike Shepherd. Image reproduced courtesy of Aberdeen Council)

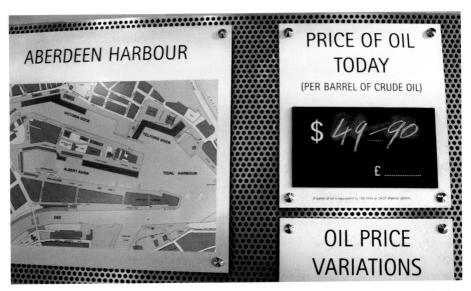

The value of Brent crude as posted in the Aberdeen Maritime Museum, February 2015. The low oil price threatens much of the current activity in the North Sea.
(Photo: Mike Shepherd)

Hydrogen Bus, Aberdeen. An alternative to oil? A fleet of 10 buses run in Aberdeen, powered by hydrogen fuel cells. The project is expensive, £19 million has been spent so far, but once the hydrogen is produced using renewable energy, the operating costs will be minimal.
(Photo: Mike Shepherd)

DEDICATED TO
THE MEMORY OF THE
ONE HUNDRED AND SIXTY SEVEN MEN
WHO LOST THEIR LIVES
IN THE
PIPER ALPHA OIL PLATFORM DISASTER

6TH JULY 1988

The Piper Alpha memorial in Hazlehead Park, Aberdeen.
The Piper Alpha oil platform caught fire in 1988 with the loss of 167 lives.
(Photo: Mike Shepherd)

The Piper Alpha memorial stained-glass window in St Nicholas Church, Aberdeen.
(Photo: Mike Shepherd)

The Clair oil platform. The Clair field, located to the west of the Shetlands, was to feature in the Scottish independence referendum campaign in 2014.
(Reproduced courtesy of the BP Archive)

The No and Yes sides campaign in Aberdeen in the lead-up to the Scottish independence referendum.
(Photo: Mike Shepherd)

anew. This would take about 12 hours and would give me the chance to get some sleep.

Sleeping accommodation on the Forties platforms for the drilling crew and fellow travellers like myself was in the South Truss, an add-on accommodation block suspended from the south side of the platforms and supported by a cantilevered truss. It was a big metal box hanging off the side of the platform, with nothing between the bottom of the South Truss and the waves of the North Sea. The production staff would sleep in what I presumed were the more luxurious state rooms on top of the platform.

I never felt too comfortable lying in bed in the South Truss; as I tried to get to sleep, worries would queue up in my mind. Not far below where I lay were the waves of the North Sea and I worried about the integrity of the cantilever support for the accommodation block in an environment where there was a never-ending battle against metal corrosion from the salt spray. Then I would worry about going to sleep on an oil platform with a high throughput of potentially flammable oil and explosive gas. The final worry in the queue was the nagging question as to how many Soviet nuclear warheads were actually pointing at me as I lay between the sheets... slumber would eventually follow.

Every now and again the platform would shudder, either a large wave would hit it or a crane operator had dropped a large container on the top deck. And the shudders would resonate that bit more on the cantilevered South Truss. Big shudders are a part of life on a North Sea oil platform.

Some time later, when I worked on the reservoir management of a field in the northern North Sea, the government-run British Geological Survey phoned me up in the office to tell me that they had recorded a magnitude four earthquake close to the field's production platform the previous day, 'and had anybody on the platform noticed the tremors?'

You would certainly notice a magnitude four earthquake onshore, because all the objects in the house or workplace would start rattling, although there wouldn't be much, if any, structural damage. I phoned the operations manager offshore and put the question to him, only to get the reply that as the platform shuddered on a regular basis; nobody would have felt anything out of the ordinary. I had somehow guessed that this would be the answer.

My first major role offshore was to decide on the casing point before drilling into the reservoir. This involved picking some distinctive red beds near the base of the Eocene, a short interval above the top of the Forties Sandstone. Although the vast bulk of the mudstone that we had been drilling through so far had been grey mudstone, a thin layer of red mudstones was found at this point. This constitutes a marker horizon that once recognised is an indication that the Forties reservoir is just underneath. It sometimes seemed that everyone knew the red beds had come in before I did, as the drilling mud coming up over the shakers to remove the rock fragments would turn a distinctive salmon-coloured tinge. Once recognised, the drill pipe would be removed and the casing then installed.

Casing is steel pipe that lines the drill hole and prevents the hole from collapsing; a well couldn't be drilled all the way through otherwise. It can also isolate certain problematic formations so that you can drill ahead safely. Several lengths of casing will be run in the hole before the well has been drilled to its total depth, each fitting inside each other like an old-fashioned telescope. A typical North Sea well will use about 400 tonnes of steel casing in total and about 365 tonnes of cement to fix it in place. Those experienced with drilling operations can recognise the various diameter tubulars at a glance. Onshore in Aberdeen, it's possible to see various trailer loads of offshore pipe being transported through the city streets, and you can pick out such as $13^{3}/_{8}$ inch casing, $9^{5}/_{8}$ inch casing and so on in transit. In this particular instance, the casing was needed to isolate the rock behind the borehole before drilling into the Forties reservoir. The pressure had dropped in the reservoir as a result of oil production and the weight of the drilling mud needed to be reduced before entering the top of the oil zone. If the mud weight wasn't reduced, then it could potentially fracture the reservoir rock, with the mud being lost into the fractures and serious well control problems ensuing.

It would take up to two days to run in and cement the outside of the casing to the borehole wall, time to relax, drink coffee and have a chat. Then drilling would recommence and we would shortly enter the top of the Forties field reservoir. The first sign that the reservoir had been penetrated would be that the drilling rate would suddenly increase. The porous sandstone in the reservoir was much easier for the rock bit to pick apart compared to the dense mudstones lying above it. The rock fragments would take half an hour or more to come up the borehole, carried up by the returning mud, and then I could confirm the first sign of oil-bearing sand grains in the samples.

I remember one particular day offshore, the well I was working on had reached its total depth, my job was finished there and I was due to fly back to the office again. I was working on the Forties Alpha platform and a small helicopter was to shuttle me to Forties Charlie where a bigger helicopter, a Sikorsky S61, would fly me home. The small four-seater Bölkow helicopter lurched off the helideck as it took off, and this gave me a spectacular all-round view of the four platforms in the field. I looked down at the sea and I mentally traced the track of the well as it lay over 2,000 metres under the seabed, deep within the rock. I had a strong sense of satisfaction at a job completed. It was teamwork and I had played a significant role; I had been involved with the well from the start, its location was based on my maps, I had provided the target for the drillers to aim at and now I had been at the well site, helping out with the final drilling stage.

A peculiar thought then took hold as I looked down. All I could see was the surface of the waves; the well track was in my mind as a concept, a very real one nevertheless. It would produce several thousand barrels of oil every day once the pipe work was put in place. I marvelled at the power of abstract thinking, mankind's ability to transform mental concepts into tangible reality.

In the first year of working on Forties, I was asked by the production management to explain how the reservoir was behaving. The Forties field had been producing for over six year and the production rates were declining slowly, after having been kept at a plateau of 500,000 barrels of oil a day. The field was starting to produce water along with the oil and the proper management of the reservoir required an explanation of where the water was coming from. Water production was a bad thing. The oil was driven up the wells to the platform by natural reservoir pressure. Any water coming into a well is heavier than the oil and loads up the fluid column making it flow more sluggishly to the surface. If too much water comes in, the well may even stop producing altogether.

Actually, less water was being produced in the Forties field than had been expected and an explanation for this would obviously help in managing the field. I was able to explain both how the water came into the wells and why there was less of it than predicted. Although the Forties reservoir looked like a very clean sandstone section with no obvious features in it that would act to hinder water moving up from below as the oil was removed, it didn't actually behave like this. I could show that the few mudstone beds in the reservoir actually formed large areal blankets which acted as barriers to upwelling water. The pressures were different either side of the mudstones and this was telling. Instead the water mostly came in from the flanks of the field with a much longer distance to travel before it reached the oil wells. In this manner, the water would have to push much more oil out of the way before it could break through. This was why the field was producing less water than it was expected to. I love detective work like this and my favourite projects in my oil company career would involve fields with similar puzzles to solve.

9

Big Money

WHEN BP DEVELOPED the Forties field, the costs were staggering. It would eventually cost over a billion pounds. What was required was the construction of four 27,500 ton steel oil platforms to stand in the North Sea 180 kilometres from Aberdeen, located in water depths of between 100 and 128 metres. They were to be linked by 169 kilometres of pipeline to Cruden Bay on the Aberdeenshire coast and from there by 209 kilometres of land-based pipeline to the Firth of Forth. Then the production wells needed to be drilled – over a hundred were required.[155]

In the first few years after first oil was produced from the field in 1975, there was a drive to get the development wells drilled as fast as possible to repay the money borrowed from the banks. The more oil produced meant the quicker the bank loan could be paid back. Once this happened, the field would make massive profits for the company (minus the large amount of tax paid to the government).

By the time I worked for the company this was already happening, as the loan had been paid off by the end of 1977. One day in the office as a break from the relentless pressure of planning wells, I got my calculator out to work out how much production from the field was needed to pay my annual salary. At a field production rate of 450,000 barrels per day and with the oil price approaching 35 dollars a barrel, I had reckoned this wouldn't take long. About a minute's worth of production was the answer.

The politicians were certainly impressed by the earning potential of fields like Forties and were rubbing their hands with glee at the potential tax take from North Sea oil. The Prime Minister James Callaghan visited the Forties field in 1977 and said that, 'God has given Britain her best opportunity for a hundred years in the shape of North Sea oil.'[156] The country certainly needed it, given the enormous balance of payments deficit at the time.

Oil had started to assume increasing importance for the UK during the First World War when Winston Churchill, then First Lord of the Admiralty, converted the country's naval ships from coal to oil, the latter having numerous advantages. Oil could produce more heat at a more rapid rate than coal, allowing a ship to pick up speed faster and it produced less smoke. Oil is also easier to load than coal at port.

After the Second World War, the discovery of large fields in the Middle East and North Africa was to provide a source of abundant cheap oil. BP in particular had interests in oilfields in Iran, Libya and Kuwait. The benefits of cheap oil would see Western European countries shift their energy consumption from coal to oil in the 1950s, '60s and early '70s. Their economies would boom as a result. Oil would stay cheap up until 1973, when the price of oil quadrupled in the aftermath of the Yom Kippur war and the price doubled again in the late '70s. The price rises were spurred by the Organisation of Petroleum Exporting Countries (OPEC) which had been formed in 1960 in order to boost the then low price of oil. The oil price hike was a major economic shock to those countries which had become increasingly dependent on cheap oil to provide their energy needs.

Faced with the windfall of North Sea oil at a time when the country's finances were under severe strain and where the nationalisation of Arab oil had led to an insecurity of supply, the government directive was clear: North Sea oil must be developed as quickly as possible. It would take two years before the first oil was produced and the country meanwhile put up with the economic turmoil. The rapid development did, however, create a drawback. There had been no time to encourage British industry to take advantage of North Sea oil with the result that many of the contracts to provide materials and infrastructure for the rigs, platforms and pipelines went abroad.

The oil production rate from the North Sea was rising fast in the late 1970s and was expected to exceed two million barrels a day in the early 1980s. Whoever won the 1979 UK general election would be in power for at least three terms thereafter. It wasn't that important what they actually did, the boon given by a vast injection of tax revenues into the government coffers would make them appear economically competent anyway. The election was won by Margaret Thatcher's Conservative Party and they won three more elections after that. After 18 years in power they finally lost at the 1997 general election.

Much discussion has been focused as to what the government should have been done with the tax receipts from oil. By 2012, the total UK tax from oil production up until then was more than £300 billion (in 2012 money).[157] To some this has turned out to be a wasted windfall. The increasing oil revenue to the UK in the 1980s drove up the sterling exchange rate, making much of British industry uncompetitive. Unemployment increased substantially as a result, exceeding three million people out of work in 1984, and some of the extra tax revenue from oil went to pay unemployment benefits. The oil revenues allowed the top rate of income tax to be reduced from 60p to 40p by 1988 and much of the extra income ended up creating a boom in house prices. There were politicians, even within Margaret Thatcher's Conservative Party, who felt that the funds would have been better used to modernise British industry and improve the country's transport infrastructure.

The previous Labour government had mooted the idea of setting up an oil fund, but this idea got tangled up with infighting within the party and it never happened.[158] This was a lost opportunity for the UK. An oil fund was established by the Norwegian government in 1990 and as of 2015 it holds £549 billion invested in 1.3 per cent of the entire global equity market, including 2.5 per cent of Europe's listed companies.[159] By comparison, there had been no effective political planning to handle the windfall of North Sea oil in the UK other than short-term economic and political expediency.

An early initiative which the Norwegians took and the British didn't was in the provision of major government-funded technological research to back up the oil industry. This was important, particularly in view of the new challenges posed by going deeper and further offshore in the North Sea. If the technology worked, it could be applied to other offshore petroleum provinces that could open up following success in the North Sea. When I visited Norway in 2010, I was told that the Norwegian government extracted a one per cent levy on oil company exploration expenditure made on any new licenses that were granted. This was to be used for funding oil and gas research in the country. The new technology and know-how gained was then given to the companies that had funded it. The difference in how Norway and the UK nurtured home-grown oil services shows today. The Norwegians have a home-grown vibrant hi-tech oil and gas service sector whereas the UK has fallen behind in this regard.

Yet the UK had a head start over the Norwegians. We had discovered gas in the southern North Sea and the development of the gas fields required platforms to be installed, albeit in shallower water compared to Scottish waters. Guy Arnold was to note in his book *Britain's Oil* that by 1975, British industry had only picked up five per cent of the engineering work; most of it went to the Netherlands. Not a single jacket for North Sea gas had been built by that time in Britain.

What went wrong? It looks to have come down to politics. Norwegian politics are largely inclusive, consensual and forward looking, although they do have their disagreements. In the UK, particularly in the 1960s, politics were divisive and governed by class differences. Elections were a tug of war between moneyed interests and the workers; industry was in decline, strikes were common and management standards were poor. The economy was in a mess and there was no unified political solution to create a way forward for British industry. North Sea oil started up in the middle and the muddle of all of this. We live with the results of this today. The only consolation is that it could have been much worse – the UK economy may have had to survive from the '70s onwards without the benefit of North Sea oil.

The Scottish Nationalist Party (SNP) would have taken a different route if it had won independence on the back of the slogan 'It's Scotland's oil'. A secret report made in 1974 to the UK government by the economist Gavin McCrone outlined the strong case that the SNP had for independence in the 1970s:

This paper has shown that the advent of North Sea oil has completely overturned the traditional economic argument used against Scottish nationalism. An independent Scotland could now expect to have massive surpluses both on its budget and on its balance of payments and with the proper husbanding of resources this situation could last for a very long time into the future.

Wealth does not automatically mean full employment and the end of net emigration. But provided sensible policies are pursued, it is possible to see how this situation could be used to re-equip Scottish industry and renew outworn social capital thereby providing the expansion necessary to absorb Scotland's excess labour and the increase in productivity required to raise incomes. Thus, for the first time since the Act of Union was passed, it can now be credibly argued that Scotland's economic advantage lies in its repeal.[160]

The SNP believe that the true extent of the oil reserves under the North Sea had been suppressed in the 1970s for political reasons. Yet, the public were only too aware at the time that there were large oil reserves under the North Sea; a few zeros at the end of some big numbers would not have made that much difference to the public perception. The reality was more mundane than a conspiracy to deceive the Scottish public. Guy Arnold in his book *Britain's Oil* written in 1975, describing the British as collective pessimists notes that, 'In the early to middle 1970s a feature of North Sea developments was a persistent public scepticism, almost disbelief, that the oil bonanza could come to anything.'

Economists give a technical name for the phenomenon that leads to this outlook – it's the 'resource curse'. It stems from the observation that countries often fail to transform the benefits of rich resources into sustainable economic development. Explanations for this include the decline in competitiveness as the country's exchange rate climbs, the damage to the economy caused by periodic commodity crashes and the diversion of the revenue stream to non-productive areas of the country's economy.

I can look back over my long career in the service of North Sea oil including the operations on the Forties field and wish that much better use had been made of the bonanza that my colleagues have worked hard to achieve. The UK government should have started an oil fund as happened in Norway, the

Shetlands and the Orkneys. More effort should have been made to invest in research and development with a view to encouraging home-grown oil-based technology companies. As it turned out, the UK government acted like lottery winners, splurging their bonanza on high living while it lasted and with little to show for it now.

By 1986, the first stage of development wells was complete on the Forties field and no more wells would be drilled until almost 10 years later. I was moved into a team carrying out equity work; that is, trying to figure out what percentage of an oil or gas field each of the partners sharing in a development owns. This sounds like a trivial exercise, but it's not – it's as close as you can get to oil companies declaring war on each other.

An equity negotiation will be called if a field is found to extend across two or more licence blocks, with a different group of oil company partners in each block. This means that a certain percentage of the field's oil will be in one of the blocks and the remainder in the other. It is common practice for the entire field to be developed by one oil company, with the other oil company owners having voting rights on how the operation proceeds. In this instance, the different partner groups need to come together and agree who owns what percentage share of the field as a whole. Once this has been done, they will then pay this percentage as a contribution to the cost of field development and will also receive the same percentage as profits from the oil revenues.

This happens because national governments usually insist on the oil companies agreeing on a single operator for a field. It was found from oil field experience in the early part of the 20th century in the United States, that the various companies involved in different leases covering a single field would try and produce as much as they could as quickly as they could expecting the other operators on the other leases to do much the same. These practices severely damage an oil field and you will only get a fraction of the oil out that you could normally expect with good reservoir management. Governments stepped in with regulation and insisted that any new oil field must be 'unitised' with one oil company responsibly managing the field on behalf of all the partners sharing an interest in the operation.

Equity work involves determining exactly what the percentage splits are for the oil companies sharing an oil field and it is a highly stressful job. The big problem is that the oil companies find it very difficult to agree the percentage shares as they will inevitably insist that there is far more oil in their block relative to the other block. A few per cent difference in who owns what where can turn out to be a very large sum of money. Hundreds of millions of pounds of asset worth can be gained or lost in these negotiations. And as oil companies think money, breathe money and are covetously desirous of money, this is as deadly serious as it gets for them.

It gets even worse if the percentage shares have been decided early on in the field development with the idea of coming back later and redetermining all the equity splits once more data is available. The redetermined percentage applies retro-actively to all the profits that have been made from the field. This brings with it the horrific outcome to an oil company of 'balancing payments': paying out big money in recompense for over-earned income if their percentage share has shrunk later on.

The responsibility for equity work is devolved to the subsurface team, whose job it is to use their models and maps to figure how much oil volume lies in each block, or as the oil company finance department would prefer, the most optimistic possible version of how much oil lies in the company's block that at the same time manages to minimise the amount of oil volume in the other block where they don't have an interest.

One of the reasons why equity work can be so difficult is that the data available from any oil field in the subsurface is sparse and ambiguous. Yet in order to make a conceptual model of the reservoir you still have to predict what is there from the scraps of information you do actually have. Consequently, it is not possible to derive a rigorously 'correct' answer as to what is down there in the subsurface; rather you provide predictive models of what could be there with various assumptions built into each of these interpretations. And if billions of pounds are at stake, some highly biased framing of the data will be pushed by both sides in the attempt to justify an increased field share.

Both sides will then get together to present their interpretations in what are almost always extremely bad-tempered meetings where nothing ever gets agreed. After much frustration, a common recourse is for the different partner groups to agree to the use of a third party independent expert to act as referee in the equity dispute. Both sides will make their case to the expert, and the expert after reviewing the data then makes the final decision as to what the final percentage split should be. The expert's decision is usually respected.

Sometimes a large oil field crosses national boundaries and then the respective governments will also take an active interest in the negotiations. Because the profits from oil fields are heavily taxed, the government on either side of the negotiation will not want to see their tax take reduced and will thus get involved. This is where an equity dispute becomes even crazier if that's at all possible.

This situation happened with the giant Statfjord oil field, which crosses the median line between Norwegian and UK waters. One of the Norwegian participants in the equity negotiations has provided a detailed account of the procedure on a Norwegian engineering heritage website.[161] The following information comes from this.

The share of Statfjord between UK and Norway had been estimated back in 1979 to be 15.91 per cent for the UK and 84.09 per cent to Norway. This had always been an interim figure liable to change later once additional data became available as more wells were drilled in the field.

The oil companies then decided to come up with a final equity split in 1985. There was big money involved in whatever figure was decided. Given that Statfjord is one of the larger fields in the world with over six billion barrels of oil in place, even a small change in the percentage equity would have a major financial impact. A one per cent change in equity share on Statfjord represented a loss or gain of £350 million. The companies on the UK side were angling for an extra 2.5 per cent, equivalent to almost a billion pounds worth of value, while those on the Norwegian side were convinced that they would gain from the deal.

The consequences of a change in equity split meant that one side would have to pay big, big money to the other side. The profits from the field to date had been allocated on the 1979 percentages and any changes in equity would mean that all the profits would have to be back-calculated using the new percentages and then balancing payments made by whoever lost out. This was always going to be one hell of a battle, and so it turned out.

The initial negotiations went on for almost four years, finally collapsing without agreement in 1989. Both sides fought 'tooth and nail' over the details in 60 meetings between the opposing sides. According to one of the participants on the Norwegian side, accusations of skulduggery were an everyday occurrence. Nobody trusted anybody else. The Norwegian side felt that the British interests were stalling for time as the Norwegians were convinced that the equity split would give an increased share to their part of the field. The British oil companies would then have to pay back the money owed in consequence and they were delaying having to do this for as long as possible.

On the other hand, the British side insisted that they needed more data from the Norwegian operating oil company. There was an unstated implication that the missing data held details that would have increased the British share of the field. The Norwegians had been slow in providing this data.

By 1989, the politicians started to get involved.[162] The negotiations were discussed in the UK House of Commons by the Energy Minister, who blamed the Norwegian side for the lack of progress. He suggested that negotiations should be taken away from the oil companies and handled instead by the UK and Norwegian governments. The Norwegian government wisely ducked out of this as they felt it would complicate what was otherwise friendly relations between the two countries.

The oil companies then decided to have another go at resolving the issue, this time using an expert to make the final decision. The highly respected Dallas-based consultancy DeGolyer and MacNaughton was called in to do the work. In August 1991, they decided that the equity share should change to 14.76 per cent for the UK and 85.24 per cent for Norway (previously it had been 15.91 per cent and 84.09 per cent respectively).[163]

This was a nasty shock to the British interests and the UK government in particular. Rather than gaining almost a billion pounds value as expected, the UK side had lost out badly. This wouldn't do. So they looked at the initial legal agreement between the oil companies drawn up before the field was developed. It created the provision that any of the oil companies could call for an equity negotiation every four years and this clause was brought into play. It meant that they were legally entitled to have another go later with the British aiming to claw back some of the lost equity. The UK side would have to accept the 1991 percentages for the time being and call another round of 'discussions' in 1995. But this time it would be final. Everyone insisted that it should be final, I suspect because nobody involved wanted to spend any more years of their professional lives than they had to over bitter and futile arguments.

By 1995, the scope of work in deciding who owned what was becoming enormous. The Statfjord field by this time had been penetrated by 140 wells with 17 years of production history. The seismic data across the field added up to the equivalent of several thousand kilometres. This all had to be analysed before any equity split could be decided on.

The 1995 equity negotiations quickly ran into a problem. The agreement had been to pick an expert but which company would do the work? The Norwegians wanted DeGolyer and MacNaughton again, while the British side demanded that someone else should do the job. After weeks of fruitless discussion, the choice of expert was eventually decided by drawing lots. The names of the Norwegian favoured expert and the UK-favoured expert were placed in a bag and one name was drawn out – it was DeGolyer and MacNaughton. The oil companies accepted this, only for the UK government to step in and veto the choice of expert. The equity negotiations had stalled again.

The Norwegian side was by this stage totally fed up. They dug in at subsequent meetings and insisted that there should be absolutely no change from the 1991 equity split. After many months of further argument, the breakthrough finally came at a meeting in the Marcliffe at Pitfodels Hotel in Aberdeen on 11 June 1997. There was by now tacit acceptance that the status quo, the 1991 equity percentages (with slightly modified percentages as extra oil zones were later included), should be kept and the discussions then moved on to the topic of how the money that was owed to the Norwegian side by the UK side should be paid. Repayment was to be drawn out over time and funded by future oil production so as to minimise the immediate financial impact.

There was one big problem, however. Nobody had a computer available that could do the necessary financial calculations for everyone to agree on. Fortunately, the hotel reception had a laptop computer and it even had

Windows 95 and the necessary applications installed. The Norwegians, however, had only used Norwegian computers and the function keys on the hotel laptop were unfamiliar to them. After some trial and error they managed to work out how to use the keyboard. It was important to do so, the multi-million pound profits of 10 oil companies and the future tax revenue of two national governments hung in the balance.

There were some further discussions between the two governments but essentially a resolution to the problem was in place. The Statfjord equity split was finally agreed at a national level in August 1998; 13 years after the initial negotiations had started.[164] It had been a protracted episode of bad temper, strategic trickery and total mistrust on an epic scale.

An equity determination doesn't always have to be like this. I know of one equity negotiation on a North Sea field that was resolved quickly and painlessly because all concerned agreed beforehand to be open, honest and fair in their discussions. It's interesting to note that the managers on both sides of the negotiation were women.

10

BP and Britoil

IT WAS SOMEWHAT chaotic working for BP in the late 1980s. The turmoil started in the Aberdeen office when it was announced in 1986 that the 300-strong exploration department was to move to London. BP's international exploration group was there and we were told that the company's intention was to create a 'centre of excellence' in the London office.

The move had some practical difficulties, not the least because the Aberdeen property market still hadn't recovered from the 1986 oil price crash and there were thousands of properties for sale with few buyers. The impending loss of 300 BP staff merely served to depress the market even further and as 1987 wore on, the number of repossessed homes in Aberdeen increased sharply. The problems that beset BP staff trying to sell houses there delayed the move for months.

The dire state of the property market in Aberdeen hit home to me personally. The family flat was on sale at the time as we needed more room following the birth of my son in June 1987. At the start of December we received a letter from the selling agents informing us that the asking price for the flat was too high at £49,000; a similar flat in the same street was on sale at £35,000, we were told, though 'not so nicely furnished'.

I had no desire to move to London and this prompted me to apply for an Aberdeen-based job with the American oil company Occidental. By the time I was offered an interview, I had been informed that the BP reservoir geologists were expected to stay in Aberdeen and that would include me. My close friend Andy Gordon had applied for the Occidental job, and seeing that he was currently out of work after the 1986 slump, I withdrew from the interview to give him a better chance of getting it. As it turned out, the vacancy was for the Piper field reservoir geologist role, and Andy's first week on the job in July 1988 was when the Piper Alpha disaster took place.

Chaos landed on BP at the national level, when the Conservative administration decided to privatise 31.5 per cent of the government-owned BP shares. The 2.2 billion shares were worth £7.2 billion. No sooner had the sell-off been launched than the stock market crashed and UK shares lost over 10 per cent of their value in one day and would fall further in the days to come. The BP share sell-off price was announced on the Thursday before the 'Black Monday' share crash of Monday 19 October 1987, and revealed to the public when a team of soldiers from the Royal Marines abseiled down the front of BP's London headquarters, trailing a huge banner with the number 330 written on it. The share offering at 330 pence per share would now be open for three weeks. This was hubris in the extreme. Perhaps as a sign of what was to come, that night the BBC weatherman, Michael Fish, made the most famous weather forecast of all time: 'Earlier on today, apparently, a woman rang the BBC and said she'd heard there was a hurricane on the way. Well, if you're watching, don't worry, there isn't.'

That night a massive storm arrived, the worst in Southern England since 1703. It caused £1 billion worth of damage and as many as 15 million trees were blown down. Six of the seven oak trees symbolising the name for the town of Sevenoaks in Kent were toppled by the wind.

On Black Monday, the BP share price fell to 316p, below the 330p offer price for the government sell-off, and it would fall further. A reporter on the BBC news announced that applying for the BP share issue was now a waste of money. He also mentioned that applications were arriving at the BP issue office in sack-loads, presumably from people who hadn't heard that the stock market had crashed. Some had even applied for more than they were entitled to – 90 people were eventually prosecuted for making multiple applications for BP shares.[165] The share price crash would cause painful problems for the banks and other institutions which had underwritten the privatisation. The government had effectively sold them 2.2 billion BP shares at the 330 pence offer price. Four American merchant banks had underwritten the $1 billion worth of shares for sale in the United States and were facing massive losses as a result.

The government were forced to try and prop up the share price by guaranteeing a part-paid share price of 70 pence to the American banks and other underwriters should the share price drop further. The argument was made that the banks, having been left with a huge tranche of unwanted BP shares, could potentially offload them whenever the price started to go up, thus depressing the BP share price for years, until they finally managed to get rid of them all. A Labour politician was unconvinced, making the sarcastic comment that the UK Government was now underwriting the underwriters.

The government's problems increased when it was announced on 19 November that the Kuwait Investment Office, which administers Kuwait's sovereign wealth fund, had bought 10 per cent of BP through the government's flotation and they intended to keep on buying the shares. Was this the start of a takeover bid for Britain's largest company by a foreign national government? Probably not – there was no way the UK government would allow this to happen, given the strategic importance of BP's oil reserves in the North Sea. Nevertheless, the Kuwaitis could still build up a share and then sell it on as a stake for a takeover bid by someone else, such as Exxon or Shell. The BP board would also have been worried that given the number of shares the Kuwaitis controlled they would be in a position to exert influence on company decisions. It was perhaps ironic that BP had been instrumental in discovering oil in Kuwait back in 1938 after helping to found the Kuwaiti Oil Company, in partnership with Gulf Oil.

BP now decided to start buying shares in Britoil, the privatised entity which had previously been the British National Oil Corporation. This looked like the start of a takeover. It was a bold move, because the UK government held the power to put a stop to this as they held a single £1 'golden' share in Britoil, designed to give them an effective power of veto over any takeover bid for the company. The idea of a possible takeover proved unpopular in Scotland where Britoil had its Glasgow headquarters. The *Scotsman* reported the BP share dealing with the headline: 'BP about to steal another Scottish company HQ?' Memories of the international drinks group Guinness absorbing the Scottish whisky company Scottish Distillers still rankled. Guinness had said that it would set up its corporate headquarters in Scotland if the takeover went ahead. When Guinness took over the company the headquarters stayed put in London. This had been revealed only a matter of weeks before BP started buying Britoil shares.[166]

On Friday 18 December 1987, BP announced that it was indeed launching a takeover bid for Britoil, valuing the company at approximately £2,270 million.[167] BP deflected criticism that this was a Scottish sell-out by announcing in a press release that they would 'set up in Glasgow a new headquarters office for its enlarged UK exploration, development and production functions, all reporting to the Chief Executive for the UK who would be based in Glasgow where BP has its head office'.

BP would eventually move their exploration department from Aberdeen to London in April 1987. As promised, they then transferred their exploration staff to Glasgow, although this would not be the final move. The department eventually completed the round trip back to Aberdeen several years later when BP shut down the Glasgow office. Some of the office staff managed to make all three moves.

BP needed oil reserves. Forties field oil production had come off plateau production in 1980 and was gradually declining, the Prudhoe Bay oil field was just about to do likewise. BP's exploration effort had been insufficient to replace their reserves so they were resorting to buying oil reserves by taking over other companies. Nevertheless, Britoil seemed an odd choice. BP was heavily involved in the high cost area of the North Sea at a time when the oil price was low. Profit margins were minimal for their North Sea operations and it would seem that the last thing they needed was to take on extra North Sea commitments by buying Britoil. It would have made more sense to balance the portfolio by buying onshore oil assets where the costs were low relative to the oil price. Indeed the previous year BP had spent £4.5 billion to secure the shares they didn't already control in the American oil company Sohio. Sohio had a major interest in the Prudhoe Bay oil field in Alaska and gave BP a strong presence onshore in the US.[168]

On Wednesday 23 December 1987, the takeover panel announced that BP could proceed with their offer for Britoil. The government suggested that they could now keep the golden share in Britoil to thwart any attempt by a foreign company to take over a merged BP-Britoil operation should a foreign company (eg the Kuwait Investment Office) move to take over BP in the future. It's plausible that this was the reason why BP made the bid for Britoil in the first place. The Kuwaitis had by this time further increased their BP shareholding. They eventually announced in January 1988 that they were not intending to bid for BP. In October 1988, the Monopolies and Mergers Commission ruled that the Kuwaitis were required to reduce their 21.68 per cent shareholding in BP to no more than 9.9 per cent within one year from the ruling. A significant Kuwaiti holding in BP was deemed a potential conflict with UK public interest. BP ended up buying back 11.6 per cent of its shares from the Kuwaitis at a cost of £2.4 billion; they did not want these shares sold on to a potential bidder. They were forced to sell assets to fund these costs.[169]

BP finally won its battle to take over Britoil in February 1988. Just afterwards, I copied into my diary this letter from John L McCall, Lochgilphead, which was published in the *Glasgow Herald* on 26 February:

I read, in growing disbelief your front page article describing the rewards Sir Philip Sherbourne [the outgoing chairman of Britoil] will receive from the BP takeover of Britoil.

To ease the pain of retirement he will receive a lump sum of £530,000. He will then be re-employed as a consultant, 'working' a maximum of three days per month at a salary of £127,000. In addition he will receive £24,000 to 'cover lunch expenses'. Assuming that he eats at home free of charge, he will be able to spend £100 each weekday on his lunch. He should be able to get a good spot of lunch for that kind of money; or about 50 fish suppers; or one fish supper and spend the change on frivolities.

More mysteriously, Sir Philip will also receive £40,000 a year 'in lieu of office services'. What can this mean? Does hard cash in some way compensate him for not having a typist?'

The Britoil takeover saw the end of any lingering traces of what had been a battle of political ideologies in the UK between those that wanted political control over the country's resources (the Labour Party) and those that preferred to leave as much as possible of the nation's economic activity in the control of private business (the Conservative Party). The coal industry had been nationalised in 1946 and the UK gas industry had also been take into public control and stayed there up until Thatcher privatised it in 1986. The steel industry became a tug of war between the opposing ideologies; it was nationalised by Labour in 1949, privatised by the Conservatives in 1952, nationalised again in 1967 and then privatised by the Conservatives in 1988. It has since been absorbed into an Indian steel company.

Before Britoil was privatised in 1982, it had been called the British National Oil Corporation (BNOC). BNOC was set up in 1976 to ensure that there was some degree of national control over the security of Britain's oil supplies. The original position of the Labour Party was to bring all North Sea oil and gas under government control with a majority share in the operation. This ambitious proposal was watered down over time – it wasn't exactly practical, the compensation costs would have been massive. The UK still needed the expertise and finance from international oil companies and they didn't want to scare them away. The government was also keen to see the North Sea developed quickly to ensure a stable supply of oil to the nation and to shore up its dire balance of payments problem.

The arrangement finally ended up with BNOC securing the right to buy 51 per cent of all the oil produced in the North Sea at market price. Where oil companies refined the oil they produced in the UK, 'buy-back' agreements were arranged whereby the oil was bought back from Britoil by the same company that had originally produced it for exactly the same price they had sold it to Britoil in the first place. This peculiar arrangement gave BNOC and the government a degree of influence over supply and refinery output in the country. BNOC was to become both a major buyer and seller of North Sea oil.

When BNOC was formed in 1976 it was given the oil interests of the National Coal Board. These included part shares of several North Sea fields. It would later acquire control of the Thistle field from Burmah when the latter ran into financial problems and would then take over the Beatrice field from the American company Mesa Petroleum, whose owner, T Boone Pickens, had named the field after his wife.

BNOC did not survive Thatcher's Conservative government for long. After gaining power in 1979, the new administration started to privatise any organisation that was not deemed to be core to the government and the publicly owned BNOC soon became the privately owned Britoil. The Labour Party responded by promising to renationalise the company if they ever returned to power. Somebody in the BP office in Aberdeen posted a cartoon on the staff noticeboard in response to this. It depicted a man wearing nothing but a safety helmet bearing the Britoil logo, clutching his nether regions with a pained expression on his face. Underneath was a newspaper cutting with the headline 'Labour Pledges to Deprivatise Britoil'.

When the oil price crashed in 1986, Britoil was in trouble. Larger integrated oil companies such as BP and Shell could partly compensate for reduced revenue from crude oil by selling their refined products at a higher margin.[170] Britoil couldn't do this and their profits were hammered. They were forced to sell assets and make large-scale redundancies. In June, 220 of the company's 2,700 employees were laid off out. This was followed by 750 staff cuts in September, 600 in Glasgow and 150 in Aberdeen.[171]

Britoil harboured aspirations of becoming an international company and had bought assets overseas, particularly in the United States. These were sold at a loss. The company was to bump along until BP was eventually allowed to take it over.

After the Britoil takeover, BP moved the Magnus production team into Britoil's operations office in Aberdeen and I went with them. Just before I arrived, an accounts assistant in the office, Alison Anders, had tried to steal £23,331,996.95 from the company. Britoil had leased an oil rig and the payment for this was due. She had been asked to process the form authorising the payment through the Bank of Scotland. However, she had other ideas for the money and substituted an international payment order to a Swiss bank account instead. It was one of the biggest attempted frauds in British history.

In the court case that followed it was revealed that the criminal plan had developed following a bridge session at an Aberdeen club. Later that evening, Anders and her bridge partner, Royston Allen, who was having an affair with her, went for a drink. She had jokingly said that if she was going to improve her play she would need bridge practice on the beach of Rio de Janeiro. She had also mentioned in passing how she was about to sign off the money for the lease of the rig.

This started Allen thinking about how to steal the money. He worked for an oil-related company and shortly afterwards had gone on a business trip to Abu Dhabi where he met someone who said he could launder cash through a Swiss bank account. This contact was an Arab-Albanian businessmen called Hajideen, who was married to a princess in Abu Dhabi. Alison Anders later described Hajideen as a duplicitous bastard.

The Swiss bank account was set up in the name of a young girl called Ann Killick who had been killed in a road accident in 1971, whose identity Anders was intending to steal, having managed to secure a birth certificate and passport in the girl's name. The idea had undoubtedly been inspired by an incident in the Frederick Forsyth novel *The Day of the Jackal*.

The morning after she had submitted the fraudulent money transfer, a manager mentioned that the payment for the rig lease had been queried by the Bank of Scotland. Anders took fright and immediately flew out to Abu

Dhabi to meet her lover and Hajideen, unaware that a stop had been put on the transaction by the oil company. Discussions about how to launder the cash continued, but relations with Hajideen broke down and he accused the couple of trying to double-cross him. He claimed he had already spent a lot of money to bribe the Swiss banker and had also cut a deal with the Mafia. He threatened to set the Mafia on Anders and Allen, saying that if they didn't cooperate their legs would be broken. Hajideen's sidekick, Omar, drove Anders out to the desert, telling her that as it was a very big place and she was small, it would be easy for her to disappear.

This was too much for Anders and she vanished for a second time, eventually ending up in the United States, where she assumed her false identity as Ann Killick and worked first as an office cleaner and then in a flower shop in Portland, Oregon.

Back in Aberdeen, life was falling apart for Royston Allen. His wife found out about his affair and confronted him. He denied everything and told her that the only reason he had been meeting up with the accounts assistant was because they had been setting up the £23 million fraud attempt. She was not impressed and asked for a divorce. This was refused, and after consulting with a lawyer she reported her husband's involvement in the fraud to the police. Anders' address in Portland was subsequently found in Allen's office. She was arrested by the FBI, having been on the run for almost 11 months. Anders and Allen were both sentenced to five years in jail. After their release, they married and went to live in a remote croft in Aberdeenshire.[172]

Meanwhile, in the former Britoil domain, not all was happy for the staff. BP had been left with some hefty bills after the Sohio and Britoil takeovers, not to mention the share buy-back from the Kuwaitis. The oil price was low and profit margins were dwindling. A large tranche of asset sales had not been enough. The company needed to cut costs and they also wanted to reduce the staff count by getting rid of duplicate staff inherited as a result of the takeovers.

The managing director of BP's exploration arm, John Browne, announced in a satellite broadcast to the BP operational centres worldwide that there would be redundancies within the organisation, initially a thousand staff to go.[173] I survived the first round of redundancies, but only just. Several of my colleagues were out the door and it was almost certain that there would be more rounds of redundancies to come. My friend Andy Gordon told me of a job going at Occidental and this time I went to the interview.

Occidental and ELF

I WAS WORKING on BP's Magnus field project in 1988 when the Piper Alpha disaster took place on 6 July. A total of 167 men were killed when the platform blew up. The first explosion took place at about 10pm and I heard an indication of it on the Radio Scotland news at 11pm, which mentioned that there had been a fire on a North Sea oil platform (unnamed), and that there were reports of men in the water. I stopped in horror. A very serious incident must have taken place for men to be in the water. And, I wondered, was this one of the platforms I had worked on and knew many of the offshore workers?

The next morning the radio news gave more details and mentioned that Occidental's Piper Alpha platform had been involved. This is what I wrote in my diary that day:

Disaster on Piper Alpha – the platform has blown up. There is not much news yet. I came into the BP office this morning and the building was buzzing, our control room downstairs is also the disaster control room for the central North Sea.

The call went around BP for blood donors with at least 400 volunteers offering blood including myself. Between 160 and 170 men are probably dead, the law of averages means that I probably know one of them. Aberdeen is not a big place.

Someone brought in the latest edition of the Aberdeen local paper and we all gasped in shock at the photograph on the front page. Only one side of the platform had been left standing and it was the side supporting the platform's two flare stacks, now dangling uselessly; much of the rest of the platform had disappeared in the explosions.

We crowded into the company's social club to listen to the lunchtime news on the BBC. They finished the bulletin with an unfortunate slant – the UK balance of payments may suffer as a result of the disaster. This got boos and hisses from us. All these bloody Londoners can think about is money.

The general feeling in the office is one of utter shock. An oil platform
blows up – bloody hell!!

The TV news later that evening was to show a never to be forgotten, most
distressing scene. A crowd of wives and girlfriends had gathered next to the
helipad at Aberdeen Royal Infirmary in anxious wait for the survivors to come
in by helicopter from the rescue vessel. Only there were no more helicopters to
come in, so many men had been killed in the disaster.

I knew one of the victims of the Piper Alpha disaster by sight. He was
one of the regulars at the Prince of Wales where I liked to go for an evening
pint. On the day it became known that he been killed, the bar stool where he
usually sat was left empty and a pint of his favourite beer was left on the bar
untouched.

An unfortunate series of events had led to the disaster. One of the two gas
condensate lines on the platform was being worked on to remove a pressure
safety valve on an injection pump for routine maintenance, but the work
remained unfinished by the end of the dayshift at 6pm and the valve wasn't
replaced. As a temporary measure, the workman had fitted a metal cap over
the opening where the valve had been removed.

Later that evening, the second gas condensate line, which had still been
in operation, stopped working, presumably having suffered a blockage. The
night shift then made the fatal mistake. They shut in the second gas line and
opened up the first gas line, unaware that it was in an unsafe condition. The
handover procedure between the day and night shifts had been ineffective and
the fatal accident enquiry later concluded that it is likely that the night crew
didn't know that the pressure safety valve was missing. The temporary cap
started leaking and gas escaped into the open air around the platform. The
gas alarms sounded, but it didn't take long for the escaping gas to catch fire.

The second misfortune then took place. The gas exploded with such force,
it blew through the fire walls and the adjacent control room was put it out
of action. The control room handled everything on the platform, including
the normal coordination of evacuation procedures in an emergency, but
what remained after the blast was a tangled debris of telephones, computer
equipment and furniture. With the control room gone and the platform on
fire, the situation was desperate. There had been no orders to evacuate. Many
of the men had gathered in the top level of the accommodation block, waiting
for a helicopter to arrive to carry them to safety. They were probably unaware
that the situation had escalated to the point where no helicopter could safely
land on the helideck. More explosions followed during the night and the men
in the accommodation block eventually died from smoke inhalation; they may
have been waiting for further instructions that never came.

Those that survived, and there were 61 survivors that night, had somehow managed to make their own way off the burning platform. Several jumped into the sea, an act that many of us who had taken offshore survival courses before Piper Alpha had been warned about doing – above a certain height, a jump into the sea is essentially an uncontrollable fall, but with a burning platform behind them, there had been no choice. All but three of those who jumped survived the fall; of the survivors, 15 had jumped from the pipe deck, 40.5 metres above the sea, five from the helideck at a height of 53 metres.

The heroes of the day were those men who set off in their little rescue crafts, speeding towards the burning oil platform to pick up the survivors in the water. One of these boats didn't come back. It was returning after having picked up survivors when it was engulfed as the flames of an explosion spread over the water; all but one onboard were killed.

A few years later, I flew offshore to a drilling rig on the Piper field. It was redrilling the production wells prior to a new platform being installed. I remember sitting outside the logging unit on a beautiful summer day, with the sky clear blue and the sea flat calm. Not far away from the rig was a yellow buoy with flashing warning lights, marking the position of what remained of the Piper Alpha platform. It was such a balmy day and difficult to imagine that 167 men had lost their lives on this spot.

I left BP in 1990 and joined Occidental. I was to work for them for a year before they sold up in the North Sea. The company today has pariah status amongst some I know in Aberdeen following the Piper Alpha disaster, but I must say that I enjoyed working for Occidental. They were a small tight-knit operation, everybody was very friendly and it had the feel of a family-run business. I was impressed when on my first day, the president of Occidental Aberdeen, Glenn Shurtz, stopped me in the corridor and, addressing me by first name, welcomed me to my new job.

Nevertheless, Occidental, like any other oil company, was a money-making machine producing oil from the North Sea. There was a telling conversation recounted in the 1996 TV documentary *Wasted Windfall* when the founder of Occidental, Armand Hammer visited the Piper Alpha platform. In response to his personal assistant, Tim Halford, mentioning that there was distinct rumbling sound coming from underneath the platform as they stood on the deck, Armand Hammer said, 'I can just feel those dollars going through underneath me and that's what it's all about.'[174]

Working for an American oil company was a total culture change. After a few weeks in the office, I mentioned to my American boss that there was potentially an untapped volume of oil that might be worth going for in the field I was working on.

He replied abruptly, 'I want a drilling proposal on my desk in two weeks' time.'

Behind the American can-do culture, there is an unspoken assumption along the lines: 'We trust you with the responsibility, but deliver or else you'll be out the door.'

Being given my head energised me and it was difficult to hold me back after that. Given a new field to investigate I would attack it like a terrier, picking it apart until I had established whether there were any pockets of oil worth drilling. If I found something promising, I would then push the concept relentlessly within the company.

Life at Occidental was hard work. The company believed in running a very lean operation with only a small number of managers. They operated a meeting-free culture, which meant that you worked eight hours or more a day without a break, except for lunch. Communication was through line management on a one-to-one basis or via the weekly report document which you were expected to read thoroughly. This working style was in complete contrast to any other oil company I've worked for, where there would be numerous daily meetings, some of which would go on for hours. One asset manager at another company got so fed up with this, he organised our weekly meeting for 11.45 am every Friday. If the meetings went on too long, we would miss lunch. They were the shortest, snappiest meetings in the company.

I was assigned to the Claymore oil field, located in the outer Moray Firth. Of all the fields I've worked on, the Claymore is my favourite in terms of geological studies, fascinating not in the least because it held a multitude of reservoirs hundreds of millions of years in age. I was part of a team planning a succession of production wells, almost all of them coming in as expected, and that was satisfying. But it was my least favourite job in terms of the working environment. For most of my time on Claymore, the field was operated by the French company ELF, which had taken over Occidental's assets in the North Sea. Following Armand Hammer's death in December 1990, his successor had instigated an immediate reorganisation of the company to address its financial difficulties and its North Sea assets were sold off. One day I was working for Occidental, the next for ELF.

ELF was a strange company to work for. Part-owned by the French government, they were bureaucratic in the extreme. When they took over from Occidental, the first French managers to arrive in Aberdeen took one look at the existing organisational structure and then added two new layers of management. Once they settled in, they sought to make further changes. The manager of the Exploration Department hopefully decreed that we should all speak French in the Aberdeen office and we were told to attend French lessons twice a week. The initiative collapsed early on, as none of the French managers could understand us, or bear to hear their beautiful French language spoken with a strong Aberdeen accent.

Most of the managers had graduated from the École Polytechnique, the top engineering college in France. They were very proud of this, and of having gained a job with ELF, at that time the biggest and most prestigious oil company in France. This marked them as part of the elite within French society. In general, I liked the French, who were mostly charming, very polished and cultured, but I had difficult relations with several of the managers. For a start, they didn't trust what they called the Anglo-Saxon culture and how it was used to make operational decisions.

The British way was to take a pragmatic approach to problems, quickly determine the key elements and then work out a solution. This would be made once there was enough information judged good enough to be able to move things forward quickly, and the decision was often based on the likelihood rather than the near certainty of a desired outcome.

If you have been brought up in an Anglo-Saxon culture, this sounds like a common-sense approach to operational problems. Yet, this attitude appals the French and they see it as essentially anti-intellectual. The continental way of thought is firmly rooted in high theory and rigorous analysis. As far as the French were concerned, operational decisions had to be based on theoretical models. The model could be a detailed computer simulation or an elaborate evidence-based analysis. Modern science and medical research works this way, but its benefit in an operational situation is questionable. Yet pragmatism was a dirty word to be mentioned with a disapproving grimace; good enough was not good enough as far as the French were concerned, it led to second-rate decisions.

This all sounds splendidly academic and perhaps a source of amusement to the bystander – the idea that two separate cultures had gone their own intellectual way over the centuries and that this was now causing discord within a modern oil company. Nevertheless, the difference in outlook caused numerous headaches for both sides. Unfortunately, in a heavily operational environment which involved the management of several offshore oil platforms, the need to make reasonably quick and often sequential decisions would be forced upon you. For instance, do you install a piece of equipment that other operators in the North Sea have found reliable, or do you take a few months to study all the options and then install what you consider to be the best choice, perhaps causing problems offshore while you are making your decision. Many of us felt that the French were impractical in their demands for lengthy analyses that would lead to much the same outcome anyway. This led to considerable tension between the two nationalities.

The ELF management system was strongly top-down: you were expected to do what you were told, and opening out a management decision into a discussion of its pros and cons could be difficult. Yet some of the demands coming down from senior management were strange. This autocratic behaviour got the company into trouble every now and again. In the 1970s, the ELF board in France were sold a technique which they felt would give them a big lead in exploring for oil and 50 million dollars had been paid for its exclusive use.[175] This was a so-called sniffer plane, an ordinary plane kitted out with a measuring device said to detect hydrocarbons from existing, yet undiscovered oil fields. It has never been too clear how this device was supposed to work. The plane would fly back and forth across any prospective territory, building up data to compile a map of concentrations of hydrocarbons over the region.

The management arranged in secret for the sniffer plane to be flown over their exploration acreage and having identified a number of interesting features, they would then order wells to be drilled without any explanations to the geologists currently searching the area for oil using conventional methods. Some of the drill sites were in places where it was extremely unlikely that oil would be found, for instance where the underlying rock was solid granite. When the geologists informed head office that the locations were dubious, the reply was to get the wells drilled and ask no questions. Senior management wanted the sniffer plane technique to remain top secret. Some of the wells were drilled but none of them found anything and the programme was eventually called to a halt.

One of our yearly requirements was to liaise with ELF research group in Pau in the South of France, not far from the Pyrenees. We were required by management to find suitable projects for the research group to work on and the budget allocated for this was sizeable. I visited the Pau research centre on three occasions and was able to learn a great deal from the experts in ELF. The standard of research was outstanding. Industrial relations amongst the ELF staff in France could get rather fraught. Sometimes passions would spill over and on one spectacular occasion the workers bricked up the front entrance to the research centre and on another, welded the front gates shut. My favourite story was the time where the striking workers found a more subtle way to bring the centre to a halt. They stole all the balls out of the computer mice in the office.

My first visit to Pau was just after the transfer. I and my fellow Brits were to be shown around and hopefully impressed with the facilities and expertise available there. At the end of the first day, we were taken to the 'château', actually a big house near Pau, where we were treated to a gourmet meal eased down with vintage French wine served by a butler. The senior ELF managers from Pau came along too and the seating plan alternated the Brits and French so as to ensure there would be some communication between the two groups. I found myself sitting next to the geology manager, Henri, who I hadn't come across previously. I introduced myself and was astonished to know that he knew a great deal about me, which oil companies I'd worked for and even that I was married with two children.

Here I was in a foreign country and talking to someone I'd never met before and he knew my personal history in some detail. I asked Henri how he knew so much about me. 'We are trying to get you posted from the Aberdeen office to work with my group here. We have lots of really smart guys here who can do great work but we really need somebody with operational experience to give them a sense of what can be done in practice.' He had somehow obtained a copy of my curriculum vitae.

When I returned to the Aberdeen office, I went to see the chief geologist and asked him what was going on. He was annoyed as he knew nothing about it and told me that Pau had previously tried to poach staff.

'But don't worry,' I was told, 'I'll put a stop to that.' I stayed in Aberdeen.

After six years of working for ELF I was finding the job more and more frustrating. I was falling behind on pay and at the same time being given more and more work to do when I could barely cope with my existing work load. I had been promised a promotion and even shown a draft of the letter confirming this, when a pay freeze was announced by head office. My British colleagues had also started to leave and the story went around the office that ELF stood for 'Everyone Leaving Fast'. One day in the office when I was feeling particularly disenchanted, a head-hunter cold-called to ask if I was interested in a consultant job in Aberdeen.

'I'll take it,' I said.

'Don't you want to know what the job is first before you accept it?' he asked in astonishment.

'Oh, I suppose so,' I replied. It was a job with the American oil company Amerada Hess. I took the job.

Shortly afterwards, ELF divested themselves of most of their assets in the North Sea and disappeared as an independent company in 2000. They were the focus of a major political and corruption scandal in France.[176] The chairman of the company, Loik Le Floch-Prigent, who had been treated with great obsequiousness when he had visited the Aberdeen office, ended up in jail.[177] When he turned up in Aberdeen, the limousine that took him from the airport to the office drove past a petrol station that had just recently appeared with an ELF logo.

There had always been murmurs about ELF's dealings in Africa, a continent which provided the profit centre for the company. ELF operated in countries there which did not necessarily come out too well on Transparency International's ranking list of global corruption. But the furtive dealings had now been shown to extend beyond Africa.[178] An investigating magistrate called Eva Joly was to uncover a network of high-level corruption in France involving business and government officials, all linked through the use of secret funds at ELF.

It was a tale of company money used to provide 'commissions' for businessmen paid through secret Swiss bank accounts and ELF credit cards handed out to the influential and used by them at the top restaurants in Paris.

The mistress of the French foreign minister, Roland Dumas, had been given a retainer from ELF. She had been bought a £1.7 million apartment in one of the most fashionable streets in the Left Bank of Paris not far from the offices of the foreign ministry. She also received the equivalent of £5,000 a month from the company and charged her ELF credit card by anything up to £20,000 a month. Her most extravagant and notorious purchase on the card was a pair of handmade *bottines* at a cost of about £1,100, bought as a gift for her government minister lover. The detail that intrigued the French press was that for that price, purchasers were invited to bring the boots back annually to the shop, where they would be washed in champagne.

Allegations were made that she was being paid to influence her lover over a deal involving the sale of six French frigates to Taiwan in 1991. The Foreign Minister was found guilty of illegally receiving funds from ELF, sentenced to jail for six months and fined for taking illegal gifts from his mistress. The conviction was later overturned on appeal;[179] it was his mistress that went to jail. This episode did nothing to change the prejudices of many a French political cynic at the time. The mistress later chronicled her experiences in a book titled *La Putain de la République – The Whore of the Republic.*[180]

When the other major French oil company, TOTAL, merged with ELF in 2000, nobody in the French government stopped them – they were happy to see the end of what had been a major embarrassment to the establishment. The merged company was initially called TOTAL-FINA-ELF; three years later it became TOTAL.

Oil Reserves

THE LATE 1990S saw difficult times for oil companies. The oil price had been fairly low, generally in the range $15–$20 per barrel since the crash of 1986. This was just above the economic floor at which oil companies could make money in the North Sea. They then instigated cost reductions on their North Sea operations in an attempt to become more efficient and to make savings on their expenditure.

When the price tumbled towards $15 per barrel or even lower in the late 1990s, the oil companies were in turmoil. In December 1998, the price of Brent crude briefly dropped below $10 per barrel. The American oil company I worked for shed 30 per cent of its UK workforce and I was lucky to keep my job. Some big oil company mergers took place at the time, notably, BP with Amoco and Exxon with Mobil.

The oil price picked up again in 2000 and rose steadily after that. Ironically, after surviving both the 1986 and 1998 crashes, I was made redundant in 2003 – during a phase of rising prices. The Canadian oil company which had bought the oil field I was working on decided to relocate the Aberdeen subsurface team to their London office. I took a redundancy payment and left the company. I could easily have picked up another job in Aberdeen, but I wanted to try something different for a change.

I took a year out of the oil industry and moved to the Aberdeen University Geology Department. I had felt frustrated that I had not completed my PhD research from my earlier years and wanted to start a new research project. My intention was to spend a year kick-starting the project and then complete it part-time once I returned to the oil industry. I talked to Professor Andrew Hurst about this. Andy had been in my geology undergraduate class, so we knew each other well. He suggested what he felt would be a more productive use of my 'sabbatical'– writing a textbook for the Production Geology Master of Science course work. There was no recent textbook and it would be an enormous benefit for the class and similar academic courses elsewhere. I thought it would take a year to write, but it took me six years to complete – a big effort, but certainly worthwhile.

Oil Field Production Geology was published by the American Association of Petroleum Geologists in 2009. Its main objective is to give new-start professional geologists an idea as to how to get more oil out of the fields they are assigned to. I know from my own experience how unnerving it is to be thrown into managing a producing oil field without really knowing what to do. The opening sets the context:

There are widespread concerns about the future of oil and gas resources. The volume added by new oil and gas discoveries has declined since the 1960s while the global demand for hydrocarbons is rising as the world population increases. Although less oil is being discovered as a result of exploration for new fields, a significant volume of reserves is being added because of improved oil recovery from existing fields. Reserves are the volumes of petroleum that a company expects to produce from a field by the end of its life. Recent data suggest that the volume of exploration finds and reserves growth in producing fields is now roughly similar.

So why is so much oil being added as reserves from existing fields? Where is this oil coming from? The basic observation is that the amount of oil recovered from the world's oil fields has historically been poor. Typically more oil has been left behind in oil fields than they have ever produced. Today, out of the total amount of oil that has been found in the world, it is anticipated that only about 30–35 per cent of this volume is likely to be recovered under current estimates. The remaining 65–70 per cent of the oil is expected to be abandoned in the world's oil fields once these have become unprofitable to produce from...

It is interesting to speculate as to how much the recovery factor can be improved globally by enhanced reservoir management. The question was addressed by Keith King of Exxon Mobil at the 2006 American Association of Petroleum Geology Oil Resources Conference. The range in the possible increase in recovery was estimated as an additional 4 per cent to close to an additional 13 per cent (based on the maximum resource case).

The low case may arise if the current improvements in recovery start to moderate. The high case will depend on future technological advances in enhanced oil recovery techniques and the application of these world-wide, particularly in the giant oil fields.

It is worthy of note that an upside improvement in recovery of 13 per cent would add almost as much oil supply as has been consumed by the world to date. It would take a heroic effort to get this much oil out of our reservoirs, but if we could, then this would go a long way to providing a solution for the world's energy problems. Whether this will happen or not is open to debate. Nevertheless, what is clear from these figures is that there is a very large hydrocarbon resource available in our existing fields.[181]

That's a bold statement Keith King makes: that improved management of our existing oil fields could produce the equivalent of all of the world's oil used to date all over again.

Here is the basic problem when you manage an oil field. You can't get all the oil out of it. In fact, it's very difficult to get even half the oil out – you need an exceptionally good quality reservoir before you can manage even that level of recovery. As I've mentioned, the world average is recovery of about 30–35 per cent of the oil, although one technical paper reckons it's as low as 22 per cent. I don't think anybody really knows. The North Sea has the best recoveries worldwide with a 46 per cent recovery predicted for both the UK and Norwegian sectors.[182]

There are several reasons why oil gets left behind. One is because a significant proportion of the oil in the reservoir rock gets trapped in a multitude of dead-end oil pockets, individually small but collectively adding up to a sizeable volume. This is oil that is not contactable by the existing production wells and which will lie there unproduced unless something is done to access them.

These oil pockets are mostly too small to target individually; sometimes they are miniscule. You could produce the oil, yes, but the cost of the operation would be in excess of the potential profit; it's just not worth it. The trick is to locate any bigger untapped pockets which are large enough to justify the expense of drilling a new well. These untapped oil pockets are to be found in most fields, but it takes a great deal of concerted analysis to find out where they are. Most of my career has been involved in doing this type of work.

If you find a new untapped pocket of oil to produce, it adds to the field's reserves. Reserves are technically the volume of hydrocarbons the oil company expects to produce from a given date (usually the current year) and the end of field life. As such, the reserve's value is a prediction of what is going to happen in the future, and as everyone knows predicting the future just ain't easy. When Ian Clark, the County Clerk of the Shetland Isles, was negotiating with the oil companies to set up the Sullom Voe oil terminal, he found himself frustrated at their inability to tell him what the volume of oil throughput over time was expected to be. He felt they were being imprecise and evasive for tactical reasons. Only later, when he became an executive for the British National Oil Corporation and encountered the same response when the subsurface technicians reported to him, did he realise how uncertain reserves prediction can be.[183]

The problem is that there are too many random factors influencing reserves. You can be reasonably certain as to your minimum reserves. Most fields show their oil production slowly declining with time in a profile that looks like a ski slope. The minimum remaining reserves can be extrapolated from this curve to a point at which the field becomes uneconomic, although even this estimate is based on assumptions about oil price. If the oil price miraculously doubles in value just as the field is about to be shut in, then that field will suddenly become profitable again and can be kept going longer.

Oil companies will always want to do something to keep their fields producing, which is why the subsurface team are asked to find new infill well locations to tap the hidden unproduced oil pockets. When you come up with candidate wells to drill like this, these provide the potential for additional reserves. It's always possible to increase the book value of reserves by including the potential projects that could get more additional oil out of the field. Now these projects haven't happened yet, so the reserves added by them are predictions made within a vague yet large volume of 'uncertainty space'. The most sensible route is to cautiously pick out the most plausible scenario, and with a sceptical eye put forward a tentative estimate of the reserves case that could result from this work. A more aggressive approach is to take a more optimistic scenario, still within the bounds of the uncertainty envelope, and to promote that version instead. Oil companies will derive the categories of proven, probable and possible reserves that are listed in oil company reports using this type of approach.

Oil reserves lie at the heart of an oil company. The value of the company is largely the value of the proven reserves on their books, so it's important for the company to keep trust with the financial markets in defining what the reserves are. The American government insist on a rigorous definition of oil and gas reserves before companies are allowed to trade on the New York Stock Exchange and they will sue for fraud if reserves are misrepresented.[184] Smaller companies get specialists such as Degolyer and MacNaughton from Texas to audit the reserves of their oil and gas fields. Larger companies will audit their own reserves.

Sometimes an oil company gets into a mess over reserves. Part of the problem is that field managers just love to increase the proven reserves for their field, in so doing, they are increasing the value of the company and with it the value of their future job prospects. Equally, they hate with a passion having to announce that their reserves have decreased. And it's always possible to derive a Pollyanna view of what the reserves might be, given the uncertainty space they reside in – Pollyanna was the young orphan girl in the book of that name who always found something to be glad about in every situation.

So there can be an innate tendency for reserves to increase one way but not so much decrease the other way. This can sometimes reach the critical point whereby the reserves start to look highly unrealistic compared to what the fields are actually producing. Ultimately, the company will be forced to take action and reduce the reserves to more plausible levels.

Nevertheless, the year-on-year increase in field reserves in oil companies is mostly valid. Technology gets better all the time. During the 20 to 30 year life cycle of the oil field, methods may be found to enhance the seismic imaging of the reservoir, drill the reservoir more effectively and new methods may arise to get the difficult oil out. It's a matter of general experience that you recover more oil with time from the bigger fields, whereas it can be much more difficult to do this with the smaller ones. The oil fields on the UK continental shelf have seen significant reserves growth over the years, the result of very hard work by my colleagues in the industry. Every decade in the North Sea brings a prediction that a significant number of fields will eventually shut down, but not many actually do.

One of the reasons for the good recoveries in the North Sea is because of the practice of injecting water into the edges of the reservoir from the start of oil production, an excellent way of keeping pressures up and moving the oil along. It is also possible to use techniques which change the chemistry and physics of the reservoir fluids in order to get more oil out. For example, detergent, steam or even microbes can be injected down hole as a means to do this. Another method is to inject carbon dioxide gas into an oil field; the gas dissolves in the oil and allows it to flow more easily through the pores of the reservoir rock.

The most extreme attempt to improve recovery involved exploding a nuclear bomb within the reservoir rock of under-performing gas fields. This had been tried five times between 1965 and 1979 in both the US and the Soviet Union.[185] The idea was that the immense energy of the atomic explosion would shatter the reservoir rock into fragments and thus allow the gas to move freely through the rubble. It didn't work. The nuclear explosions failed to get that much more gas out. Not only that, there was considerable contamination of the natural gas with radioactive gases and the vaporisation products of the rock itself.

A good example of reserves growth in the North Sea is shown by BP's Magnus field.[186] The field was discovered in 1974 in the northern North Sea. BP originally considered the discovery marginal. Although there were indications of a reasonable amount of oil there, about 450 million barrel reserves were estimated at that time, the water depth of 186 metres was a critical factor. It was at the extreme limit of what could be done with 1970s North Sea technology.

The field outline is elongate in shape, extending north–south for 14 kilometres. If the water depth had been shallower, then two fixed platforms would have sufficed to access the full length of the field. However, at a water depth of 186 metres, the cost of the two platforms would have swallowed up much of the subsequent revenues. BP decided to build one fixed steel platform to be placed in a central location on the field and then develop the northern and southern ends of the field with subsea wells linked back to the platform. The platform stands at a height of 312 metres above the seabed, just 12 metres short of the Eiffel Tower in height.

The field came on production in 1983 at a development cost of £1.3 billion. It was initially thought that the reservoir sandstone had been deposited as a fairly simple connected body of sand and would need only a small number of wells to develop it. As a result, the platform was built with the capability of drilling only 20 wells; by comparison, the first four Forties platforms each had the capability to drill 36 wells. Twenty drilling slots were not enough, as it later turned out.

The six appraisal wells showed that the field would produce more oil than initially thought; the reserves were now estimated as 450 million barrels out of total oil in place of over a billion barrels. I started work on the Magnus field in 1987 and wrote two technical papers on the early production phase.[187] By this time, the ultimate recoverable reserves had grown to 665 million barrels out of a total oil in place of 1,665 million barrels. We knew more about the geometry of the field by that time and the seismic resolution was improving.

One of the curiosities of the second paper I wrote on the Magnus field is that I also include a production profile, not just showing how much oil had been produced by the field up until 1987 but also giving the estimated forward production beyond then. The profile stops at the end of 1999 when the field was expected to be shut in. In 2015 as I write, the Magnus field is still producing at a rate of about 12,000 barrels per day.[188] This is typical of the North Sea; the oil fields have lasted considerably longer than they were expected to. And when a field produces for longer than expected, it produces more reserves than had been originally anticipated.

I also mention in this technical paper that the Magnus reservoir is somewhat more difficult to manage than previously thought. Instead of behaving as one big connected volume, the geology proved to be somewhat more complex, with faults and blanket mudstones dissecting the reservoir. As a result, the field could be shown to be divided up into a number of self-contained compartments, a bit like the bulk-head of a ship.

I've kept an eye on Magnus over the years, reading the latest technical papers and attending conference presentations. As more and more data comes in from the wells, it's clear that the reservoir is even more complex than I had thought. Intimate understanding of field performance has led to improved recovery of the remaining oil and although the field team have had to do some juggling with the limited number of drilling slots on the platform, that hasn't impeded the reservoir management. New wells have successfully targeted undrained volumes of oil. Today, BP is trying to push the ultimate recoverable reserves for the field towards a target of one billion barrels.

BP has implemented enhanced oil recovery methods on the Magnus field using a technique called Water Alternating Gas (WAG). This works by alternating six months of gas injection into the wells followed by six months of water injection, repeated in yearly cycles. The gas mixes with the oil and makes it more fluid. When the water is subsequently injected into the reservoir, the cushion of water is able to push more oil out.

The Magnus field is just one of many large oil fields in the North Sea showing reserves growth. The technological prowess demonstrated in the North Sea is the reason why oil field recoveries are better here than anywhere else in the world. Magnus is still going strong while some of the other fields on production 30 years ago have ceased production. Nevertheless, it has become a trend to open up previously abandoned fields in the North Sea and to use new methods of getting extra recovery from these old reservoirs. These fields had been shut in by previous operators with a significant volume of oil left behind. At the time there would have been good reasons to do this, perhaps the field had become uneconomic.

I was lucky to be in the team that was the first to open up a previously abandoned North Sea field; this was the Angus field which came back on production in 2004 after having been shut in since 1993. This was a success. We drilled a new well which came on stream at 23,000 barrels per day, comparable to a Forties field well in the early days of production. The rejuvenated field went on to produce an extra 4.7 million barrels of oil, not bad for a field that was supposed to have seen the end of its days.[189]

Evaluating how much oil is left to produce in any one field is in the realm of arm-waving prediction. This puts into perspective any attempt to do this for all the world's oil fields and thus predict how much oil is left globally. Nobody really knows how much oil we have got left to produce. Oil is a finite resource, so eventually we will find out one day. You will notice that oil supplies are running low when sailing ships return to the world's oceans and everybody is riding around on bicycles.

The drive to maximise the reserves in the world's oil fields depends to a large extent on the activity of nationalised oil companies. These are state-owned entities which in many countries control the entire oil resource. They either produce the oil directly or in some cases provide a production sharing agreement with private oil companies. Sometimes they venture abroad. For instance, the National Iranian Oil Company has a 50 per cent share of the Rhum field in the northern North Sea.

The World Bank in 2011 estimated that national oil companies control approximately 90 per cent of global oil reserves, 75 per cent of global oil production and 60 per cent of the world's yet-to-find reserves.[190] The future of our supplies depends on the performance of these companies, whose reputation varies considerably. Top in class is Statoil, 67 per cent of which is owned by the Norwegian state. At the other end of the scale, a number vastly underperform, starved of resources by the controlling government, where political cronies who don't understand the business are given well-paid management jobs and experienced professionals leave to progress their careers elsewhere.

We could get the world's oil all over again, and we would, if oil company performance in the North Sea became the global benchmark to aim for. As it stands, the oil industry is likely to fall short unless the underperforming national oil companies become more efficient. The alternative is for countries with national oil companies to allow access to private oil companies. A recent development has been a decision by Mexico to break the monopoly of the national oil company and open up to foreign oil companies for the first time since the industry was nationalised in 1938. The government hopes to see an influx of outside investment and an increase in oil production.[191] In March 2015, I witnessed the Mexican president, Enrique Peña Nieto, turning up in Aberdeen to sign 'a memoranda of understanding on collaboration in the energy sector' between Mexico and the UK.[192] This could be a significant development if more governments follow this example.

There is a tremendous resource available in our existing oil fields if we could do more globally to get more oil out of them. As the OPEC oil minister Sheikh Yamani once said, 'Oil will be left in the ground. The Stone Age came to an end not because we had a lack of stones, and the oil age will come to an end not because we have a lack of oil.'[193]

Out West

BACK IN THE early 1980s, I remember being among a large crowd of BP geologists on an outing to the Odeon in Aberdeen to see *Local Hero*. The film concerns the efforts of an American oil mogul, played by the actor Burt Lancaster, to secure a shoreline terminal base for the offshore oil fields. As mentioned in Chapter Five, it was based in part on the true story of Armand Hammer, the head of Occidental Petroleum, in his deal to secure an oil terminal on the Orkney island of Flotta. One of the scenes shows the oil mogul 'Arnold Happer' in his Houston office discussing the negotiations. On the wall behind him is a map of the UK continental shelf, showing the location of the oil company's fictitious oil fields, most in the sea area to the west of the Shetland and Orkney Isles.

After the film, we nipped across the road to the Glentanar Bar for a pint. I remember one of the exploration geologists saying: 'Did you see the map with all the oil fields west of Shetland? If only that was true!' There were no producing fields in the area at the time, although BP had already discovered the Clair structure in July 1977 but had yet to work out how to develop the oil there. Following an initial burst of enthusiasm in the 1970s, the area to the west of Shetland had failed to excite any sustained interest. The Department of Energy, the government body responsible for the UK oil licenses, was determined to get the oil companies to drill there by whatever means. In one of the early licensing rounds, they indicated that if oil companies applied for the blocks west of Shetland, applications for the much sought-after blocks in the central North Sea would be considered favourably. This was one way of ensuring that the west of Shetland blocks would be drilled. Part of the deal of securing a UK oil license was that the oil company had to make a commitment to a work programme, including such items as shooting seismic and drilling one or more wells.

Britoil had applied for the plum acreage in the central North Sea in addition to applying for the blocks West of Shetland. They were none too happy when they were subsequently awarded the blocks to the west of Shetland, but none of the blocks they particularly wanted in the central North Sea. Britoil was later taken over by BP, who then discovered that they had also secured the West of Shetland acreage with the accompanying baggage of a number of expensive commitments to drill wells. The government insisted that the company should honour these commitments.

The first commitment well drilled by BP in 1990 discovered the Foinaven field, but only the thin updip crest with 11 metres of sandstone containing both gas and oil. It was an 'undiscovery' well that was considered distinctly unpromising at the time. According to a published technical paper, a decision was then made by BP and their partners Shell to exit the area west of Shetland. In the meanwhile, BP had reprocessed the seismic data using a technique designed to highlight any hydrocarbon-bearing reservoir should it be there. This proved promising, as it gave an indication that there was oil down structure from where they had drilled the well. A second well in 1992 proved the concept and the Foinaven field was 'rediscovered'.[194] Shortly after, the even larger Schiehallion field was found nearby. These discoveries caused much excitement in the UK oil industry. A new area had opened up in the mature UK continental shelf that had previously been discounted as prospective.

The Foinaven and Schiehallion fields, named after Scottish mountains, were discovered relatively late in the exploration history of the UK continental shelf. Exploration geologists hadn't taken the area west of Shetland very seriously up until then, which is surprising, as the giant Clair oil field had been discovered there and proved that large volumes of oil had been generated in the area. The early efforts to explore the West of Shetlands had been unsuccessful. Before the Clair field was found, 16 wells had been drilled in the area, some with oil shows but nothing turned up that looked commercial.

These initial results from the West of Shetlands must have been discouraging and it wasn't clear at the time that Clair had commercial potential. It was not an easy area to drill in; The water extends to vastly greater depths than the North Sea in places. BP has to date drilled an exploration well in a water depth of almost 1,300 metres, while Chevron are sitting on the potential Rosebank oil and gas field development, which is located in area where the water depth is 1,100 metres.[195] The Clair field is in relatively shallow waters by comparison, at 140 metres. The weather conditions are also more extreme as the area receives the full impact of wave and storm as they build up over the full length of the Atlantic Ocean; the North Sea is sheltered from much of this by the British Isles landmass. The expense of exploration and appraisal wells ramp up because of lost drilling time waiting for the storms to blow over.[196] These factors have affected the cost of exploration and development and explain why the oil companies have been slow to sanction developments there.

There is much more incentive to drill in the North Sea where, if you found something, you could always produce it via the existing infrastructure. To the west of Shetland, the scope for tapping into existing infrastructure as a means of reducing transportation costs is more limited.

The seismic data can be tricky to interpret in the area. Sometimes you get an indication that a reservoir is present and this ultimately proves to be an artefact when you drill the feature and find nothing. The seismic response is weak at prospective reservoir depths over large areas to the north-west, including the entire continental shelf offshore from the Faroe Islands. Thick piles of basalt lava obscure the signal here. The seismic pulse tends to bounce off the hard lava in the upper part of the rock succession and the response from below is fuzzy and weak. Much of the yet-to-be-found oil and gas fields to the west of Shetland probably lie within or below the lavas.[197] Oil companies have been working hard to develop new techniques to try and enhance the signal from this area.

Let's jump ahead to 2014 and pick up the story again. Scotland has just had a referendum on independence. To the question, 'Should Scotland be an independent country?' – 55 per cent of those who voted replied no. North Sea oil figured prominently in the debate on both sides. Much discussion focused on how much oil is left to produce, the yes camp promoting independence, claiming that a larger volume of oil remains around Scotland's shores than the figures put forward by the no camp. The yes agenda claimed that because of the abundance of offshore oil reserves even today, Scotland will have years of prosperity to come as an independent nation.

Unfortunately, an element of misinformation had crept into the debate. If some in the yes camp were to be believed, there are large oil reserves in the Firth of Clyde, the world's largest oil field lies to the west of Shetland and there is a conspiracy by all, up to the level of Prime Minister, to suppress the true amount of remaining reserves in the Clair oil field. According to one survey carried out before the referendum, 42 per cent of those asked believed that it is probably true that new oil reserves had been discovered off Scottish shores and that the UK government was keeping these secret.[198] On the basis of online comments on social media and newspaper articles, many believed these stories.

The Clair field reserves story was shared by over 15,000 people on Facebook and this is the post as it appeared on my timeline:

My mate is back from the rigs and confirmed that his friends on the Clair oil field (supposedly the biggest reservoir in the world) were stood down and sent home on full pay until the end of September.

The results of the prospecting showed that the field was three times bigger than expected and that the oil is premium grade. Execs were flying in from all over the world and Mr Cameron sneaked up to meet them. Immediately after this, they were stood down.

This could be the single biggest and most devious act of treachery

Westminster has committed in Scotland. This simply cannot happen. We must tell everyone. Sadly, many Scots are complicit in deceiving the Scottish people and directing them into a future of bondage, servitude and humiliation. We have the chance to stop them and MUST. This is Scotland's birthright and it's our children's future they are stealing.

It's nonsense of course. The Clair field has the largest amount of oil in place of all the fields on the UK continental shelf at 8 billion barrels, according to BP, but only a fraction of the oil will be recovered – one to two billion barrels is my guess. That's not bad, but it is still less than the Forties field, which has produced over 2.5 billion barrels of oil to date. The mythology that the Clair field is somehow the world's biggest oil field and the basis for an independent Scotland to become rich is at best described as mischievous. Not everybody in Scotland took these tales seriously. I saw one online parody which stated that the biggest oil field in the world was to be found under Loch Ness – 'It's a monster!'.

Clair has proved a difficult reservoir to develop and this may explain why it was discovered in July 1977, yet only came on production in February 2005. The reservoir and oil properties are moderate in the Clair field by comparison to oil fields in the North Sea. The sandstone porosity is on the low side at about 13–15 per cent of the rock volume and the oil is of medium-grade density. The field covers a very large area at 220 square kilometres, and the reservoir is shallow, the bulk of it lying above 2,000 metres depth. This is a rather awkward reservoir to develop because a large amount of oil is spread out over an enormous area. The oil flows at lower production rates than the typically lighter oil in the fields under the North Sea. The shallow reservoir depths are also a hindrance. This potentially limits the drilling radius of wells from a platform as there is not much room to spread out your wells before reaching the reservoir. Additionally, the reservoir rock is shot through with open fractures and the oil tends to move through these fractures more rapidly than through the porous rock itself.

BP obviously agonised over the development of the Clair field; there is so much oil in place, yet it is not easy to get it out. A sign of the uncertainty involved is that after discovering Clair they drilled 23 appraisal wells and sidetracks before they decided to sanction the development.[199] The company are developing the field in phases, with the first phase aiming to access up to 300 million barrels of reserves from the core area of the field. The second phase will involve the installation of two linked platforms (currently under way at time of writing) with the intent of accessing 640 million barrels of reserves from the Clair Ridge.[200] With experience, BP has found the best way to access the oil; they drill horizontal wells through the reservoir so that they can penetrate as many of the fractures as possible. BP have also discovered that by injecting fresh water into the reservoir as opposed to the much more readily available sea water, they can push more oil towards the production wells.

The existing oil fields west of Shetland look to have long-term potential although only four of them have been developed so far. The giant Clair field could trundle on producing for many a year. The Foinaven field is still producing oil. BP is spending £3 billion to redevelop the Schiehallion and adjacent Loyal field where there is significant reservoir potential.[201] They are replacing the existing FPSO vessel and anticipate that the new vessel will be on station for at least 35 years. Yet, several of the fields discovered to date have still to be developed. One of these is the Rosebank field with reserves of about 240 million barrels of oil equivalent and discovered in 2004.[202]

One of the discoveries to the west of the Shetlands is the Marjun oil pool which extends across the maritime boundary into the maritime area under the jurisdiction of the Faroe Islands.[203] The discovery well in November 2001 was drilled on the Faroes side and found a 170 metre thick interval of light oil and gas. As such it is the first oil discovery in Faroese waters. If oil discoveries pick up off, the Faroe Islands (population just under 50,000) could end up as the richest nation on the planet. However, there is no sign of this happening yet. The Marjun find has not so far proved commercial. Oil and gas shows have been seen in two of the other exploration wells drilled on Faroese acreage but the oil industry has yet to find the equivalent of an Ekofisk or Forties field in this part of the world.

The west of Shetland has been the area getting the most attention on the west side of Britain. Further south, the UK offshore acreage takes an enormous salient around the islet of Rockall, 480 kilometres to the west of the Scottish mainland. Rockall was claimed as UK territory in 1955, when the Royal Navy visited to cement a proprietary brass plaque near the summit of the rock and then hoisted the Union Jack aloft. Thereafter, Rockall has been the subject of diplomatic wrangling with Ireland, Iceland and Denmark (on behalf of the Faroes).

Rockall at 31 metres long, 25 metres wide and 17 metres high is smaller than a modern office block.[204] It has no trees or bushes of any kind, just seaweed, lichen, algae and moss. The tiny lump of granitic rock sticking out of the sea and forming the islet of Rockall is clearly not the specific interest for all concerned hoping to clarify the ownership issue. Rather, its strategic position is the basis for securing both fisheries and potential subsurface oil resources under the seabed in the surrounding area. Claiming Rockall as sovereign territory has been difficult to support. International legislation passed in 1982 states that 'rocks which cannot sustain human habitation or economic life of their own shall have no exclusive economic zone or continental shelf'.

Yet according to the annals of the Rockall Club, the society that is open to all those who have set foot on the islet, it is possible to live on Rockall. The living space is provided by an area known as Hall's Ledge located just below the summit. It is 3.5 metres long and 1.3 metres wide.[205] It was here in 1985 that Tom McClean, a former SAS soldier, proved that Rockall was habitable when he spent 40 days on the islet; that is, 'habitable' perhaps to the satisfaction of the UK government. The feat has since been repeated, in 1997 by Greenpeace activists, protesting against oil exploration in the area and in 2014 by the adventurer Nick Hancock.

Maritime boundaries have now been agreed with Ireland in the south and the Faroe Islands to the north. The sea around Rockall has been carved up by the UK licensing authority into quadrants and licence blocks for the purposes of exploration. It's an enormous area and a glance at the map shows that it is almost as big as the whole of the UK North Sea areas combined.

Drilling is difficult here, the sea deepening rapidly all around the Rockall islet, with water depths over 1,000 metres typical. A basin of sedimentary rocks is found beneath the Rockall Trough south-east of Rockall itself. This is an enormous trough that extends 800 kilometres in length from west of the Hebrides down the west coast of Ireland. The oil companies have drilled at the edges, where the sea water is relatively shallow, 14 wells to date. One has found gas – the Benbecula discovery made by Enterprise Oil in 2000. According to a UK government presentation, the well found 19 metres of gas and has proved a gas accumulation with an estimated volume of about 500 billion cubic feet.[206] That would be OK if it was in the North Sea but stand-alone in the Atlantic Ocean, it's not going to be commercial. It would need more gas fields in the area to justify constructing what would be a very expensive pipeline and a dedicated gas terminal onshore. In this instance, the nearest landfall is the Isle of Lewis, 80 kilometres to the south-east. The pipeline would have to cross Lewis and then on to Sutherland on the Scottish mainland, from where an onshore pipeline would be needed to provide access to gas consumers in the UK.[207]

Another well drilled by the Italian oil company AGIP found minor oil shows. As the UK government like to point out, there is a proven petroleum province in the Rockall area, yet the oil industry remain to be convinced.[208] The area has many drawbacks which it shares with the area to the west of the Shetlands. The water is deep, the weather terrible and thick lava flows obscure the seismic response. A major discovery would clearly help in establishing a basic infrastructure for the area: a hub platform, pipelines and onshore terminals.

There has been minor interest in the Inner Hebrides, where rocks similar to the Brent reservoir interval outcrop on the islands of Skye and Raasay. A well was drilled in the north of Skye in the 1970s but it failed to find anything. There probably isn't any mature oil source rock present in the area and the oil companies have not returned.[209]

Another area to the west of Scotland which has not gained much interest from the oil companies is the Firth of Clyde. Nevertheless, the Scottish independence rumour mill has been active in playing up this part of the west coast on account of a BP seismic survey shot to the south of Arran in 1981. BP never followed up with an exploration well and there is absolutely no evidence that any hydrocarbons are present in the Firth of Clyde, yet it is sometimes claimed that oil exploration was stopped because the Ministry of Defence were concerned it would interfere with its training and exercise ground for nuclear submarines.[210]

The prosaic reality would appear to be that BP shot seismic and then gave up on the area, most likely because they saw nothing of interest. I don't know what the outcome of BP's investigations were and so far no data has been published, although I suspect they were looking for a structure similar to the Morecambe Bay fields further south, but didn't find anything promising. BP almost certainly had gas in mind and not oil. Sandstone intervals of the same age as those that provide the reservoir for the Morecambe gas fields and the gas fields of the southern North Sea are found on the Isle of Arran. The Coal Measures, a potential gas source rock, are present onshore to the east. Nevertheless, hints are given in technical publications that the presence of any significant mature source rock is doubtful and this is probably why the oil companies have not shown any sustained interest in the area.

14

The End of Oil

IN 1999 I attended a meeting in the oil company's London office. The aim was to discuss our latest development well proposal with management and to get their approval for it. I flew down from Aberdeen to London, catching the 'red eye' at 6.30am and returned later that same day. The London offices were very plush and the board room directly overlooked the back garden of Buckingham Palace. I had a sneaky peek, but the borders were so densely tree-lined you couldn't actually see if anyone was there.

The meeting didn't last long as the managers liked the well proposal and nodded it through quickly. I had about an hour to spare before catching the taxi to Heathrow Airport so I nipped down to the office's impressive geology library to have a look through the books there. One title caught my eye as it was totally out of place in amongst all the geology books – *How Many People Can the Earth Support?* by Joel Cohen.[211]

I thought, 'How strange, what's this book doing here?'

I asked the office librarian if I could borrow it and read it on the plane home. The book was academic rather than popular in style, and although it didn't directly answer the question the title of the book posed, the analysis made it clear that the human population is rapidly approaching unsustainable levels on the Earth's surface. I wondered if one of the senior managers in the London office had ordered it. I suspect many oil company managers harbour secret concerns about the future of our energy requirements. After all, they work in an industry that depends on making predictions about resource availability over a time frame of 20–30 years, or longer. Oil company personnel are acutely aware that global energy demand is increasing at the same time as cheap and easy-to-produce oil resources are diminishing fast. We are now sweating the difficult stuff as far as oil is concerned.

The Joel Cohen book reminded me of another on the same topic, Paul Erlich's *The Population Bomb*.[212] When it came out in 1968 it controversially predicted that rapidly increasing human numbers meant that the world would run short of resources in the next decade and mass starvation would ensue. Of course, this never happened, and the book lost credibility as a result.

Yet, what has happened since the 1960s is that humans just got a bit smarter, and that's about it. We have kept things going that bit longer. New strains of wheat and rice were developed that produced many more grains per head; the plants are smaller and more resistant to being knocked flat by wind and rain. This kicked off the so-called 'Green Revolution' in the late '60s, massively increasing the yield of wheat and rice planted per hectare. It proved to be an amazing initiative that undoubtedly headed off famine in Asia and Central America. Synthetic fertilisers developed in the early part of the 20th century have also helped with modern agriculture and the use of these has been complemented by mechanised agriculture.

The world population is growing at 200,000 people per day and in 2015 has been estimated to be in excess of seven billion individuals. How did the global human population get so large?

You have to go back a long way to get the answer, indeed as far back as the early Stone Age. Our ancestors became omnivores some two and half million years ago, adding meat to their diet, whereas previously their predecessors had hung around trees and had eaten mostly fruit and nuts. They had thus become predators, scavenging and hunting for animal produce. Biologists inform us that predator numbers tend to be limited by the available prey to be eaten. As a result of this equilibrium, there are only so many hunter-gatherers that a land area can support. The carrying capacity for the pre-agricultural UK is thought to be very low and may have been not much more than about 22,000 hunter-gatherer individuals; it could even have been as low as 5,000, although the estimates are somewhat uncertain. The equivalent number for the world as a whole could be a few million people.

That balance changed when farming arrived, starting from about 11,000 years ago in Europe. By being able to store food for the lean times, humans managed to transcend the normal predator-prey balance and populations rocketed. It was at this point in Earth history that we left behind our precarious existence as just another mammal scrabbling to survive in the natural environment.

Intrinsic to the development of farming was the need for new technology and sources of energy to drive the technology. At first, draught animals provided the 'horsepower' and much later watermills and windmills were put to use. The global human population remained below about half a billion individuals until the Industrial Revolution started in the 18th century. Steam technology driven by coal then became a dominant energy source. Another source of energy, electricity, arrived in the century afterwards. The human population started to increase significantly after the Industrial Revolution reaching an estimated one billion in 1804 and two billion in 1927. What is incredible is that our numbers then increased substantially since the Second World War ended in 1945, with over an additional four and a half billion humans now on our planet. The advent of oil as a cheap and highly efficient energy source from the 1950s onward has been a factor in supporting these population numbers. This was a time when a vast amount of oil came on stream from the Middle East and North Africa.

The year 1950 has been described as the start of what has been described as 'the great acceleration'. It was the date when human global activity ramped up enormously. Thousands of new dams were built, the demand for water increased substantially, the use of fertiliser on the fields increased by almost a factor of 10, the amount of vehicles on the roads increased from 50 million to over a billion today, mass international tourism started to become a major industry and many other economic indicators show the frenetic increase in human activity. The world saw increasing urbanisation on the back of cheap oil, from about 30 per cent of the total world population to 54 per cent in 2014 and currently growing by just under two per cent every year.[213] We have thus attained a new level for the carrying capacity of our planet for human beings, propped up by modern agriculture, mechanisation and oil.

We could be in a tricky situation. Maurice King and Charles Elliot writing in the medical journal *The Lancet* in 1993, define the concept of 'entrapment':[214]

A population is demographically trapped if it has exceeded, or is projected to exceed, the combination of: (a) the carrying capacity of its own ecosystem; (b) its ability to obtain the products, and especially the food, produced by other ecosystems except as food aid; and (c) its ability to migrate to other ecosystems in a manner that preserves (or improves) its standard of living (voluntary migration).

We could all be in a situation of entrapment if energy resources start to dwindle. Oil is currently needed in a world with so many people on it. Crude oil is mainly used for fuel, heating oil and petrochemicals. It is not so much used for power generation; coal, gas, nuclear and increasingly renewable energy sources predominate here.

The discovery of cheap, plentiful oil has not only seamlessly supported a massive growth in the human population, it has also brought a very high standard of living to those of us in the richer countries of the world. Modern economic life needs oil – we could possibly do without it, but our standard of living would be substantially diminished in consequence. Without oil, there would be no efficient mass transport and haulage of goods; international air flights and modern mechanised agriculture also depends on it. I find myself writing this book at my kitchen table enjoying a typical western life style. I'm drinking coffee from Indonesia in a cup that was made in China. The bowl of fruit on the table holds oranges from Spain and bananas from Central America. Cheap oil helped to bring them here. In my cosy flat, I am experiencing a far better and richer standard of living than most of the kings and queens of past ages. If you own a car, you depend on people like me finding oil. You are driving one of over 1.2 billion cars that are currently using the world's roads.[215] The oil industry copes with all of this by producing 92 million barrels of oil a day.[216]

Unfortunately, the drawbacks of oil are considerable. Oil makes a horrendous mess when it pours into the environment accidentally; the various pollution disasters taint everybody who works in the industry. Oil is 'the devil's excrement' wrote the Venezuelan politician Juan Pablo Pérez Alfonso (and one of the founders of OPEC).[217] Fossil fuels contribute to the pollution of the atmosphere which in turn causes global warming. Climate change will cause problems for agriculture amongst other issues, and something we definitely don't need with 7 billion plus people on the planet. Almost a quarter of the pollution leading to global warming is emitted by cars, trucks and buses using oil products. The fine particles emitted in diesel fumes are known to be a significant health hazard.

The big problem with oil is that it is difficult to find alternative sources of energy to replace it. There is so much energy within a single teaspoon of oil, not much else compares as an energy source except for nuclear energy. The idea of replacing petrol-driven with battery-driven cars is to be applauded, yet the energy-density of batteries is at the moment substantially less than that of oil. Another advantage of oil is that it is light and compact as an energy source and can be carried around with the car. Perhaps fuel cells are the answer, and as of 2015 a fleet of 10 buses has appeared in my home city of Aberdeen, powered by hydrogen fuel cells and emitting water as the sole exhaust product. The intent is to produce the hydrogen using electricity generated by wind power to split the gas from water molecules. The project is expensive, £19 million has been spent so far, but once the hydrogen is produced using renewable energy, the operating costs will be minimal.[218]

It's not difficult to make predictions as to where all these trends might lead. A point will come at which the world population surpasses any credible means of supplying them with resources, and that includes oil. Before that happens, there is an imperative to develop and build alternative energy resources to cope with the transition from fossil fuels. It's possible that we could ease ourselves out of a dependence on fossil fuels and make a gradual but successful transition to alternative energy resources. It is only to be hoped that we can do so.

I'm writing this book in my spare time – the day job involves me working on a field development project in the Brent Province of the northern North Sea. Although the oil pool is small, it's a multi-million pound development if it can be shown that the operation is a money-making proposition. I work as part of a team of professionals and we each provide input to the larger decision. The degree of differing expertise that needs to meld together for an oil operation to work is impressive; nobody can do it all on their own. Team work is essential.

It's likely to be my last job of work in the industry before I retire after over 34 years in the toil for oil. I'm a member of what the industry calls the great crew change. Many new professionals were brought into the industry in the 1970s and '80s as offshore areas like the North Sea opened up. We are all of an age in our late '50s/ early '60s and it's time to wind down and retire. We represent a large pool of experienced professionals that are about to depart from oil companies never to come near them again. Unfortunately, a couple of oil price crashes in 1986 and 1999, coupled with severe redundancies, displaced many professionals from the industry. The oil company clear-outs could be brutal. This type of behaviour discouraged many promising youngsters from joining the industry and left a major gap in their staff demographics.

This has created the unfortunate situation whereby oil companies today have a combination of a few experienced staff on the verge of retiring and a lot of youngsters who are smart but less experienced. None of the projects are getting any easier. Indeed the lot of oil companies today is to sweat the tricky oil fields. Gone are the days when you could milk a relatively easy project like the Forties field.

I attended a conference in London in 2012 organised by the Society of Petroleum Engineers. The theme concerned what could be done to maximise oil production from existing fields and I gave a talk on the geological methods of doing so. The conclusions of the workshops held as part of the conference particularly interested me. What came out was that there is still a tremendous amount of additional oil that could be produced from ageing fields with the right set of practices and techniques. However, two major problems beset companies in trying to do this. The first is that there is not enough staff to go around in the industry and many projects scrape along understaffed. The second problem is that it is not only the staff that is ageing, the platforms and related infrastructure are ancient too. Many North Sea oil platforms were built and installed in the 1970s and '80s and were not expected to be used for as long as they have been. For the North Sea oil industry as a whole, it's important to keep them in place for as long as possible. They act as hubs for any new developments which probably wouldn't be economically standalone and would need an existing infrastructure to tap into. However, the older platforms are expensive to maintain and they have numerous integrity issues. They are not producing that much oil, so the expensive maintenance costs eat into what profits can be eked out of them. None of this is easy…

As the North Sea ages, the oil fields are changing hands. Slowly but surely, the large oil companies such as BP and Shell are selling their oil fields to smaller operators who can survive at a different economic scale without the same overheads. One success story has been the American oil company Apache who took over the Forties field from BP. By an aggressive campaign of drilling on the field they have managed to reverse the production decline on the field. They are still drilling 40 years after the field started production.

Technical experts landed on the range of 15–24 billion barrels of oil equivalent as a most likely prediction for the UK continental shelf remaining reserves including those in the North Sea (about 42 billion barrels of oil equivalent had been produced up until 2013). The time frame going forward to produce this oil will probably be 30–40 years, although there is much uncertainty about all of this.[219]

The oil price started to drop in the latter half of 2014 and is still low (2015). Global oil production has increased as a result of the success of the American shale oil industry together with other factors and the Saudis have decided not to support the oil price by cutting production. A sharp decrease in the oil price, such as was seen in 1986, could easily bring North Sea oil production to a halt much sooner. Another detrimental factor is that the North Sea has become a high cost area and the return on capital invested there has dropped as a result. There is a danger that global finance will seek better returns elsewhere. The reduction in oil tax announced in the March 2015 budget statement should help to secure North Sea oil as a vital strategic resource for the nation.

Eventually, North Sea oil and gas production will be no more as the last drop of oil is produced around the mid-century. As each field is finally shut in between now and then, a massive tidying-up job will be required to remove the entire infrastructure. This will involve the dismantling of about 475 offshore installations, 10,000 kilometres of pipeline and 15 onshore oil and gas terminals. Between 2013 and 2040, the overall cost of abandonment is expected to be a whopping £31.5 billion.[220]

Some of the smaller fields have already been abandoned. The first major abandonment exercise in the North Sea will be Shell's Brent field which is currently in planning.[221] Three out of the four platforms have already ceased production. Shell had considered alternative uses for the Brent platforms such as wind power and even offshore prisons and casinos were proposed, but all these options proved untenable not the least given the remote location of the field area. The abandonment will be a massive job as it will not only involve removing all four platforms but also 24 pipelines. In addition, 130 wells will have to be made safe to ensure that there is no chance of any oil leaking up them and polluting the sea.

The regulations governing platform abandonment were agreed between 15 European countries. Since 1998, after there had been controversy over the proposed dumping of the Brent Spar loading buoy in the Atlantic Ocean, the dumping or the leaving of offshore installations in place is prohibited. Permission may be given to leave installations or parts of installations in place (eg for steel platforms weighing more than 10,000 tonnes in air or gravity-based concrete platforms).[222]

Once everything has gone, a major episode in Scotland's history will be over and it will be the end of North Sea oil. I consider myself very lucky to have had the chance to take an active role in all of this.

Geological Period/ Epoch	Age MYA: Million Years Ago	Comments
Holocene	0–11, 700 years	
Pleistocene	11,700 years – 2.6 MYA	Ice Age
Pliocene	2. 6–5.3 MYA	
Miocene	5.3–23 MYA	
Oligocene	23–34 MYA	
Eocene	34–56 MYA	Youngest oil fields in the North Sea.
Palaeocene	56–65 MYA	Forties, Montrose, Nelson and Foinaven fields amongst others
Cretaceous	145–201 MYA	Chalk fields including the Ekofisk field in Norway.
Jurassic	145–201 MYA	Numerous fields including Brent, Magnus, Ninian, Beryl, Piper and Claymore fields. The Kimmeridge Clay Formation which provides the source rock for most of the oil in the North Sea is Jurassic in age.
Triassic	201–252 MYA	
Permian	252–299 MYA	Auk oil field, southern North Sea gas fields.
Carboniferous	299–359 MYA	Coal Measures. Some southern North Sea gas fields and central North Sea oil fields.
Devonian	359–419 MYA	Clair field.

15

The Geological Story

THE HISTORY OF North Sea oil goes back further than 1969 and the discovery of the first commercial oil fields; indeed, it extends back through millions of years of geological time to when the first reservoirs formed, whether as desert sands, delta deposits or submarine landslides. It's a fascinating history and I propose to cover it in this section much as a drill bit would encounter the rock – from the top down. We will drill a fictional well down through the rock under the North Sea; nevertheless the geology we will encounter is real. We can regard the drill bit as a time traveller. As we go deeper, evidence will be uncovered that allows us to tell the story in the rocks – the ancient worlds of volcanoes, earthquakes and the creatures that lived back then.

The drill bit is lowered down from the rig to the bottom of the North Sea and from there cuts through the uppermost sediments – our narrative now begins.

Geological Report No. 1

Depth: 0–20 metres subsea.
Lithology: Unconsolidated mud, silt and sand.
Age: Holocene, 0–11,700 years before present.

The uppermost sediments lie directly below the sea floor and are made up of loose mud, silt and sand recently deposited in the North Sea by current, wave and tide. A few metres deeper and the material that formed during the Ice Age will be reached. The sediments are getting older and older with depth, not quite rock yet; they are too loosely bound to be called that.

Before we get to the Ice Age sediments, we pass through an important timeline at about 8,200 years before the present day.[223] This was when one of the world's largest known tsunamis was set off, and it happened here in the North Sea. Over a 100 kilometres length of the underwater Norwegian continental shelf collapsed, possibly triggered by an earthquake. A massive submarine landslide, involving about 3,500 cubic kilometres of rock debris, poured down onto the seabed offshore from mid-Norway, displacing an equivalent volume of water. This spread out in an enormous underwater pulse from the area of the slide. The tsunami hit the coastal regions of the North Sea, piling ahead of it a chaotic mixture of debris, tree trunks and silty sand; sedimentary deposits that can be dug into and examined today around the North Sea coastline. The upper limit of the tsunami deposits has been recorded at 20 metres or more above sea level in the Shetland Isles, three to six metres in north-east Scotland and 10 to 12 metres' elevation in western Norway. The high level reached by the tsunami in the Shetlands and Norway was due to the narrow inlets and fjords acting to funnel the surging water beyond the shoreline.

The small population of humans living on the North Sea coast must have been affected by the tsunami. These were hunter-gatherers, subsisting on any food that came to hand such as shellfish and plant roots. They would also have hunted for elk, deer, wild boar and aurochs, the ancestors of domesticated cattle.

We have evidence that humans were probably around at the time. The oldest known 'house' in Scotland was discovered in 2012 during the excavations to build the new Forth road bridge at South Queensferry. The building, dating from 10,250 years before present, shows an oval structure seven metres long which was probably roofed with grass turf.[224] Agriculture was not yet known in Scotland, although it had been established on the eastern fringes of Europe from about 11,000 years ago. The spread of farming through Western Europe had been slow and it wouldn't be practiced in Britain until about 6,000 years ago.

Some intriguing archaeological finds in Inverness, Broughty Ferry and on the Norwegian coast near Bergen show the tsunami deposits immediately overlying what appears to be evidence for hunter-gatherer camps complete with flint implements.[225] The condition of moss caught up in the tsunami sediments show a seasonal maturity consistent with a late October timing for the tsunami.[226] For the hunter-gatherers this was the worst possible time of year to cope with the disaster as they would have already started to overwinter on the coastline after their summer season hunting in the hills. Any survivors would not only have been faced with a devastated landscape, they would also have lost their winter camps and all their tools at a time of year when the worst of the winter conditions was yet to come. It is possible that all human life disappeared from the east coast of Scotland in consequence.

Geological Report No. 2

Depth: 20–600 metres subsea.
Lithology: Unconsolidated mud, silt and sand.
Age: Pleistocene (Ice Age), 11,700 years – 2.6 million years before
            present.

The top of the Ice Age sediments dates to 11,700 years before present. Ice sheets and glaciers were widespread in Britain, indeed throughout much of the northern hemisphere. The Ice Age wasn't entirely chilly throughout; the climate kept swinging back and forth between cold and warm phases for the two and half million years it lasted. In its later stages the warm intervals in each 100,000 year cycle would persist for about 11,000 years and the climate during these phases looks to have been much like it is today. Such an imbalance between the length of the cold and warm intervals suggests that freezing conditions mostly prevailed. The ice would come and go during each cycle. Every time it warmed up, the glaciers would retreat as the ice melted, piling sediment-laden torrents of water into the North Sea. This happened between 30 and 50 times since the start of the Ice Age. The cycles were influenced by long term variations in the Earth's attitude and orbit relative to the sun.[227]

The cause of the Ice Age was probably an accident of circumstances. The Earth's tectonic plates had been shifting around and rearranging the continents and oceans. In particular, both Australia and South America had split off from Antartica. The patterns of oceanic circulation changed as a result, causing the Antarctic area to become much colder. By about 15 million years ago, ice sheets had formed in Antarctica and glaciers were present in Greenland. The tipping point probably came when the gap between North and South America closed and the Panama Isthmus formed about three to three and a half million years ago. This land bridge barred any direct connection between the warm waters of the Caribbean and the Pacific, forcing warm oceanic currents to flow northwards. It may seem paradoxical that a warm ocean current sent northward would cause an Ice Age. Nevertheless, it had the effect of generating warm, moist air that would cool and fall as snow in and below the Arctic Circle. The area had long been bitterly cold with glaciers present, but now there was an abundant supply of moisture that allowed the snow and ice to build up. Vast, thick ice sheets were now forming in northern climes.[228]

The ice sheets at their full development during the last glacial episode 20,000 years ago reached over three kilometres thickness in North America; in Scotland over a kilometre thick.[229] So much of the world's water was bound up in the ice that the sea level during the Ice Age was substantially below where it is today, 130 metres lower at one point. Ireland was linked by land to Great Britain which was in turn linked to continental Europe. Japan and

China was a continuous land mass and so was Australia and New Guinea.[230] Much of the North Sea was dry land at intervals during the Ice Age albeit frequently covered in thick ice.

A remarkable find was made by the British Geological Survey in 1981. They had been sampling the uppermost seabed sediments in the northern North Sea as part of a big study. A flint artefact of human origin was found in one of the cores recovered from the sea floor, 150 kilometres north-east of Lerwick. The flint, which had clearly been worked by knocking flakes off to form an edge, was lying in a bed of sand 28 centimetres below the top of the core (the seabed) and has been described as a scraper. Although it appeared to be unused, it would have helped Stone Age humans to scrape and clean animal hides or perhaps carve wood for spears. The flint scraper could have been accidently dropped overboard from a primitive boat, but it's also possible that it was lost on land by the early humans that were living there.[231]

The massive weight of glacial ice imposed a tremendous load on the Scottish mainland and was heavy enough to cause the crust of the Earth to sag under its weight. At the human scale, the Earth appears to be rigid and unyielding, yet it doesn't take that much weight to depress the surface. The loading of the ice onto the Scottish land surface acted to push it down by several tens of metres. When the weight on the land was released as the ice melted, the Scottish mainland started to rise up again. It is still coming up at a rate of up to two millimetres a year. Around the coast of Scotland you can see former beaches and even cliff lines, now inland and at heights of up to 35 metres above present-day sea level. Global sea levels are currently rising but Scotland for the moment is popping out of the sea a touch faster. Curiously enough, as Scotland is rising out of the waves, the south of England, where the glacial ice had been thin to absent, is gradually shrinking in areal extent as the sea encroaches inland.[232]

An event of great significance to the British Isles occurred about 425,000 years ago. Before this time, a ridge of land had connected England and France between what is now Dover and Calais. To the north of the ridge was a very large lake of water dammed in between the ridge and the glaciers occupying the North Sea further to the north. As the ice melted, the water levels of the lake continuously rose until eventually they overwhelmed the ridge to the south.[233] This created a massive waterfall which gouged out the Dover Strait. Some 200,000 years later a similar episode forced water to cascade south-westwards in an even bigger flood, and this enlarged the Dover Strait to close to its present size. Britain had thus become an island isolated from Europe.

Geological Report No. 3

Depth: *600–1800 metres subsea.*
Lithology: *Predominantly medium-grey mudstone, minor siltstone and*
             sandstone intervals.
Age: *Oligocene / Miocene /Pliocene, 2.6–34 million years before*
             present.

Our hypothetical well is now drilling through sediments older than the Ice Age. The time line is 2.6 million years before the present day. The rock samples will be starting to get a bit more monotonous now, grey mudstones and siltstones representing the mud and silt that continuously fall into and clog up the seas and oceans of the world. Rivers and streams continuously erode the emergent land masses dumping the resulting sediment into the sea. Sand grains and pebbles are the heaviest and will fall out quickly, forming the deltas and sand bars seen offshore from many rivers. The mud and silt is lighter and will travel further out to sea. The samples coming back up the wellbore are now starting to look like proper rock. They have had so much weight of sediment lying on top of them, much of the original pore space has collapsed, the water driven out and the remaining clay and silt has been compacted.

What is happening elsewhere in the world 2.6 million years ago? Over in Africa, our ancestors are walking upright. They are not quite modern human beings; we didn't appear until somewhere between 100,000 and 200,000 years ago, but they are on the way to us. The world is becoming dryer and cooler than it had been previously and grassland has been gradually replacing the extensive forests of old. The apes are becoming less common, while large herds of herbivores range over the grass plains that are just starting to open up. Our ancestors are the exception amongst the apes; they are on the verge of giving up eating fruit as their main diet and will soon be scavenging from the carcases of game animals lying on the open savannah.

Back to the well again and we are drilling even deeper below the Ice Age sediments. The rock fragments coming back up the borehole will be much the same for several hundred metres. The drilling bit will cut down slowly through this section, sandstone drills faster than the mudstone but we will not see much sandstone in this section, maybe the occasional thin sandy interval and that's it. The mud and silt was sediment that was mostly sourced from the erosion of the of the British Isles landmass and to some extent, Norway.

We can pick out some more of the highlights on the way down. Dramatic events were taking place in the Mediterranean about five to six million years ago. About 6 million years ago, the Straits of Gibraltar started to rise above sea level and this blocked off the connection between the Atlantic Ocean and the Mediterranean Sea. The water in the landlocked Mediterranean started to evaporate leaving two large isolated salt lakes at a much lower water level than today surrounded by arid scrubland. What had been the Mediterranean islands of Corsica, Sardinia and Majorca now stood out as big mountains in the middle of this desert.

This situation lasted for about 640,000 years, at which point the Straits of Gibraltar was breached by the sea and the waters of Atlantic Ocean flowed back in again. This episode formed the Mediterranean Sea as we largely know it today. Initially the flooding of the Mediterranean started in a slow, leisurely manner, but as the Straits of Gibraltar started to erode and deepen to a significant extent, water cascaded into the basin. The level of the Mediterranean inland sea then rose at least 600 metres in 10,000 years.[234] This produced what would have been an enormous and very spectacular waterfall at the entrance to the Mediterranean.

At about 7 million years ago, the last common ancestor of both humans and chimpanzees was swinging through the trees of tropical Africa.[235] We are not descended from chimpanzees; our two lines branched off at this stage. This wasn't that long ago compared to the age of the rocks we will eventually uncover. The bit is drilling at 700 metres below the seabed by this point; we still have over 3,000 metres of rock column left to go before we finish this well.

The Alps of Switzerland and Austria were growing fast between 9 and 18 million years ago in the Miocene Epoch.[236] This was the result of the collision between the African and European tectonic plates, the first phase of which had started 46 million years ago. The early versions of the large European rivers such as the Rhine were sourced from the emerging mountains and started to pour sediment into the southern North Sea from then on.[237]

Sediments of the Oligocene Epoch appear 23 million years before present. It was a time when forests were being increasingly replaced by grass pastures.[238] The Antarctic continent was located at the South Pole and glaciers were starting to form there. More and more water became locked up in the ice and the global climate became drier. This favoured the development of grass pastures as opposed to extensive forests. Grass can survive periods of drought, whereas trees cannot do so easily.

Grass had undergone a major evolutionary breakthrough. Previously grass plants could not tolerate continuous grazing and were restricted to environments such as swamps where they could largely escape the attentions of animals. The new adaptation was simple but effective, grass kept on growing continuously (hence the need to mow the lawn every week in the summer). Grass pastures could thus survive grazing as there would always be just enough leaf on show for the plant to absorb sustaining energy from the sun.

The gradual loss of forests and the expansion of grasslands would have a significant effect on the mammals at the time. Upon until now, the mammals had adapted to living in forests. Now the mammals that we see today started to flourish. The expanding grassy plains benefitted the hoofed animals including the early horses and predators such as the cats also adapted. Fast running and good long-distance eyesight were now required skills for both the predators and the preyed upon.

Geological Report No. 4

Depth: *1,800–2,100 metres subsea.*
Lithology: *Predominantly medium-grey mudstone, minor siltstone and*
                sandstone intervals. Minor oil shows.
Age: *Eocene / Palaeocene, 34–65 million years before present.*

The shallowest oil fields in the North Sea area are found in sediments of the Eocene Epoch dating from over 34 million years ago. The oil fields are located in the lower part of the Eocene within sandstone reservoirs that formed in submarine channels. The sand that filled these channels was provided from the shoreline of the Scottish landmass. Sea levels had fallen so that the shoreline now coincided with the edge of the shelf, beyond which the North Sea deepened considerably. Beaches and deltas building up on the shelf edge would become unstable causing the sand to tumble down the submarine slope beyond. The sand eventually ended up splayed out as sand channels over the seabed in the central area of the North Sea having travelled several hundred kilometres from their source.[239]

Some of these Eocene reservoirs have a curious history. When the pile of Ice Age sediment filled up the North Sea, the reservoirs were buried so rapidly, the pressures in the porous rock ramped up to very high levels. Many of the reservoirs simply burst like a balloon and the surrounding rock cracked open as the pressures dissipated. The cracks and fissures were injected full of sand; indeed, some of the larger structures formed in this way are big enough to form commercial oil reservoirs in their own right.[240]

It was very hot during the Eocene, although the climate had cooled down towards the end of the epoch. Extensive forests were to be found near the poles and the London area was covered in jungle with similar plant species to that found in present-day Malaysia.[241] During the early Eocene and for some time previously, carbon dioxide concentrations in the atmosphere were much higher than they are today. The carbon dioxide was sourced from volcanoes and there had been numerous large scale eruptions for a long interval of the geological record leading up to the early Eocene.[242] Carbon dioxide is a greenhouse gas. It will absorb some of the energy of the sun's rays that have been reflected from the Earth's surface and thus prevent some of this energy from escaping into space. By re-emitting the energy, greenhouse gases cause heat to be retained in the lower atmosphere that would otherwise have been lost. The higher the concentrations of greenhouse gases in the atmosphere, the higher are the temperatures at and above the Earth's surface.

Near the base of the Eocene are rocks representing an episode from 56 million years ago when rapid global warming gave the world's life forms a major heat shock.[243] Over an interval of only a few thousand years, the world became five to eight degrees Celsius warmer and then cooled again 200,000 years later. An increase in average temperature of five to eight degrees Celsius doesn't seem that much, but bear in mind the narrow temperature range at which animals survive. Temperatures consistently below zero degrees will kill animals, while on the other hand, temperatures over 40 degrees Celsius reaches the upper critical stress levels for most creatures. The Earth was indeed baking. It's thought that the gradual rise in global temperatures over millions of years previously had reached a tipping point just before the start of the Eocene Epoch. A slight rise in temperature due to the normal cyclical variation in the Earth's inclination and orbit had been enough to push the global environment over the edge. One popular theory is that the increased temperature caused large areas of permafrost in the Polar Regions to melt. Organic material that had been previously frozen within the peaty layers effectively defrosted in enormous quantities. The subsequent feeding frenzy by bacteria added considerably to the amount of carbon dioxide released into the atmosphere. This episode has been the subject of much research as academics reckon it can potentially give an insight into the potential consequences of human-driven global warming in the present day, a consequence of rising carbon dioxide levels in the atmosphere from the burning of fossil fuels.

Many organisms were substantially affected by the heat shock. One group of marine shell-life suffered badly as the seas became more acid as it absorbed more carbon dioxide; some 30–50 per cent of the species in the group went extinct. Mass migration took place on a global scale as many animals moved *en masse* towards the poles where it was cooler. This happened both on land and in the oceans. Animals underwent rapid evolution as they adapted to the climate change. They became smaller on land, tending towards dwarf versions of their original form; many mammals shrunk to half their original size. This was probably because food supplies were in short supply during the ecological crisis and this was the major factor influencing short-term evolution. Smaller animals need less food and will survive; larger animals starve.

The thermal shock ended when the climate cooled as the normal variation in the Earth's orbital cycles caused the poles to chill again. Two smaller heat shocks followed, with the Earth returning to a more equitable climate from then on.[244]

Below the heat shock horizon are found the rocks of the Palaeocene Epoch. The Palaeocene was the first geological epoch following the demise of the dinosaurs at the very end of the Cretaceous, 65 million years ago. About two million years after the start of the Palaeocene, a dramatic event took place in the UK/ Greenland area.[245] An enormous blob of molten magma broke free from deep below the Earth's crust and pushed its way upwards towards the surface. The crust domed up over a very large area centred on East Greenland,

and the resulting highlands extended as far as the west coasts of both Norway and the northern British isles. The UK and Greenland were part of the same landmass with only a small sea in between. Although the southern part of the Atlantic Ocean had started to form earlier, the northern branch of the Atlantic Ocean between Greenland and Norway had yet to break apart.

By 60 million years ago, the dome had grown to its maximum height and it then ruptured. As the Earth's crust cracked open, volcanoes erupted through the fissures, the first phase lasting for two and half millions years, followed by a second episode of eruptions between 50 and 56 million years ago. An enormous quantity of lava poured out, solidifying to a rock pile some two kilometres thick in the Inner Hebrides and five kilometres thick around the Faroe Islands. The remnants of some of these volcanoes can still be found on the west coast of Scotland and in Northern Ireland. The craggy islands of Skye, Rum, Mull and Arran, together with the peninsula of Ardnamurchan, all have volcanic rock at their core. The volcanic rocks in Scotland and Greenland had been the outcome of enormous crustal convulsions with the weakened crust providing the locus for the northern part of the Atlantic Ocean to open up between Greenland and Norway. This started 55.5 million years ago and the process continues today; every year the Atlantic Ocean widens by another 25 millimetres.

As the Greenland dome bulged upwards in the Palaeocene, the Scottish land mass was pushed sideways and tilted eastwards. The Orkneys and Shetlands area was a major extension of land from Scotland at the time and suffered considerable erosion.[246] Rivers and streams fed off the newly formed highlands flowing down slope towards deltas in the Moray Firth. From there, large volumes of sand would set off down submarine canyons towards the centre of the North Sea forming a thick extensive network of channels clogged up with sand, each one building on top of the other. These provide the reservoir interval of the Forties, Nelson and Montrose fields amongst others.

Geological Report No. 5

Depth: *2,100–3,200 metres subsea.*
Lithology: *White to grey white chalk in the upper section; predominantly grey marl, minor black mudstone, and minor sandstone intervals beneath.*
Age: *Cretaceous, 65–145 million years before present.*

The uppermost part of the Chalk is Palaeocene in age, although the bulk of the Chalk is older than this, mostly forming the upper part of the Cretaceous interval. (Chalk with a capital letter refers to the geological interval; chalk in lower case refers to the rock.) The Cretaceous Period, ranging from 65 to 145 million years old is named after the chalk; the root *'creta'* being the Latin name for the rock. The Chalk was deposited over large areas around the world. It is found in Northern Europe, Texas and Western Australia.[247]

Chalk is a white to grey rock, almost pure calcium carbonate, and technically a limestone. Examined through a microscope, it is largely composed of minute shell fragments. These belong to fossil microplankton – tiny marine plants with a big name – coccolithophores. The microplankton bloomed in abundance in the warm seas of the time and in turn would have been subject to a feeding frenzy by predators, tiny crustaceans mostly. The resulting detritus rained down in clumps onto the seabed.[248]

The Cretaceous Period was a time of great global heat. Geologists can find no evidence that polar ice caps were present. Forests which you would find at our latitudes today reached beyond both polar circles in the Cretaceous Period, to the North of Alaska for instance. This created the unusual setting of forests located in a part of the world that was dark for almost half the year. It must have been warm up there as the fossilised bones of cold-blooded dinosaurs are found in amongst the fossil trees. The dinosaurs probably migrated northwards in the summer and then lumbered south as the day-long winter nights started to set in.[249]

Much of the continental land masses had been drowned by the sea during the Cretaceous. Sea levels were very high, as much as 300 metres above present-day sea level at one point. The land mass of the continents had shrunk as the sea encroached and there were not many mountain ranges around at the time. Small flat-lying islands persisted, such as the Scottish land mass.

It was a world rich in carbon dioxide, perhaps as much as four times the atmospheric levels that we record in the atmosphere today. A vast complex of volcanoes, covering an enormous area on the floor of the Pacific Ocean, pumped out lava into the sea. This is one of the reasons why sea levels were so high in the Cretaceous, the huge volume of lava pouring out into the ocean displaced an equivalent volume of water onto the continental shelves. It also explains why the Cretaceous was so warm; the volcanoes were releasing a tremendous amount of carbon dioxide gas into the atmosphere.

The Chalk straddles the Cretaceous/ Palaeocene boundary, famous as the time when the dinosaurs died out in a mass extinction event. We human beings should be manifestly grateful for this fortuitous event as the mammals survived and the dinosaurs went extinct. The extinction event is thought to have resulted from the impact of a 10-kilometre diameter asteroid into the ocean floor near what is now offshore Mexico, although large-scale volcanic eruptions taking place in India have also been implicated as a background contribution to the stresses that life faced at this juncture. The impact created a crater about 180 kilometres wide and the oblique impact threw much of the resulting debris and molten glass northwards over the North American continent. A large volume of carbon dioxide and sulphur dioxide was released on impact following the vaporisation of the rocks hit by the impact and this was washed out of the atmosphere into the oceans.[250]

I've seen a core sample taken from the Chalk in the central North Sea which straddles the Cretaceous/ Palaeocene boundary. It's possible to put your finger on the exact point when the dinosaurs died out. The mass extinction at the end of the Cretaceous not only wiped out the dinosaurs, but was also catastrophic for many other groups of animals, especially marine creatures with calcium carbonate shells. The seas were acidified by the material thrown up by the asteroid impact and this affected the ability of these creatures to form their protective shells. The chalk changes in character as a result, the shell plates and fragments are much smaller in the chalk layers which formed after the boundary than they were before.

Chalk is a rather improbable reservoir rock because it is so fine-grained, much like the mudstone that forms the cap rock for many reservoirs. One geologist was so impressed that chalk produces any oil at all in North Sea fields he described it as a 'modern miracle'.[251] Chalk stores oil in large volumes at depths in the North Sea where the weight of the overlying rock could have been expected to crush out much of the pore volume. For example, the top of the Ekofisk field reservoir lies at a depth that is just over three kilometres below the seabed.

So how did the modern miracle come about? The chalk is made up of individual pellets of fossil shell material and it is this feature that makes the chalk a different type of rock. The pellets in pure chalk weld together under only a limited tonnage of overlying rock weight and keep a strong rigid structure that resists much in the way of further compaction as the rock is buried deeper. Chalk can survive burial with much of the pore space intact, up to 45 per cent of the rock can be pores in the best reservoirs. The fluid in the pore space sustains high pressures and this acts as a cushion preventing the chalk from being crushed by the mega-tonnage of rock lying on top of it. Another fortuitous feature is that when the oil filled up the reservoir, it pushed the water that had previously filled up the pore space out of the way. Thus there was much less dissolved rock material that would otherwise have crystallised out into the pore space and clogged it up.

Although a chalk reservoir can store tremendous volumes of oil, the fine-grained rock has low permeability and will not yield to oil production readily. Special techniques are needed to produce oil from chalk. One of these is to deliberately fracture the rock in the well by pumping fluid under great pressure and then pouring large volumes of sand down the well to prop the fractures open. Several boat-loads of sand may be needed for the big jobs. A cheaper alternative is to pump acid down the well and into the fracture planes. The acid etches wormholes that allow the oil to be produced more readily through the fractures.

The big chalk oil fields are located in the Norwegian and Danish sectors of the North Sea, although there are some smaller ones in the UK. Production from chalk reservoirs has its own peculiar problems. Chalk can at times deform like putty under pressure and in the presence of water. The Norwegian Valhall field not only produces oil but also large volumes of chalk flowing like toothpaste into some of the wells accessing the crestal area of the reservoir. The chalk will also compact as the oil is extracted. The pore spaces get squeezed closer together as the oil is removed, and the overlying rock column pressing down on the chalk will start to subside too. This has caused problems in the Ekofisk field where the seabed has subsided by several metres. The oil platforms are firmly anchored to the seabed and the lower decks of the platforms have over time sunk close to the level at which they could be overwhelmed by high seas in extreme storm conditions.

This was gradually becoming a potentially hazardous situation and in 1987 the operator Phillips Petroleum raised all six of the Ekofisk platforms in a highly impressive feat of engineering. The oil pipelines were disconnected and the legs were cut, taking extra care to avoid cutting any interconnected pipes or wires. Four of the platforms were jacked up simultaneously, and this involved lifting a combined weight of 23,000 tons. The topsides were raised by 5.5 metres and leg extensions were inserted.[252]

Chalk has provided one other major benefit to mankind, indeed to all of life on Earth. The Chalk is vastly thick in parts of the North Sea, over a kilometre in the deep basinal areas offshore from Norway and Denmark. Together with buried limestones elsewhere in the world, it has locked up a tremendous volume of carbon dioxide in the form of calcium carbonate. Much of the limestone has formed as a result of plant and animal activity, carbon dioxide is readily dissolved in sea water and from there can be extracted and combined with calcium to form shell and skeletal material. The extraction and subsequent burial of carbon dioxide products within lime rock has been a life-saver for all organisms in the planet. If all the carbon dioxide locked up within limestone, including chalk, was released into the atmosphere, we would end up with 98 per cent carbon dioxide in the atmosphere and an atmospheric pressure at the Earth's surface 60 times greater than it is at the moment. These conditions would then be similar to those of the atmosphere of planet Venus; a planet where the surface temperature is 460° Celsius, a temperature far too hot for life to survive.[253]

At or near the base of the Chalk lies a thin interval rich in black mudstone called the Plenus Marl, (or more precisely, the Black Band Member) named after a distinctive fossil called *Actinocamax plenus*. The black mudstones of the Plenus Marl are easy to spot when they come up in the drill cuttings and are used as a way-post to confirm where you are drilling in the geological interval. Sometimes you can get a bit lost due to the monotony of the rock fragments coming back while drilling several hundred metres of the Cretaceous interval, but you can usually spot the Plenus Marl when it turns up. When the offshore geologist reports the depth of the Plenus Marl as it comes in, this can cause anxiety for those back onshore in the oil company office. Before the well started, the seismic interpreter would have provided their prognosis of where the depths of the formation tops could be expected to be found while drilling. There is a degree of uncertainty involved in calculating these depths, often plus or minus 100 metres. If the Plenus Marl comes in hundreds of metres deeper than predicted, this can cause panic as something will have gone badly wrong with the prognosis. It probably means the underlying reservoir target will also be much deeper than was thought, that is if it is there at all.

Black mudstones like the Plenus Marl are not only found in the North Sea, they occur in sedimentary basins worldwide wherever Cretaceous rocks are present. They mark episodes called oceanic anoxic events where global environments went totally out of kilter for up to a million years or so and caused much stress to life on the planet.

The likely sequence of events leading to an oceanic anoxic event is as follows. A massive volcanic eruption releases enormous volumes of carbon dioxide into the atmosphere resulting in rapid global warming. Sea levels will also rise and the continental shelves will be flooded. The temperature of the oceans increases and with higher temperatures less oxygen is absorbed into the sea water. The warmer atmosphere soaks up more water and the resulting increased rainfall on land swells the rivers and causes an increased amount of sediment to pour into the sea. This brings in large volumes of phosphate and iron sourced from the weathering of rock on land and key nutrients for plankton in the sea. Normally, there is never enough phosphate and iron in the ocean and low phosphate levels act as a natural brake on the plankton population numbers. Once the brake is off, plankton will bloom in very large quantities eventually consuming all the oxygen below the surface waters. Almost the entire world's oceans will become dead zones as a result and marine life stutters in response. Many species went extinct during these periods.

We drill through the base of the Chalk and into the lower part of the Cretaceous interval. The sediments are generally less pure than chalk, and they mostly consist of lime-rich mudstones called marls. The shoreline along the Moray Firth was shedding sand into the basin at this time and this forms the reservoir interval for oil fields in the area such as the Scapa field.

Geological Report No. 6

Depth: *3,200–3,800 metres subsea.*
Lithology: Interbedded grey mudstone and sandstone intervals.
Age: *Jurassic, 14 –201 million years before present.*

Rock of the Jurassic Period underlies the Cretaceous and spans an age of between 145 and 201 million years before present. The Jurassic is where the vast
bulk of the oil in the fields of the North Sea was sourced from and many oil
fields have reservoirs in Jurassic sandstones. The furthest north of the offshore
oil fields, the Magnus field, has a Jurassic reservoir. The furthest south of the
North Sea oil fields, the Fife and Fergus fields, are in Jurassic reservoirs. It is
also the time when the North Sea substantially split apart to form the basin
it is today.

A big marker occurs at the boundary between the Cretaceous and the
Jurassic. In most oil companies it is called the Base Cretaceous Unconformity,
or the BCU for short. The marker gives off a prominent seismic reflection; it
is such a strong reflection that it was even visible on the early seismic shot in
the 1970s. The quality of the seismic was so poor back then, it's a wonder you
could see anything resembling an oil field, but nevertheless you could pick the
BCU with reasonable confidence.

An unconformity is where you find a discontinuity in the rock interval with
a large time gap marking the boundary between the rock sitting above and
below it. Commonly the beds lie at an angle to each other. The lower beds
may be tilted at say 40 degrees from vertical, whereas the upper beds may be
lying flat on top of the eroded remnants of the tilted lower beds.

Some of the first unconformities to be recognised in the history of geological
science were found in Scotland by James Hutton in the 18th century. The best
exposed example can be seen at Siccar Point on the coast of Berwickshire.
Here in 1788 Hutton found beds of the Old Red Sandstone lying on the
eroded stump of older sediments which were dipping vertically below the
surface between them.[254] The older sediments contained ripple marks showing
that they had once been deposited by currents in an ancient sea.

It was a great moment in science. Hutton immediately grasped the significance
of what he was looking at; it was nothing less than an insight into the vastness
of geological time. Before James Hutton found unconformities such as those
at Siccar Point, no one had considered the Earth to be that old. The prevailing
wisdom had been established by James Usher, the Church of Ireland Archbishop
of Armagh and Primate of All Ireland: from the chronology of events in the
Bible, he worked out that the Earth had been created on the night of Saturday,
22 October, 4004 BC. Hutton realised that this could not possibly be right.
What he saw before him was evidence that the Earth was far older.

Hutton would later state that deep geological time was unimaginable in scale, finishing his book *The Theory of the Earth* with the words, 'The result of our enquiry is that we find no vestige of a beginning, no prospect of an end.'

His colleague James Playfair, who accompanied him on the visit to Siccar Point, had been similarly awestruck:

The mind seemed to grow giddy by looking so far into the abyss of time; and while we listened with earnestness and admiration to the philosopher who was now unfolding to us the order and series of these wonderful events, we became sensible how much further reason may sometimes go than imagination can venture to follow.[255]

The older rocks had been sediments laid down within an ancient sea. They had then been buried under the weight of younger sediment, consolidated into hard rock, and then uplifted by the colossal movements involved in a mountain building episode, hence the vertical angle of repose of the beds which had once been laid down as flat-lying strata. The eroded stump of the mountain, long gone by now, had then been inundated by rivers and the sediments lying above the unconformity were then laid down. All this must have taken millions of years to have happened.

What caused the Base Cretaceous Unconformity? In this instance, it wasn't due to a mountain building episode as had been the case with Hutton's unconformity; rather, it was the result of the opening of the North Sea in response to major crustal forces that were causing oceans to form elsewhere, in particular the birth pangs of the Atlantic Ocean.

The cracks in the crust had already appeared before the start of the Jurassic. The stretching of the North Sea area then continued in fits and starts, culminating in a significant episode of rifting at the end of the Jurassic. It is possible that the North Sea was on the way to becoming an ocean, but then the stretching suddenly stopped never to start again. Crustal weaknesses elsewhere would now become the locus for the Atlantic Ocean to form.

The stretching episode caused individual blocks of rocks to crack apart and then tilt over at an angle. This created a multitude of traps for oil fields in the northern North Sea area. Once the tilting ceased, the steady drizzle of mud and silt that normally piles into the North Sea continued anew. This eventually built a considerable thickness of sediment which buried the tilted blocks and formed the cap rock for the reservoirs underneath.

The Jurassic tilting episode corresponded to a regime of frequent and strong earthquakes in the North Sea area. Some major faults happened at this time, the product of thousands of individual earthquake episodes. Faults are major fractures in the rock whereby the rock mass on one side of the fault has moved relative to the other side.

Faults are rarely simple smooth planar surfaces; it is more likely the fault plane will be a rough rock surface with both sides interlocking in an irregular fashion. As the stress builds up prior to an earthquake, the forces will be acting to try and push separate masses of rock along the fault plane into the same space. This is impossible of course, so enormous stresses will ramp up to the critical point when the rocks fracture. It takes great energy to overcome the resistance of the interlocking rock in the fracture plane which is why earthquakes are such powerful events.

Yet, even a big earthquake may only cause the rock either side of the fault to be displaced by a metre or so. But once the fault has formed in this way it acts as plane of weakness to accommodate the great crustal stresses in the region. In this way it acts as the location for many subsequent earthquakes. The oil fields in the North Sea are commonly bounded by faults which can show 30–100 metres' displacement between the strata on either side of the fault. Sometimes, much bigger faults are seen.

There are so many oil fields within the Jurassic reservoirs of the North Sea, it's best to start describing a selected sample of them, starting in the north and then proceeding south.

At the northern end is the Magnus field. The reservoir comprises a thick series of submarine sand channels rather fortuitously encased top and bottom by the Kimmeridge source rock. No problem in getting oil in there and there is a lot of it. With oil in place in excess of 1,500 million barrels, the field's a giant.

To the south of the Magnus field is located numerous fields with their reservoir in the Brent Group. The moniker 'Brent' is a crafted acronym derived from the constituent rock formation names that make up the Brent Group. These are named after Scottish lochs and from the base upwards comprise the Broom, Rannoch, Etive, Ness and Tarbert Formations. Shell was successful in grabbing many of the big Brent Group oil fields ahead of the competition. The biggest was the Brent field itself, but the others were fairly sizeable too.

The Brent Group fields are found within a large delta system that built out northwards along the North Sea axis in the Middle Jurassic. This has been established by an enormous amount of detailed analysis by oil company geologists of rock samples and other data from the wells. As a geologist, you keep in mind how modern sediments are laid down and you look for similar features in the core samples to get an idea as to what processes were responsible for depositing the ancient sediment. For example, sand ripples forming on a beach are symmetrical because they have been moved back and forth by the waves; in contrast, sand ripples formed by currents are lopsided with the long side of the ripple pointing upstream. You collect clues like this and if you can understand how the reservoir rocks formed, it's possible to map out what they look like in the subsurface. If you know you are looking at what was once a river delta, then you can produce maps that are consistent with the shape, size and forms of the various features that are found in deltas. You can define the individual river channels that fed the delta, the mouth bars where the sand dropped out as the river currents slowed down on entering the sea, and where beaches had formed around the edge of the delta.

Proceeding further south past some notable fields such as Beryl and Brae, we come into the outer Moray Firth where there is a cluster of big oil fields with Jurassic reservoirs, including the Piper and Claymore fields.

I spent seven years working on the Claymore field, a complex field containing a multitude of reservoirs but with much of the oil located in Jurassic sandstones. It has been developed by a pair of linked platforms located along trend from the Piper field. Like the Magnus field further north, the main sandstone reservoir is sandwiched within the Kimmeridge Clay Formation source rock. The first exploration well drilled at the crest of the Claymore structure failed to find the main reservoir, only uncovering poorer quality rock in the deeper interval. Just after the well was drilled, some of the details of field structure in the northern North Sea started to become widely known. These fields were discovered on the edges of major faults formed during the frenzy of seismic activity during the Jurassic. As the faults formed, the rock on one side of the fault would rise upwards and tilt backwards, often with the leading edge rising above sea level to create an island. The island would then be subjected to erosion by the elements over time, ultimately reduced to a flattened stump. The erosion can totally remove the reservoir interval at the highest point, yet further back from the fault it is fully preserved as the structure slopes down under the sea.

The tilted fault block can provide an excellent trap structure for the containment of oil. The trick in finding these type of traps is to be aware that the reservoir can be absent in the crest where it had been subject to erosion, but could be found in full lower down the structure. Two years later the Claymore operators, recognising this as a possibility, drilled another well down structure from the first well and found what eventually proved to be a major oil field with over a billion barrels of oil in place.

The lower part of the Jurassic in the area between the Piper and Forties fields consists of volcanic lavas and associated ash deposits. When the North Sea was stretching open at this time, magma found its way up the crustal weaknesses that formed in the central North Sea.[256] Volcanic activity occurred further south too. ELF drilled an exploration well in the Dutch sector after they had spotted an interesting structure that looked as if it could trap gas. They found the gas field but they were also to discover the feature that had been propping up the reservoir for the gas field. As they progressed further with the well, they found that they were drilling down through the cone of an extinct volcano, later named the Zuidwal Volcano.[257]

I once looked at some core samples taken through the volcanic deposits in a well that had been drilled in the Telford field. In amongst the slurry of mixed up volcanic ash and silty sediment was a perfectly preserved fossil pine cone. This was in rock that had been retrieved from almost 3,000 metres below the seabed and is about 170 million years old, yet the pine cone is recognisable as the familiar object we see today. It's a connection between present day reality and the evidence of a long gone reality that was once a moment in time.

It is difficult to convey a true sense of the awe that a geologist feels on occasions like these. John Playfair got close with 'The mind seemed to grow giddy by looking so far back into the abyss of time.' But it's more than that. As a professional geologist, you are continuously making an abstract mental framework of space and time as a means of predicting the location of resources such as oil and gas. Your mind hardly ever locks on to any sense that you are dealing with something that was very real those millions of years ago. It is indeed all real, but you never normally connect with the data that way. That is, until you find something like the fossil pine cone and it causes your abstract framework of geological knowledge to crystallise into a vivid sense of the meaningful reality of the whole lot of it, all of it... and somehow your awareness of day-to-day living becomes conjoined with this awakened connection to Earth history and out of this emerges an overwhelming feeling of human frailty in the vastness of geological time.

Geological Report No. 7

Depth: *3,800–4,400 metres subsea.*
Lithology: *Interbedded red mudstones siltstones and sandstone.*
Age: *Permian / Triassic, 201–299 million years before present.*
Current activity: *Pulling out of hole after reaching the well's total depth.*

I've worked on fields with reservoir rock immediately older than the Jurassic, one lot with Triassic-age reservoirs and the other – southern North Sea gas fields with a Permian-age reservoir.

The Triassic Period dates from 201 to 252 million years before present and below, the Permian Period ranges from 252 to 299 million years ago. A thin veneer of coastal sediments at the top of the Triassic in the North Sea gives way downwards to a pile of sediments deposited on land by rivers flowing across a vast arid continent and in lakes. The sediments are mostly rusty red in colour due to the reaction of the iron in the sediment with the oxygen in the air.

An enormous supercontinent was present during the Permian and Triassic, which geologists have called Pangaea. It came together when two already enormous continents collided. Mountains were thrown up by the collision in a giant belt that extended across the world from what is now the Gulf of Mexico to Eastern Europe.[258]

The northern margin of the continent contained the land mass that would later separate to form north-west Europe. The seasons affecting this part of Pangaea are thought to have alternated between dry winters and wet summers. Oil and gas condensate fields in the central North Sea are found in the continental red beds of Triassic age. These include the Heron, Skua and Egret fields and further south the Judy, Josephine and Jasmine fields among others. The reservoirs comprise sediments that were laid down in seasonally flowing rivers or by flash floods during torrential downpours.

The underlying Permian sediments have been extensively studied in Germany, where geologists have subdivided the upper Permian rock sequence into the upper Zechstein and lower Rotliegendes intervals.

The Zechstein is rich in deposited salt which has been mined onshore in Northern England and continental Europe. The salt probably formed in inland seas. On occasions, the entrance to the sea would become blocked during a sea level fall. The inland sea would then dry out leaving extensive flats of evaporated salt. This was a cyclic process, with the result that layer upon layer of salt would build up.

Salt as a rock is a peculiar substance. Whereas most normal rocks are brittle and will shatter under stress, salt is plastic in the subsurface and tends to flow rather than break. The tremendous pressure exerted by the weight of the overlying rock column squeezes the salt to a much greater degree than normal rock. If there are any weaknesses in the overlying rock, such as a fractured fault plane, the salt squeezes upwards into the cracks, often in very large quantities. In the central North Sea, the salt has forced its way up major faults at particular points of weakness, forming enormous mushroom-shaped structures, some of which encroach close to the seabed.

The force of the upwelling salt can cause the overlying rock to be pushed up into large domes. If there is any porous rock in the uplifted domes, they are commonly structures that trap oil. Several oil fields in the central North Sea show structures that formed above upwelling salt, notably creating traps for oil in the chalk, the Ekofisk field for example. The forceful intrusion of the salt into or just below the chalk not only forms the oil field structure, it can also fracture the brittle chalk and the fractures provide a major pathway for oil production into the wells.

The deeper Rotliegendes interval includes thick intervals of desert sandstone. It provides the reservoir interval for the Auk oil field in the southern part of the central North Sea, but has not proved to be a common oil reservoir. The Rotliegendes is nevertheless the major reservoir interval for the gas fields in the southern Northern Sea, offshore from eastern England. Here, the underlying Coal Measures provide the source rock for the gas. I have worked on these fields too. Although these fields are located in eastern England, several of them are managed out of Aberdeen.

On one field I worked on, it was actually possible to map out the individual sand dunes within the desert sandstone reservoir. One of the peculiarities of desert sandstone is that they make excellent gas reservoirs but poor oil reservoirs (the oil struggles to flow through the dusty laminae whereas these merely slow down the gas a touch but doesn't stop it from moving). Shell is particularly adept at producing from these gas fields. The giant gas field in Groningen, onshore Netherlands, is getting close to producing almost its entire gas volume.

A handful of oil fields are found with reservoirs older than the Permian on the UK continental shelf, most notably the Clair field west of Shetlands. Otherwise, this is the end of our theoretical well. We have found the economic basement for the North Sea – our well, and indeed our story, stops here.

Endnotes

CHAPTER 1 Finding a North Sea Oil Field

1   *Wasted Windfall*, Channel 4: 1996 Fine Art Productions.

2   ssa.nls.uk/film/5973

3   Interview with Roger Loper, *Wasted Windfall*, Channel 4: 1996 Fine Art Productions.

4   www.og.decc.gov.uk/pprs/full_production.htm

5   www.og.decc.gov.uk/pprs/full_production.htm

6   www.og.decc.gov.uk/pprs/full_production.htm

7   Interview with Jack Birks, *Wasted Windfall*, Channel 4: 1996 Fine Art Productions.

8   A barrel of oil equivalent is a quantity that not only includes oil, but also the gas that is produced with it. A specific volume of gas will be deemed equivalent to a barrel of oil on the basis of its energy content.

9   www.dana-petroleum.com

10   www.statoil.com

11   Banner JA, Chatellier J-Y, Feurer JR and Neuhaus D, 1992. Guillemot D: 'A successful appraisal through alternative interpretation'. In Hardman, RFP (ed.) *Exploration Britain: Geological Insights for the Next Decade*, Geological Society Special Publication, No. 67, p. 129-149.

12   Hardman RFP, 2003. 'Lessons from oil and gas exploration in and around Britain' in Gluyas, JG and Hichens HM, United Kingdom Oil and Gas Fields, Commemorative Volume, Geological Society, London, Memoir 20, p. 5-16.

13   www.rigzone.com/data/dayrates/

14   www.facebook.com/RigData/posts/517179774990763

15   Krause H, 2011. 'An 'Enterprising' North Sea Discovery', in *AAPG Explorer*. www.aapg.org/publications/news/explorer/column/articleid/2064/an-%E2%80%98enterprising%E2%80%99-north-sea-discovery

16   *Financial Times* 5/11/87.

CHAPTER 2 The First Oil Fields are Found

17   van Hulten FFN, 2009. Brief history of petroleum exploration in the Netherlands. Conference note from the symposium: *50 Years of Petroleum Exploration in the Netherlands after the Groningen Discovery*. f-van-hulten.com/Geology/Geology_FvanHulten.htm

18   www.pgknet.nl/the_pgk/monument

19 Kvendseth SS, 1988. *Giant Discovery: A History of Ekofisk Through the First 20 Years.* Phillips Petroleum, Norway. www.nb.no/ekofisk/funn_eng.pdf

20 www.norskoljeoggass.no/en/Facts/Petroleum-history/

21 Kvendseth SS, 1988. *Giant Discovery: A History of Ekofisk Through the First 20 Years.* Phillips Petroleum, Norway.

22 *Convention on the Continental Shelf 1958,* United Nations, Treaty Series, vol. 499, p. 311.

23 Kvendseth SS, 1988. *Giant Discovery: A History of Ekofisk Through the First 20 Years.* Phillips Petroleum, Norway.

24 www.kcl.ac.uk/sspp/departments/icbh/witness/science/NorthSea.aspx

25 Jorgensen LN and Andersen PM, 19911. 'Integrated Study of the Kraka Field', *Society of Petroleum Engineers* paper number 230282-MS.

26 www.maerskoil.com/operations/denmark/pages/oil-and-gas-production.aspx

27 Kvendseth SS, 1988. *Giant Discovery: A History of Ekofisk Through the First 20 Years.* Phillips Petroleum, Norway.

28 www.gov.uk/oil-and-gas-wells

29 Mackie B, 2004. *The Oilmen: The North Sea Tigers.* Birlinn Press, Edinburgh.

30 www.og.decc.gov.uk/fields/fields_index.htm

31 Hardman RFP, 2003. 'Lessons from oil and gas exploration in and around Britain' in Gluyas JG and Hichens HM, United Kingdom Oil and Gas Fields, Commemorative Volume, Geological Society, London, Memoir 20, p. 5-16.

32 *Daily Mail* 24/11/2011.

33 Birch RL, 1969. 'The search for gas in the North Sea'. *Geology,* Journal of the Association of Teachers of Geology.

34 Kvendseth SS, 1988. *Giant Discovery: A History of Ekofisk Through the First 20 Years.* Phillips Petroleum, Norway.

35 Kvendseth SS, 1988. *Giant Discovery: A History of Ekofisk Through the First 20 Years.* Phillips Petroleum, Norway.

36 www.bp.com/en/global/corporate/about-bp/our-history/history-of-bp/post-war.html

37 Peter Walmsley in Moreton R (ed) *Tales from Early UK Oil Exploration 1960-1979.* PESGB.

38 Hardman RFP, 2003. 'Lessons from oil and gas exploration in and around Britain' in Gluyas JG and Hichens HM, *United Kingdom Oil and Gas Fields, Commemorative Volume,* Geological Society, London, Memoir 20, p. 5-16.

39 Hardman RFP, 2003. 'Lessons from oil and gas exploration in and around Britain' in Gluyas JG and Hichens HM, *United Kingdom Oil and Gas Fields, Commemorative Volume,* Geological Society, London, Memoir 20, p. 5-16.

40 Mackie B, 2004. *The Oilmen; The North Sea Tigers.* Birlinn Press, Edinburgh.

41 Peter Walmsley in Moreton R (ed) *Tales from Early UK Oil Exploration 1960–*

1979. PESGB.

42 Kvendseth SS, 1988. *Giant Discovery: A History of Ekofisk Through the First 20 Years.* Phillips Petroleum, Norway.

43 Interview with Brendan McKeown. Wasted Windfall Channel 4: 1996 Fine Art Productions.

44 Dick Selley *PESGB Newsletter* June 2014.

45 *Financial Times* 8 /10/1970.

46 *Financial Times* 6 /10 /1970.

47 pensionline.bp.com/content/pl/system/galleries/download/Pensioner_newsletter/ Pensioner_Newsletter_-_Autumn_2010.pdf

48 *Financial Times* 20 /10/70.

CHAPTER 3 Appraisal and Production

49 Barr D, Savory KE, Fowler SR, Arman K and McGarrity JP, 2007. Pre-development fracture modelling in the Clair field, west of Shetland. In Lonergan L. et. al., (eds) *Fractured Reservoirs.* Geological Society, London, Special Publications, 270, p. 205-225.

50 D'Heur M., 1990. West Ekofisk field – Norway. Central Graben, North Sea, in Beaumont EA and Foster NH, (eds) *Structural Traps IV*, American Association of Petroleum Geologists, Tulsa.

51 Dickinson B, 1996. The Puffin Field: the appraisal of a complex HP-HT gas-condensate accumulation, Geological Society, London, Special Publications, 114: p. 299-327.

52 Shepherd M., Kearney CJ and Milne JH, 1990. 'Magnus Field' in Beaumont EA and Foster NH, (eds) *Structural Traps II*, American Association of Petroleum Geologists, Tulsa.

53 Dromgoole P and Speers R., 1997. 'Geoscore: a method for quantifying uncertainty in field reserve estimates'. *Petroleum Geoscience*, 3, p. 1-12.

54 Mackie B, 2004. *The Oilmen: The North Sea Tigers.* Birlinn Press, Edinburgh.

55 www.kulturminne-frigg.no/

56 Cresswell J, 2000. *Black Gold and the Silver City.* Balmoral Group, Aberdeen.

57 Mackie B, 2004. *The Oilmen: The North Sea Tigers.* Birlinn Press, Edinburgh.

58 www.bp.com/

59 www.talisman-energy.com/

60 *Daily Express* 19/6/1975.

61 Peter Kassler, transcript of speech, The Development of North Sea Oil and Gas Conference, London, 1999.

62 Coward RN, Clark NM and Pinnock SJ, 1991. 'The Tartan Field, Block 15/16, UK North Sea'. From Abbots IL (ed), *United Kingdom Oil and Gas Fields, 25 Years*

Commemorative Volume, Geological Society Memoir No. 14, p. 377-384.

63   www.unep.fr/scp/xsp/disaster/casestudies/china/gaoqiao.htm

64   Gill C, Shepherd M and Millington J, 2010. 'Compartmentalization of the Nelson field, Central North Sea: Evidence from produced water chemistry analysis.' In *Reservoir Cpmpartmetalization*, Geological Society, London, Special Publications 347, p. 71-87.

CHAPTER 4 Aberdeen

65   Pye M and Brown S, 2002. 'Hydrocarbons', in Trewin NH (ed) *The Geology of Scotland*, 4th edition, The Geological Society, London.

66   Hallett D, Durant GP and Farrow GE, 1985. 'Oil exploration and production in Scotland'. *Scottish Journal of Geology*, 21, p. 547-570.

67   Hutcheson, AM and Hogg A, 1975. *Scotland and Oil*, Oliver and Boyd, Edinburgh.

68   Mackie B, 2004. *The Oilmen: The North Sea Tigers*. Birlinn Press, Edinburgh.

69   Kemp A, 2011. *The Official History of North Sea Oil and Gas*. Routledge, London and New York.

70   Cresswell J, 2000. *Black Gold and the Silver City*. Balmoral Group, Aberdeen.

71   Davidson K and Fairley J, 2000. *Running the Granite City Local Government in Aberdeen 1975–1996*. Scottish Cultural Press, Dalkeith.

72   Sprott TF, 1981. 'The Impact of North Sea Oil on the Grampian Region and Aberdeen'. In *Onshore Impacts of Offshore Oil*, Cairns WJ and Rogers PM (eds), Applied Science Publishers, Barking.

73   Davidson K and Fairley J, 2000. *Running the Granite City: Local Government in Aberdeen 1975–1996*. Scottish Cultural Press, Dalkeith.

74   www.scotland.gov.uk/Publications/2014/02/4500/downloads

75   Kemp A, 2011. *The Official History of North Sea Oil and Gas*. Routledge, London and New York.

76   Sprott TF, 1981. 'The Impact of North Sea Oil on the Grampian Region and Aberdeen'. In *Onshore Impacts of Offshore Oil*, WJ Cairns, PM Rogers (eds), Applied Science Publishers, Barking.

77   Morgan D, 2002. *Lost Aberdeen: The Outskirts*. Birlinn Press, Edinburgh.

78   Hutcheson AM and Hogg A, 1975. *Scotland and Oil*. Oliver and Boyd, Edinburgh.

79   Mackie B, 2006. *Klondykers*. Birlinn Press, Edinburgh.

80   *Noroil Magazine* August 1977.

81   Mackie B, 2006. *Klondykers*. Birlinn Press, Edinburgh.

82   Ferguson JD, 1984. *The Story of Aberdeen Airport 1934–1984*. Scottish Airports, Glasgow.

83   Mackie B, 2004. *The Oilmen: The North Sea Tigers*. Birlinn Press, Edinburgh.

84   http://www.macrotrends.net/1369/crude-oil-price-history-chart

85 Mackie, B 2004. *The Oilmen: The North Sea Tigers*. Birlinn Press, Edinburgh.

86 Mackie B, 2006. *Klondykers*. Birlinn Press, Edinburgh.

87 Aiken GJM and McCance C, 1982. 'Alcohol Consumption in Offshore Oil Rig Workers'. *British Journal of Addiction* 77 p. 305-310.

88 *Glasgow Herald* 22/2/89.

89 *Daily Record* 27/10/08.

90 *Daily Telegraph* 20/8/14.

91 *The Scotsman* 24/7/13.

92 http://www.footballdatabase.eu/football.coupe.aberdeen.real-madrid.39935.en.html

CHAPTER 5 Local Heroes

93 Myles Bowen in Moreton R (ed) *Tales from Early UK Oil Exploration 1960–1979*. PESGB 1999.

94 *Ibid.*

95 Hardman RFP, 2003. 'Lessons from oil and gas exploration in and around Britain' in Gluyas JG and Hichens HM, *United Kingdom Oil and Gas Fields, Commemorative Volume*, Geological Society, London, Memoir 20, p. 5-16.

96 Myles Bowen in Moreton R (ed) *Tales from Early UK Oil Exploration 1960-1979*. PESGB 1999.

97 Fenwick JM, 1978. The Shetland Experience, A Local Authority Arms Itself for the Oil Invasion. *Scottish Government Yearbook 1978*.

98 www.undiscoveredscotland.co.uk/shetland/sullomvoe/index.html

99 *Ibid.*

100 *Glasgow Herald* 22/6/89.

101 *The Times* 25/4/73.

102 *Aberdeen Press and Journal* 12/9/2005.

103 *Financial Times* 26/6/73.

104 *The Times* 19/5/73.

105 *Financial Times* 16/2/73.

106 *Financial Times* 10/5/73.

107 *The Scotsman* 31/12/04.

108 Mackie B, 2006. *Klondykers*. Birlinn Press, Edinburgh.

109 www.shetlandcharitabletrust.co.uk/assets/files/accounts/SCT-Financial-Statements-to-31-March-2014.pdf

www.shetland.gov.uk/news-advice/documents/ShetlandIslandsCouncilDraftAccounts11-12.pdf

110 Wills J, 1991. *A Place in the Sun.* Mainstream Publishing, Edinburgh.

111 www.talisman-sinopec.com/pdfs/uploads/Flotta_2013.pdf

112 www.audit-scotland.gov.uk

CHAPTER 6 New Challenges

113 Hutcheson AM and Hogg A, 1975. *Scotland and Oil.* Oliver and Boyd, Edinburgh.

114 home.versatel.nl/the_sims/rig/transocean3.htm

115 home.versatel.nl/the_sims/rig/seagem.htm

116 oljepionerene.no/index_eng.php

117 home.versatel.nl/the_sims/rig/o-prince.htm

118 *Flight International Magazine* 5/12/68.

119 www.twi-global.com/news-events/case-studies/alexander-l-kielland-accommodation-platform-145/

120 home.versatel.nl/the_sims/rig/alk.htm

121 Kvendseth SS, 1988. *Giant Discovery: A History of Ekofisk Through the First 20 Years.* Phillips Petroleum, Norway.

122 *Wasted Windfall* Channel 4: 1996 Fine Art Productions.

123 Mackie B, 2004. *The Oilmen: The North Sea Tigers.* Birlinn Press, Edinburgh.

124 Rosengren P, 1986. Accidents and Safety in Offshore Diving, in Walker PA (ed) Safety of Diving Operations, Springer.

125 *Noroil Magazine* March 1975.

126 Linning MM and Larminie FG, 1981. Forties Field Development: The Environmental Aspect, in *Onshore Impacts of Offshore Oil,* Cairns WJ and Rogers PM (eds), Applied Science Publishers.

127 Rosengren P, 1988. Saturation Diving: Diving Deeper Than 300 m. Submersible Technology; Adapting to Change. *Advances in Underwater Technology, Ocean Science and Offshore Engineering* 14, p. 129-132.

128 www.norskolje.museum.no/

129 Henderson A, 2001. Dynamic Decisions. *Cranes Today Magazine.* www.cranestodaymagazine.com/features/dynamic-decisions

130 *Glasgow Herald* 28/6/77.

131 Beliveau D, 1995. Heterogeneity, geostatistics, horizontal wells and blackjack poker. *Journal of Petroleum Technology,* 47, p. 1068-1074.

132 www.statoil.com/en/about/worldwide/unitedkingdom/pages/mariner.aspx

133 www.spe-uk.org/aberdeen/knowledgefiles/SPE_Aberdeen_Mariner-250913-%20 Final.pdf

134 Loth WD, 1998. HPHT Wells: Perspective on drilling and completion from the field:

UK Government Health and Safety Executive, Offshore Technology Report. HSE Books.

135 www.offshore-technology.com/projects/elgin/

136 home.versatel.nl/the_sims/rig/o-odyssey.htm

137 *The Independent*, 9/11/91.

138 *The Times* 24/9/88.

CHAPTER 7 Offshore

139 *The Guardian* 22/11/1980.

140 BBC News 29/11/2000 news.bbc.co.uk/1/hi/sci/tech/1047249.stm

141 jenniedavisonyr1.wordpress.com/2014/01/17/people-to-people/

142 Robertson DH, and Simpson ME, 1996. Review of Probable Survival Times for Immersion in the North Sea, *Offshore Technology Report OTO 95 038*, UK Health and Safety Executive.

143 *Noroil Magazine* January 1978.

144 www.nuav.net/haltenbank.html

CHAPTER 8 The Forties Field

145 Wills JM, 1991. The Forties Field, Block 21/10, 22/6a, UK North Sea. In Abbotts IL (ed) *United Kingdom Oil and Gas Fields*, Geological Society of London, Memoirs 1991, 14, p. 301-308.

146 Aircraft Accident Report 2/88 Air Accidents Investigation Branch Department of Transport Report on the Accident to Boeing Vertol 234 LR, G-BWFC 2.5 Miles East of Sumburgh, Shetland Isles on 6 November 1986.

147 news.stv.tv/video/1257656287001/ Interview with Eric Morrans, Chinook helicopter crash survivor, from 1987.

148 Mackie B, 2006. *Klondykers*. Birlinn Press, Edinburgh.

149 *The Times* 27/1/76.

150 *The Times* 20/9/77.

151 nom.nb.no/eng/Work/Unions-and-strike/Foreigners-unions-and-a-strike

152 news.bbc.co.uk/1/hi/scotland/north_east/7910373.stm

153 www.oilandgasuk.co.uk/

154 *Herald Scotland* 14/5/14.

CHAPTER 9 Big Money

155 Mackie B, 2004. *The Oilmen: The North Sea Tigers*. Birlinn Press, Edinburgh.

156 *The Guardian* 13/9/77.

157 *Oil and Gas UK Economic Report*, 2013.

158 Interview with Lord Donaghue *Wasted Windfall* Channel 4: 1996 Fine Art Productions.

159 www.nbim.no/en/the-fund/

160 www.oilofscotland.org/MccronereportScottishOffice.pdf

161 nom.nb.no/eng/Economy-and-society/The-final-redetermination

162 *The Times* 19/5/89.

163 *The Times* 20/8/91.

164 nom.nb.no/eng/Economy-and-society/The-final-redetermination

CHAPTER 10 BP and Britoil

165 *The Observer* 29/11/87.

166 *Financial Times* 3/10/87.

167 *Financial Times* 19/12/87.

168 *The Guardian* 28/10/87.

169 *The Independent* 14/9/89.

170 *Financial Timess* 28/8/86.

171 *Financial Times* 4/9/86.

172 *The Independent* 6/9/89; *Herald Scotland* 31/8/89; *Daily Record* 7/10/14.

173 *The Independent* 14/9/89.

CHAPTER 11 Occidental and ELF

174 Tim Halford interviewed in *Wasted Windfall* Channel 4: 1996 Fine Art Productions.

175 *New York Times* 22/11/84.

176 www.legalaffairs.org/issues/May-June-2002/story_ignatius_mayjun2002.html

177 *The Guardian*13/11/03.

178 *The Guardian* 13/11/03.

179 *The Guardian* 31/5/01. BBC News website news.bbc.co.uk/onthisday/hi/dates/stories/may/30/newsid_2542000/2542475.stm

180 *The Economist* 5/11/98, *Daily Telegraph* 2/2/04

CHAPTER 12 Oil Reserves

181 Shepherd M, 2009. *Oil Field Production Geology*, American Association of Petroleum Geologists, Memoir 91.

182 Sandrea I. and Sandrea R, 2007. Global oil reserves – Recovery factors leave vast

target for EOR Technologies. *Oil and Gas Journal.* Part 1: November 5th, 2007. Part 2: November 12th, 2007.

183 Interview with Ian Clark, Memorial University of Newfoundland, Digital Archives Initiative. collections.mun.ca/cdm/ref/collection/extension/id/559

184 Scott MT, 2012. Oil and gas reserves and resources reporting – The Market Rules. *Society of Petroleum Engineers,* paper number 155398.

185 Lorenz JC, 2000. The Stimulation of Hydrocarbon Reservoirs with Subsurface Nuclear Explosions. *Oil Industry History Journal.*

186 Shepherd M, Kearney CJ, and Milne JH, 1990. Magnus Field, in *Structural Traps II* Compiled by EA Beaumont and N.H.Foster. American Association of Petroleum Geologists, Tulsa.

187 Shepherd M, Kearney CJ, and Milne JH, 1990. Magnus Field, in *Structural Traps II* Compiled by EA Beaumont and NH Foster. American Association of Petroleum Geologists, Tulsa.

Shepherd M, 1991. The Magnus Field, Block 211/7a, 12a, UK North Sea, In Abbotts, IL (ed) *United Kingdom Oil and Gas Fields,* Geological Society of London, Memoirs 1991 v. 14, p. 153-157.

188 www.og.decc.gov.uk/pprs/full_production.htm

189 www.og.decc.gov.uk/pprs/full_production.htm

190 Tordo S, Tracy BS and Arfaa N, 2011. National Oil Companies and Value Creation, World Bank Working Paper No. 218

191 BBC News 7 August 2014 www.bbc.co.uk/news/business-28685504

192 BBC News 5 March 2015 www.bbc.co.uk/news/uk-scotland-31745822

193 *Daily Telegraph,* 25/6/00.

CHAPTER 13 Out West

194 Carruth AG, 2003. The Foinaven Field. In Gluyas JG and Hichens HM (eds) *United Kingdom Oil and Gas Fields, Commerative Millennium Volume.* Geological Society, London, Memoir, 20, 121-130.

195 www.offshore-technology.com/projects/rosebank-field-shetland-islands-uk/

196 www.offshore-technology.com/features/featurerisky-business-deepwater-drilling-north-sea/

197 Austin J A, Cannon SJC, and Ellis D, 2014. Hydrocarbon exploration and exploitation West of Shetlands, In Cannon SJC and Ellis D. (eds) 2014. Hydrocarbon Exploration to Exploitation West of Shetlands. Geological Society, London, Special Publications, 397, 1–10.

198 www.scotsman.com/news/politics/top-stories/half-of-scots-say-oil-finds-are-kept-secret-1-3534186

199 Barr D, Savory KE, Fowler SR, Arman K and Mcgarrity JP, 2007. Pre-development fracture modelling in the Clair field, west of Shetland. In Lonergan L et. al., (eds)

Fractured Reservoirs. Geological Society, London, Special Publications, 270, 205-225.

200 www.bp.com/en/global/north-sea-infrastructure/Infrastructure/Platforms/Clair.html

201 www.bp.com/en/global/corporate/about-bp/bp-worldwide/bp-united-kingdom/bp-in-the-north-sea/quad204.html

202 Austin JA, Cannon SJC and Ellis D, 2005. Hydrocarbon exploration and exploitation West of Shetlands, In Cannon SJC and Ellis D (eds) 2014. Hydrocarbon Exploration to Exploitation West of Shetlands. Geological Society, London, Special Publications, 397, 1–10.

203 Smallwood JR and Kirk WJ, 2014. Paleocene exploration in the Faroe–Shetland Channel: disappointments and discoveries. In: Dore AG and Vining BA (eds) *Petroleum Geology: North-West Europe and Global Perspectives—Proceedings of the 6th Petroleum Geology Conference*, 977–991.

204 www.scotland.gov.uk/Topics/marine/marine-environment/ecosystems/Rockall

205 www.therockallclub.org/The_Rockall_Club_Facts.html

206 www.og.**decc**.gov.uk/

207 Comhairle nan Eilean Siar 2007, West of Hebrides Oil and Gas Strategic Environmental Assessment: Comhairle Response.

208 www.og.**decc**.gov.uk/

209 Naylor D and Shannon PM 1982. *The Geology of Offshore Ireland and West Britain*. Springer.

210 *Sunday Post 6/10/13*.

CHAPTER 14 The End of Oil

211 Cohen JE, 1995. *How Many People Can the Earth Support?* WW Norton & Company.

212 Erlich PR, 1968. *The Population Bomb*, Sierra Club /Ballantine.

213 www.igbp.net/globalchange/greatacceleration.4.1b8ae20512db692f2a680001630.html

214 King M and Elliott, C., 1992. *Lancet*. 341 p. 669-672.

215 www.navigantresearch.com/research/transportation-forecast-light-duty-vehicles

216 The International Energy Agency.

217 Pérez Alfonso JP, 1975. *Hundiendonos en excremento de Diablo* (We are sinking in the devil's excrement). Editorial Lisbona.

218 aberdeeninvestlivevisit.co.uk/Invest/Aberdeens-Economy/City-Projects/H2-Aberdeen/Hydrogen-Bus/Hydrogen-Bus-Project-Funding.aspx

219 *Oil and Gas UK Economic Report* 2013. www.bbc.co.uk/news/uk-scotland-scotland-politics-26326117

220 *Oil and Gas UK Economic Report* 2013.

221 Beckman J 2012. Shell grapples with uncertainties of Brent field decommissioning *Offshore Magazine*.

Shell: Brent E news March 2014: s07.static-shell.com/content/dam/shell-new/local/country/gbr/images-notext/supporting/photo/BrentDecommissioning/LandingPage/brent-enews-issue-13-homepage.pdf

222 www.ospar.org/content/content.asp?menu=00120000000057_000000_000000

CHAPTER 15 The Geological Story

223 Bondevik S, Mangerud J, Dawson S, Dawson A and Lohne Ø, 2003. Record-breaking height for 8,000-Year-Old Tsunami in the North Atlantic. *EOS 84* p. 289–300.

Smith DE et al., 2004. The Holocene Storegga Slide tsunami in the United Kingdom. *Quaternary Science Reviews* 23: p. 2,291–2,321.

Dawson AG, Long D and Smith DE, 1988. The Storegga Slides: Evidence from eastern Scotland for a possible tsunami. *Marine Geology* 82 p. 271–276.

Dawson AG et al. 2011, Relative timing of the Storegga submarine slide, methane release, and climate change during the 8.2 ka cold event. *Holocene.* 21 p. 1,167-1,171.

Bondzvik S, Lovholt F, Harbitz C, Mangerud J, Dawson A and Svendsen JI, 2005. The Storegga Slide tsunami – comparing field observations with numerical simulations. *Marine and Petroleum Geology* 22 p. 195-208.

224 *Herald Scotland* 18/11/2012.

225 Dawson AG, Smith DE and Long D, 1990. Evidence for a tsunami from a Mesolithic site in Inverness, Scotland. Journal of Archaeological Science, 17, p. 509-512.

226 Rydgren K and Bondevik S, 2015. Moss growth patterns and timing of human exposure to a Mesolithic tsunami in the North Atlantic. Geology, 43, p. 111-p.114.

227 Anderson DE, Goudie AS, Parker AG, 2007. Global Environments through the Quaternary. Oxford University Press.

228 Marshak S, 2007. *Earth: Portrait of a Planet*, 3rd edition, WW Norton.

Martin R, 2013. *Earth's Evolving Systems*, Jones & Bartlett Learning.

229 Boulton GS, Peacock JD and Sutherland DG,2002. Quaternary, in Trewin NH (ed) *The Geology of Scotland*, 4th edition, The Geological Society, London.

230 Anderson DE, Goudie AS and Parker AG, 2007. Global Environments through the Quaternary. Oxford University Press.

231 Long D, Wickham-Jones CR and Ruckley NA, 1986. A flint artefact from the northern North Sea. In Roe DA (ed), *Studies in the Upper Palaeolithic of Britain & North-west Europe* (British Archaeological Reports), 55–62.

mikepitts.wordpress.com/2009/07/29/plinth-box-3/

232 Anderson DE, Goudie AS and Parker AG, 2007. Global Environments through the

Quaternary. Oxford University Press.

233 Gupta S, Collier JS, Palmer-Felgate A and Potter G, 2007. Catastrophic flooding origin of shelf valley systems in the English Channel. *Nature* 448, p. 342-345.

234 Rouchy JM and Caruso A, 2006. The Messinian salinity crisis in the Mediterranean basin: A reassessment of the data and an integrated scenario. *Sedimentary Geology* 188–189 p. 35–67.

Bache F, et al., 2012. 'A two step process for the reflooding of the Mediterranean after the Messinian Salinity Crisis', *Basin Research* 24, p. 125–153.

235 Anderson DE, Goudie AS and Parker AG, 2007. Global Environments through the Quaternary. Oxford University Press.

236 Martin R, 2013. *Earth's Evolving Systems*, Jones & Bartlett Learning.

237 Woodcock NH and Strachan R (eds), 2012, *Geological History of Britain and Ireland*. Wiley / Blackwell.

238 R Martin, 2013. *Earth's Evolving Systems*, Jones & Bartlett Learning.

239 Woodcock NH and Strachan R (eds), 2012, *Geological History of Britain and Ireland*. Wiley / Blackwell.

240 Løseth H, Raulline B and Nygård A, 2013. Late Cainozoic geological evolution of the northern North Sea: development of a Miocene unconformity reshaped by large-scale Pleistocene sand intrusion, *Journal of the Geological Society*, London, 170, p. 133-145.

241 Stanley SM, 1993. *Exploring Earth and Life through Time*. WH Freeman and Co.

242 Zachos JC, Dickens GR and Zeebe RE, 2008. An early Cainozoic perspective on greenhouse warming and carbon-cycle dynamics, *Nature* 45, p. 117.

243 Martin R 2013. *Earth's Evolving Systems*, Jones & Bartlett Learning.

244 DeConto RM et.al., 2012. Past extreme warming events linked to massive carbon release from thawing permafrost, *Nature* 484, 87.

McInerney FA and Wing SL, 2011. The Paleocene Eocene Thermal Maximum: A perturbation of carbon cycle, climate, and biosphere with implications for the future. *Annu. Rev. Earth Planet. Sci.* 39, p. 489-516.

245 Woodcock NH, and Strachan R (eds), 2012. *Geological History of Britain and Ireland*. Wiley / Blackwell.

246 O'Knox RWB, 2002. 'Tertiary Sedimentation' in Trewin NH (ed), *The Geology of Scotland*, 4th edition, The Geological Society, London.

247 Skelton PW, Spicer RA, Kelley SP and Gilmour I, 2003. *The Cretaceous World*, Cambridge University Press.

248 Woodcock NH and Strachan R (eds), 2012. *Geological History of Britain and Ireland*. Wiley / Blackwell.

249 Skelton PW, Spicer RA, Kelley SP and Gilmour I, 2003. *The Cretaceous World*, Cambridge University Press.

250 Cowen R 2013, *History of Life*. Fifth edition. Wiley / Blackwell.

251 Scholle P 1977 Chalk Diagenesis and its Relation to Petroleum Exploration: Oil from Chalks, a Modern Miracle? *AAPG Bulletin* 61, p. 982-1009.

252 *New York Times* 19/8/87.

253 Mason SF, 1991. *Chemical Evolution*. Clarendon Press.

254 www.snh.org.uk/publications/on-line/geology/elothian_borders/hutton.asp

255 Playfair J, 1805. Biographical account of the late Dr James Hutton, FRS, Edinburgh. Transactions of the Royal Society of Edinburgh, vol. V, pt. III.

256 Woodcock NH and Strachan R (eds), 2012. *Geological History of Britain and Ireland*. Wiley / Blackwell.

257 www.npowetenschap.nl/nieuws/artikelen/2002/juni/Zuidwalvulkaan.html

258 Woodcock NH and Strachan R (eds), 2012. *Geological History of Britain and Ireland*. Wiley / Blackwell.

Some other books published by **Luath Press**

The Hydro Boys
Emma Wood
ISBN 1 84282 047 8 PBK £8.99

'I heard about drowned farms and hamlets, the ruination of the salmon-fishing and how Inverness might be washed away if the dams failed inland. I was told about the huge veins of crystal they found when they were tunneling deep under the mountains and when I wanted to know who "they" were: what stories I got in reply! I heard about Poles, Czechs, poverty-stricken Irish, German spies, intrepid locals...'

The hydro-electric project was a crusade, with a marvellous goal: the prize of affordable power for all from Scottish rainfall.

This book is a journey through time, and across and beneath the Highland landscape... it is not just a story of technology and politics but of people.

Nobody should forget the human sacrifice made by those who built the dams all those years ago. The politicians, engineers and navvies of the era bequeathed to us the major source of renewable energy down to the present day. Their legacy will continue to serve us far into the 21st century.
BRIAN WILSON MP, Energy Minister, THE SCOTSMAN

Tunnel Tigers: first-hand account of a Hydro Boy in the Highlands
Patrick Campbell
ISBN 1 84282 072 9 PBK £8.99

Tunnel tigers belong to an elite group of construction workers who specialise in a highly paid but dangerous profession: driving tunnels through mountains or underneath rivers or other large bodies of water, on locations as far apart as Sydney, Australia, and San Francisco. At the turn of the last century, they tunnelled out the subways under New York and London; in the 1940s and 1950s, they were involved in a score of huge hydroelectric tunnels in Pitlochry and the Highlands of Scotland. They continue with their dangerous craft today in various locations all over the world.

Many of these daring men were born in north-west Donegal, Ireland, where the tunnel tigers were viewed as local folk heroes because they had the bravado to work in dangerous working conditions that few other working men could endure.

Tunnel Tigers is a colourful portrait of the off-beat characters who worked on the Scottish projects, and of the tensions that were created when men of various religious and ethnic groups shared the same space.

Reportage Scotland: History in the Making

Louise Yeoman

Foreword by Professor David Stevenson

ISBN 978 1 842820 51 3 PBK £7.99

Events – both major and minor – as seen and recorded by Scots throughout history.

Which king was murdered in a sewer?
What was Dr Fian's love magic?
Who was the half-roasted abbot?

The answers can all be found in the eclectic mix covering nearly 2,000 years of Scottish history. Historian Louise Yeoman's rummage through the manuscript, book and newspapers archives of the National Library of Scotland has yielded an astonishing amount of material ranging from a letter to the King of the Picts to Mary Queen of Scots' own account of the murder of David Riccio; from the execution of William Wallace to accounts of anti-poll tax actions and the opening of the new Scottish Parliament.

...marvellously illuminating and wonderfully readable... SCOTLAND ON SUNDAY

Louise Yeoman makes a much-needed contribution to the canons of Scottish historiography, providing eyewitness, or as near as possible, to events which have shaped the country over two millennia.
THE HERALD

Scotland's Still Light: A Photographer's Vision Inspired by Scottish Literature

Andy Hall

ISBN: 978-1-908373-79-3 PBK £12.99

This beautiful partnership of photography and poetic language seeks to encapsulate perfectly the essence of the moment, and the often indescribable feeling of being solitary within a landscape. The words of highly-esteemed Scottish writers are vividly brought to life by the evocative photography of Andy Hall.

Any photographic work by Andy Hall takes your breath away. This book demonstrates his love of Scotland and highlights the mystic beauty and raw energy of our country.
SIR ALEX FERGUSON CBE

A masterful fusion of word and image that helps us to see a little better. SALLY MAGNUSSON

Breathtaking images of Scotland... and then I came upon the last one... the Little White Rose... and it did break my heart. JOHN BYRNE

These pictures and brilliantly chosen quotations dramatically reopen your eyes to Scotland's glories.
LORD GEORGE ROBERTSON

The Highland Geology Trail

John L Roberts

ISBN 0-946487-36-7 PBK £5.99

- Where can you find the oldest rocks in Europe?
- Where can you see ancient hills around 800 million years old?
- How do you tell whether a valley was carved out by a glacier, not by a river?
- What are the Focoid Beds?
- Where do you find rocks folded like putty?
- How did the great masses of rock pile up like snow in front of a snow-plough?
- When did volcanoes spew lava and ash to form Skye, Mull and Rum?
- Where can you find fossils on Skye?

This journey of geological discovery through the diverse landforms of the north and west Highlands of Scotland offers the answers to these and many other questions of interest to visitors and local residents alike.

Nort Atlantik Drift

Alan Jamieson

ISBN 978-1-906307-13-4 HBK £15.00

NORT ATLANTIK DRIFT – the warm ocean current that runs past Shetland, keeping the climate mellower than equivalent latitudes anywhere else in the world.

For centuries Shetland's artistic tradition has been nurtured by the rhythms of the sea and the lyrical cadences of a unique dialect. Set halfway between Scotland and Norway, these North Atlantic isles have produced a distinct and vibrant culture. Robert Alan Jamieson mixes mythology, autobiography and history with photographs in a beautiful book not only for Shetlanders, but everyone who has visited, or dreams of visiting, 'Da Aald Rock'.

Details of these and other books published by Luath Press can be found at
www.luath.co.uk

Luath Press Limited

committed to publishing well written books worth reading

LUATH PRESS takes its name from Robert Burns, whose little collie
Luath (*Gael.*, swift or nimble) tripped up Jean Armour at a wedding
and gave him the chance to speak to the woman who was to be his wife
and the abiding love of his life. Burns called one of the 'Twa Dogs'
Luath after Cuchullin's hunting dog in Ossian's *Fingal*.
Luath Press was established in 1981 in the heart of
Burns country, and is now based a few steps up
the road from Burns' first lodgings on
Edinburgh's Royal Mile. Luath offers you
distinctive writing with a hint of
unexpected pleasures.
Most bookshops in the UK, the US, Canada,
Australia, New Zealand and parts of Europe,
either carry our books in stock or can order them
for you. To order direct from us, please send a £sterling
cheque, postal order, international money order or your
credit card details (number, address of cardholder and
expiry date) to us at the address below. Please add post
and packing as follows: UK – £1.00 per delivery address;
overseas surface mail – £2.50 per delivery address; overseas airmail –
£3.50 for the first book to each delivery address, plus £1.00 for each
additional book by airmail to the same address. If your order is a gift,
we will happily enclose your card or message at no extra charge.

Luath Press Limited
543/2 Castlehill
The Royal Mile
Edinburgh EH1 2ND
Scotland
Telephone: +44 (0)131 225 4326 (24 hours)
Fax: +44 (0)131 225 4324
email: sales@luath. co.uk
Website: www. luath.co.uk